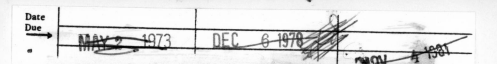

*A Textbook in*

**RORSCHACH TEST DIAGNOSIS**

*A Textbook in*

# RORSCHACH TEST DIAGNOSIS

*For Psychologists, Physicians and Teachers*

---

*By* EWALD BOHM, PH.D.

*Translated by* ANNE G. BECK, M.A. *and*
SAMUEL J. BECK, PH.D., *Professorial Lecturer,*
*University of Chicago, Associate, Michael Reese Hospital*

---

GRUNE & STRATTON

New York and London                                    1958

Library of Congress Catalog Card No. 55-6011

Printed and bound in U.S.A. (A)

# Contents

v

## PART THREE: EVALUATION

# Translators' Preface

THE AMERICAN RORSCHACH test scene has long been ready for this volume by Ewald Bohm. The European literature concerning Rorschach's test has to be sure been extensive, and burgeoning with the years. But it has been largely a journal literature, and hence scattered. A contributor to this literature Doctor Bohm had prior to the appearance of the present volume in its original German, established himself as a keen exponent of the test as clinical instrument. He now renders the important service that between the covers of one book he is presenting us with a thoroughgoing description of present European practice in using the test, and of the principles on which this practice rests. It is a systematic text, one which is certain to find a place in the examiner's authoritative resources close to that of Rorschach's *Psychodiagnostik* itself.

Doctor Bohm covers the field meticulously. He starts the fresh student at that initial point when the test cards are first presented to the Subject, leads him through the valleys of uncertainty and perplexity which are a part of every examiner's learning experience. From administration he guides him to and through processes of scoring, psychologic significances of scoring variables, then to the principal task and the *raison d'être* of the test,—clinical interpretation.

The more experienced investigator will meanwhile also find absorbing reading in Bohm. For one there is his reformulating of certain principles of personality essential towards understanding Rorschach's test logic. He does this both with relation to personality types,—a concept in eclipse in American psychology; and with relation to clinical pictures. Among the latter are the great groups of the neuroses, depressions, manic conditions, schizophrenias and epilepsies; and in addition certain "psychopathies," known but only vaguely to American clinical ears. A section on the test in children is included. All these chapters can not but stimulate one's clinical thinking afresh. With regard to the meaning of separate variables, there is the exposition—more fully than hitherto in English—of Binder's important monograph on the shading response. For this alone Rorschach test investigators will be more than grateful. Of specific interpretive interest will be Bohm's list of "Special Phenomena" in his Chapter V. Here are perplexing and elusive data appearing in any Rorschach examiner's experience. Many of these are known to the sophisticate. Some point up behaviors which had not hitherto arrested attention or interest. In Bohm's exposition of these, whether they are old or new, the reader will find valuable interpretive leads, and points of departure for research, both in terms of test validity and of clinical significance.

Another merit of the book is its wide coverage of the literature. To the predominantly monolingual American psychologists, this is an especial boon, since Bohm has access to literature which we are bound to miss, except in trickles. He has liberal recourse to these writers, and so makes a number of insights and inferences accessible for the first time to the hither side of the Atlantic. At the same time he has pored over the American texts, and shows a confident acquaintance with the Klopfer-Kelley writings, those of Bochner-Halpern, Piotrowski, Beck; with scattered references to others. Throughout, meanwhile, Bohm adheres to Rorschach's symbols and format in scoring and organizing the test variables into the formal structural summary. These are the data from which he reasons to psychologic significance.

One omission from the German text is that of the actual case samples, with the Rorschach test protocols and interpretive summaries. The German reading student will find much instructive profit in these. Space did not permit our including them.

The book, in conclusion, has the merits both of building on the solid foundation of the test as Rorschach published it and of bringing into view the superstructure that has been erected thereon. Another and keen interest attaches to it in the exposition that it is of Rorschach's test as currently filtered through the minds of its European practitioners. The translators feel privileged in the opportunity to render this valuable text into English.

Chicago                                          Anne G. Beck, M.A.
September, 1958                                   Samuel J. Beck, Ph.D.

*A Textbook in*

RORSCHACH TEST DIAGNOSIS

# PART ONE
# INTRODUCTION

## CHAPTER I

# *Applicability of the Rorschach Test*

## APPLICABILITY OF THE TEST

THE RORSCHACH TEST is useful both as a clinical instrument and for purposes of research. Hence it possesses extraordinarily rich possibilities.

1. As a *clinical instrument*, the test applies to all situations in which it is desirable to discover the pattern of a person's character in a relatively short time.

(a) In *industrial psychology*, the test offers an excellent medium, along with graphology, through which the psychometric special examinations for determining the character picture may be supplemented. It is of great service in dealing with specialized work, in counseling higher officials in industry and trade, and especially in relation to problems arising from the handling of subordinates, those in higher posts in particular, and their transfer to other positions.

An important use of the Rorschach test in today's industrial psychology is in *accident prevention*. Above all, the test can aid in screening out the neurotically accident-prone, both in railway and in street car services; in selection of drivers of motorized vehicles; and most of all in selection of flying personnel. It is true that persons who suffer accidents passively (as described by Koelsch), as well as those who have a neurotic need for punishment, can be spotted by this method only in exceptional cases. On the other hand, the test is a very good medium for determining the actively accident-prone, i.e., persons blind to danger, the fool-hardy, or the frivolous.

It can be said generally that modern psychotechnology, since it has taken the step from a merely negative to an actually positive stand in vocational counseling, can no longer ignore the matter of investigating personality.

(b) Rorschach test work has enormous relevance for the psychology of youth. In this area the test has become an indispensable instrument. Aside from its use in *vocational counseling*, it is most valuable in *child guidance*. The causes for difficulties in training and in adjustment can quite easily be established by this method. In some instances it may even happen that by testing a parent or a teacher we may discover in them a neurotic attitude which has set up the difficulties in the child's development. For a fuller

1

treatment of this important sphere, the reader is referred to Zulliger's numerous writings.

(c) The Rorschach test can also accomplish important tasks in *military psychology*. It may be used in doubtful cases during the selection of recruits. It is even more valuable as an aid to the selection of officer candidates, for it can uncover with considerable certainty the kind of character traits that would make the candidate unfit to be an officer. The same applies to the selection of specialized personnel such as radio operators and other technicians.

(d) The Rorschach test has also proved applicable to *marriage* and *family counseling*, services which have been developed in a number of countries. The problem here will often prove to be as much one of diagnosing a neurosis as of establishing some characterological feature.

(e) The use of the test in *experts' testimony in courts* is an important one in a field bordering on both the normal and the pathologic. Here the problem is first of all one of investigating the credibility of important witnesses. (Zulliger's text on the Bero Test treats this problem in more detail.) In addition there are, of course, problems of criminal psychology, as well as forensic psychiatry.

(f) From this area it is only one step to the classical application of the Rorschach test, namely, to *psychiatric diagnosis*. Since virtually half of the present book is concerned with problems of psychiatric diagnosis, we need not go into further detail at this point.

On the other hand, it might be appropriate here to say a few words about the *collaboration between physician and psychologist*. Very few physicians have the time and the patience required to learn the basic principles and technique of the Rorschach test, hampered as they are by the heavy demands of their profession, whether they are in medical institutions or in private practice. For this reason, the approach developed by clinical psychology in America has gradually become a necessity in Europe also. The only sensible collaborative arrangement is the "team," a method practiced in the United States which allows psychiatrist, psychologist, and social worker to collaborate on an equal footing. In Europe, unfortunately, the rule of the "pecking order," as it has been called by the American psychiatrist James G. Miller, one of the leading personalities in the Veterans Administration,[1] still prevails. In America it is now generally abolished. But the fact that in many other places the work of the clinical psychologist is still looked upon as a subordinate aid is not only a question of professional prestige and of the "narcissism of the little differences," but actually detrimental to a fruitful collaboration. Such circumstances are not conducive

[1]Miller, J. G.: Clinical Psychology in the Veterans Administration. The American Psychologist *1*: 181-182.

to proper working conditions and are unfair to the psychologist. One evil in particular must be emphasized and criticized. Psychiatrists who do not know the test, or know it only superficially, sometimes demand that the psychologist prepare his opinion without having first referred to the clinical chart and the questions at hand, only afterward studying the chart. This demand rests on the erroneous opinion that the "scientific" value of the investigation is enhanced by ignorance of the problems of the case. The contrary is actually the fact. Just as the physician must review the results of the biologic and psychologic investigations in order to make his diagnosis, so must the psychologist be acquainted with the clinical and biologic facts in order to arrive at his decision. It is only against the background of this material that the test results can be thrown into proper relief. The x-ray specialist, for example, will be unable to offer an opinion as to his findings without having studied the chart. The Rorschach test is an aid to diagnosis, nothing more.

As a matter of routine, the psychologist should study the test protocol before he acquaints himself with the chart. He first goes over the test itself and makes a rough sketch of the results without making use of the clinical data. Then he acquaints himself with all the relevant facts, including any laboratory investigations that have been made. With all this data in mind, he takes his stand regarding the unsolved questions raised by the test. Any points that are still not clear, he thus identifies, and they become points of departure for further investigation. Such a procedure will preserve the value and prestige of the test and set its achievement potential in a proper light. The fact is that not infrequently it is the Rorschach test which first directs suspicion to an organic factor, or brings questions of constitutional or environmental cause into the picture. Or it may shift the focus from one etiological possibility to another. Any of these questions can then be clarified by further clinical investigation.

2. We now turn to the applicability of the Rorschach test to *research*. The manifold possibilities of the method as a research instrument have not been fully exploited by far. The test may be used for comparing groups, either by arranging them according to types or by correlating psychologically relevant test factors, providing that this is done in accordance with some rationale. (But the test must be made individually.) Used in this way, the test can provide a valuable medium for various investigations of constitution and heredity.[2]

Another possibility presents itself in regard to studies following up the influence of environmental factors on development of intellect and character of normal as well as psychopathic individuals. The test has much unused

[2]Refer, for example, to the excellent work by Manfred Bleuler, "Der Rorschachsche Formdeutversuch bei Geschwistern." Zeitschrift f. Neurologie *118*: 366-398, 1929.

potential for investigating the psychology of vocational aptitudes, sex differences, age differences, and on the whole the differential psychology of groups. It can also be used with success in pharmacopsychology.[3] It would also be interesting to put the test to work studying the disputed question of a so-called national character. A beginning has already been made in the case of primitive peoples, i.e., in ethnology. One need only point to Oberholzer's treatise in Cora DuBois' book "The People of Alor." Last but not least, investigations in the field of mental health have set up an imposing array of tasks which are still awaiting the industry of Rorschach test investigators. These relate to the etiology and prevention of neuroses, psychoses, family problems, work and vocation, and also to the highly essential task of preventing war.

3. It is becoming more and more widely advocated, especially in regard to court cases, to *repeat* the test. Kuhn and Zulliger, among others, have shown the great advantages of this procedure. Depending on the particular situation, it is sometimes advisable to repeat the test after an interval of days, for instance, with persons under observation or criminals, and sometimes after an interval of weeks, months or even years, as in control studies of the effect of therapy. When the test is repeated after a long interval, the original series may be employed. Should the interval be only a few days, it is better to use the alternate series (Zulliger, the Bero-Test. Note the bibliographical references).

4. It will frequently be expedient to use the Rorschach test together with some other test. This may be a psychometric technique (the Binet-Simon, Terman, Wechsler, analytic intelligence test of Meili), or it may be some special instrument devised to test a particular problem, such as attention, concentration, the ability to make combinations, aptitude for drawing, music, etc. In cases of doubt as to children's intellectual endowment, the Maze test (Porteus)[4] makes possible a quick orientation regarding intellectual potential. Should there be suspicion of disturbances of recent memory in organic cases, it might be well to undertake a Ziehen, also known as Ranschburg, test (word pairs). The ability to concentrate can best be tested by means of a simple or complex form of the Bourdon test. For the ability to make combinations, the Ebbinghaus, or possibly the Masselon, techniques are indicated. Kraepelin's calculation technique applies to testing for fatiguability. Should there be suspicion of color blindness, Ishihara's cards are the simplest to employ.

It must be noted that intelligence tests and other psychometric methods should never be used prior to the Rorschach test, as this will cause the

[3]See Bleuler's and Wertham's report on the effects of mescal, Arch. Neurol. & Psychiat. *28,* July, 1932.

[4]Porteus, S. D.: The Maze Test and Mental Differences. Vineland, N. J., 1933.

subject to assume an "examination attitude," which will prevent the Rorschach test from being accomplished smoothly.

In individual cases, specifically in the so-called "situation" neuroses, two tests that can be used with advantage to supplement our investigation are Murray's Thematic Apperception (TAT) and the Wundt-Jung word association test. A condition with relation to the word association test is that the Rorschach is to be administered first and thoroughly processed. A number of responses suspected of stemming from neurotic "complexes" are then drawn out of the Rorschach test protocol and interspersed throughout the standard list of the one hundred stimulus words. For example, Kretschmer's "Medizinische Psychologie" contains such a list. From it a like number of other presumably non-significant words are removed. The response words and reaction times are usually set down and timed by stop watch, and this is followed by the reproduction experiment. It must be emphasized, however, that while this technique may shorten the psychoanalytic exploration to some extent, it can by no means replace it.

The Wartegg-Test has commended itself as a supplementary technique in getting character material from normals. In Swiss practice, a particular variation has been the use of colors.[5]

A number of special tests are available for discovering disturbances in abstracting ability, whether in cases of organic or of schizophrenic deterioration. These are the tests of Gelb, Goldstein, Scheerer and Weigl, reported in Goldstein's and Scheerer's "Abstract and Concrete Behavior."[6]

In certain cases where the problem is to differentiate between epilepsy, tetany, hysteria, and injury of the skull, or where other organic disturbances are suspected (lues cerebrospinalis, tumor cerebri), after-image diagnostics devised by Vujic and Levi[7] may be used, provided that the necessary technical facilities are available.

In pre-school children, the Rorschach test is best used in combination with the Bühler-Hetzer test for the young child, which establishes the level of development. The "World Test," or Margaret Lowenfeld's "Mosaics" are also in order, should neurotic disturbances manifest themselves.

A number of American clinics, the Menninger Clinic, for example, work as a matter of routine with entire test batteries, among which the Rorschach is sometimes included.[8]

The Rorschach test does not lend itself to group use. It would consequently be unwise to apply a method for group testing which, after having

[5] Verbal statement by Hanns Spreng and Hans Zulliger.

[6] Goldstein, K. and Scheerer, M.: Abstract and Concrete Behavior. An Experimental Study with Special Tests. Psychological Monographs 53, 2. Evanston, 1947.

[7] Vujic, V. and Levi, K.: Die Pathologie der optischen Nachbilder und ihre klinische Verwertung. Basel, 1939.

[8] Rapaport, D.: Diagnostic Psychological Testing, vol. I and II. Chicago, 1945.

been used for this purpose, could not be used for possible individual test-
ings. In some situations, larger groups must first be sifted so that the doubtful cases may later be investigated by means of individual tests. This is
particularly true of military or vocational selection of personnel. The Z test
is advisable for group purposes, as it has proven itself exceptionally valuable
during the second World War.[9] The Z test is now available also in the form
of cards which lend themselves to carrying out short tests.

The Rorschach test can also be combined with other techniques for investigating the personality. The Rorschach and the Szondi[10] complement
each other very well. This combination, too, is employed in the Menninger
Clinic. Graphology may equally well be combined with the Rorschach,
since this method reveals much which the test alone misses. On the other
hand, the creative potential of the genius cannot be patterned out by the
analysis of handwriting,[11] while this can sometimes be done by the Rorschach
test (especially through the M and the original responses). Then again,
graphology does not usually make possible a psychiatric diagnosis;[12] the
Rorschach test, to say the least, very often does so.

One other technique is finally to be mentioned which makes possible
a superficial orientation regarding self expression which has a psychologic
significance, especially in neurotic patients. This is the tree-test of Koch[13]
(Luzern [in accordance with Jucker's idea]). It can be helpfully employed
for the completion of Rorschach test findings. Familiarity with graphology
is, however, a prerequisite.

5. A word is also in order concerning the so-called *blind diagnosis*. Strictly
speaking, this consists in one person obtaining the protocol, and another test
expert interpreting it.

When this is done in a spirit of "fun" in order to demonstrate the possibilities of the test to skeptical souls, there can naturally be no objection.
It may also be used as a way of checking a newly derived Rorschach test
syndrome; or for making other scientific comparisons. But this kind of procedure is most emphatically to be rejected if personality conclusions are to
be drawn from it, whether for purposes of psychiatric diagnosis, expert
testimony in court, vocational counseling, or the like. Where the physician
himself cannot give the test, only the closest collaboration between physician
and Rorschach test investigator can achieve the desired results. Morgenthaler
has declared that, where practical applications are to be made, reliance on

---

[9]Zulliger, H.: Der Z-Test, Ein Formdeut-Verfahren zur psychologischen Untersuchung von Gruppen. Berne, 1948.

[10]Szondi, L.: Experimentelle Triebdiagnostik. Berne, 1947.

[11]Klages, L.: Was die Graphologie nicht kann. Zürich, 1949, p. 33.

[12]Klages, L.: op. cit., p. 34.

[13]Koch, K.: Der Baumtest, Der Baumzeichenversuch als psychodiagnostisches Hilfsmittel, Berne, 1949.

the test alone absolutely is not permissible,[14] and Binder has expressed essentially the same opinion.[15] In this respect the test is not unique. The same conclusions apply to the Wartegg, the Szondi, and the TAT. Its results are to be considered working hypotheses to be confirmed by further investigation. Professor Murray might well have written about the Rorschach test when he asserted, "A blind analysis is a stunt which may or may not be successful; it has no place in clinical practice."[16]

## THE EQUIPMENT OF THE EXAMINER

Can just anybody master the Rorschach test? In principle, yes, assuming that he possesses the requisite intelligence and the special aptitude. These are also necessary for becoming a good physician or a good engineer, since here, too, special aptitudes are required. Yet the professions of medicine and engineering are among those that can be learned. So there are good and poor Rorschach experts just as there are good and poor engineers.

Aside from the necessary intelligence and the training in psychology, the Rorschach test demands first of all much time and much patience. It is necessary to remember, however, the fact that the test—like graphology and the Szondi test—is only an instrument, and to merely master it technically offers no guarantee of success. Most important of all is an orientation in regard to psychologic processes. Szondi once expressed it perfectly: "A tester without psychology is much more dangerous than a psychologist without tests." And we can well apply to the Rorschach test what Murray once wrote: "The future of the TAT hangs on the possibility of perfecting the interpreter (psychology's forgotten instrument) more than it does on perfecting the material."[17]

Still, what fields of knowledge does the Rorschach examiner need? Many students maintain that academic courses in experimental psychology are sufficient to qualify a person to give the Rorschach test. This is not altogether correct. Courses in experimental psychology are useful and necessary. However, it is almost more important to undertake studies in character structure and medical psychology along with their several special branches. Since these are not taught at all universities, the prospective student of the test must often acquire them by himself. To put it bluntly, the prerequisites for a practical and successful use of the test are: a basic and comprehensive training in general psychology; plus a knowledge of character structure,

---

[14]Morgenthaler, W.: Einführung in die Technik von Rorschach's Psychodiagnostik. In: Rorschach, H.: Psychodiagnostik, p. 233.

[15]Binder, H.: Die klinische Bedeutung des Rorschach'schen Versuches. In: Psychiatrie und Rorschachscher Formdeutversuch. Zürich, 1944, p. 18.

[16]Murray, H. A.: Thematic Apperception Test, Manual, pp. 14 and 6.

[17]Murray, H. A.: op. cit., p. 6.

psychological types, developmental and child psychology, medical psychology, theoretical and clinical psychiatry. It goes without saying that present-day psychological training includes physiology, heredity, anthropology, sociology and statistics.

We hold one other view, and this in contrast to some other psychologists: the indispensability of at least an introduction to the theory of psychoanalysis and to depth psychology in general. This is necessary for a creative understanding of the "complex" responses not infrequently displayed in the richly productive tests of some neurotics, and in character neuroses. As in all theoretic work in the psychoanalytic field, it is naturally an advantage if the interpreter has himself been analyzed. Still, such demands can hardly be made to apply as strictly to an examiner as to a person engaging in therapy.

# PART TWO

# THE TEST TECHNIQUE

## CHAPTER II

## *Taking the Test Record*

RORSCHACH'S "PSYCHODIAGNOSTICS," beginning with its fourth edition, contains a contribution by the editor, Dr. W. Morgenthaler, dealing with the technique of the test. His purpose in this contribution was to provide the practical Rorschach worker with a constant, as far as possible, irreproachable technical procedure, so that the ever widening use of the test would not result in splits and divergent trends. For the same reason, and so as not to impede the attempts at a constant method, we can do no better than to depend essentially on Morgenthaler's work. We do it all the more willingly, since we could not conceive of a better introduction to the technique of the test. The following summary is offered in the interest of completeness and for the convenience of the reader. We are thus reproducing a condensation of Morgenthaler's directions, adding or omitting something here and there. The reader will serve himself well in studying Morgenthaler's work directly.

### THE TEST SITUATION

As in all psychological tests, especially in individual tests, the greatest possible quiet during the examination is needed. The best arrangement is to have the Examiner and the Subject retire by themselves to a quiet room. A third person can easily cause distraction. The presence of relatives, particularly, interferes with the freedom of many people and embarrasses them, especially children. When it is necessary to have a third person present— doctors, other psychologists, students—it is best to have the Subject's consent in advance.

All possible care must be taken to prevent interruptions: telephone calls should be answered by someone else. It is best to administer the test in daylight. The use of artificial light should be noted. Sudden variations in light conditions should be avoided as far as possible. In the case of older persons, and the far-sighted, care should be taken to have their eyeglasses at hand. The near-sighted are less of a problem since they usually wear theirs constantly.

Suspicion of color blindness may arise, growing out of the anamnesis of the patient, the family, or from strikingly erroneous color responses. With

9

such persons it is necessary to investigate the adequacy of their color reactions. This is most simply done with the pseudo-isochromatic test cards of Stilling or Ishihara.

The best seating arrangement is to have the Examiner and the Subject sit at right angles to each other at the same table in such a way that the Examiner's light is on his left, making it possible for him to keep the test cards in view. The Examiner and the Subject also can sit next to each other, but in such a way that the Examiner sits a little behind the Subject in order to be able to follow the test.

It is best for the Examiner to have the cards ready at his left; at the same time, it is very important that the Subject does not see the next card beforehand. One may therefore either have the cards turned down on the table or else lying with the test card up and in the correct order, but covered with a sheet of paper or a book.

Worn-out or shabby test cards, or those with distinctly visible spots, should not be employed, as far as possible. With time the cards become unsightly: greasy, sweaty, "thumbed." Morgenthaler therefore has suggested that two sets always be kept on hand, a new and attractive set for fastidious persons—more especially for neurotics and schizophrenics with obsessions for cleanliness—and another, older set for Subjects whose hands are not too well washed.

Of great importance is the so-called "psychologic preparation." This must be brief but, at the same time, as effective as possible. It is always necessary that contact be made, especially with children. One must bring about a natural atmosphere of confidence, and with anxious or timid patients a certain minimizing of the situation or a joke is in order. The deciding factor here must be the Examiner's understanding of human nature and his practical clinical sophistication.

Morgenthaler's admonition to avoid the words "test" and "testing" as much as possible should be emphasized. Anything that flavors of "examining" should be avoided. One may talk about an investigation or, in the case of the more educated, of an experiment, but this word has its hazards when dealing with simple people who may be a little suspicious.

As Kuhn[1] has emphasized, the attitude of the Subject toward the Examiner plays an important role. In some circumstances the purpose will better be served by turning the test administration over to some other person or, at the least, should there be a temporary adverse reaction or indisposition, one should wait for a better opportunity rather than bring pressure on the Subject. This precaution is especially pertinent with patients of paranoid disposition.

[1]Kuhn, R.: Über Maskendeutungen im Rorschach'schen Versuch. Basel, 1944, p. 47.

The factor which most commonly affects the attitude to the Examiner is the so-called "sexual component" in the experiment. Mathilde Vaerting[2] has already pointed to the significance of the sexual component in psychologic testing. It is a component which excites the feelings and inhibits the thought processes so that the Subject deludes himself into believing that he has done better than he really has. In the Rorschach test there is the additional fact that a male Subject suppresses sexual associations when examined by a woman. With the situation reversed—male Examiner, female Subject—the constriction, although less marked, must always be taken into consideration.

Before starting to give the test, it is well to inquire of the Subject whether he knows the test already, i.e., whether he has heard of it, read about it or taken it before. In the clinic, patients often tell one another what one is "supposed" to see. This too may influence the investigation and must be inquired into.

## INSTRUCTIONS

Rorschach himself simply placed the first test card before his subject with the question, "What could this be?" Others have expanded this directive, frequently more than was necessary. Naturally, the particular circumstances of each case determine, to some extent, the words with which to begin. The best rule is to say as much as is necessary, but as little as possible, particularly in the beginning. To explain how the test is made, or to go so far as to demonstrate it, must be precluded if we wish to study the clarity of the Subject's interpretive awareness. We consider the employment of a "trial blot" a serious error, even with children.[3] Such procedure removes from the test such important phenomena as dark shock in card I and initial test inhibition. On the same grounds, the explanation that the blots do not represent anything specific must never be given in advance as a general thing. Only under urgent conditions, when the question of going through with the test or not is in balance, is such an explanation or demonstration warranted. This fact, however, must be noted in the test protocol.

A comparison with cloud shapes is hazardous since it easily evokes cloud associations. Even the expression "ink blots" should not be employed if it can be helped. Even when the Subject is not clear as to the procedure and asks such questions as "What do the blots really mean?", it is still best to be evasive and put the Subject off with a promise, as long as possible. Should

[2]Vaerting, M.: Wahrheit und Irrtum in der Geschlechterpsychologie. Braun, Karlsruhe, 1921, pp. 105 and 120.

[3]Mary Ford (The Application of the Rorschach Test to Young Children, Minneapolis, 1946), who uses "trial blots," admits (p. 34) that the children understood the simple instructions "What could this be?" without further ado.

the Subject demonstrate that he regards the experiment as a test of his fantasy, he may safely be left with his opinion.[4]

The test card is handed over in the normal $\wedge$ position. However, the Subject is permitted to turn it and move it about at his pleasure. Klopfer[5] reports that Rorschach's comment on this point (p. 16) has given rise to long discussions as to whether or not it is permissible to inform the Subject that he is free to turn the test card, and, if permissible, when he should be so informed. Morgenthaler recommends saying nothing at the beginning on this point, preferring to wait until the Subject spontaneously turns the card. Should the Subject not do any turning of his own accord, the Examiner may hand over the second card in another position, saying, "From now on you may turn the test cards if you wish." Klopfer, too, advises (p. 33) against saying anything to encourage turning except at the appropriate moment. The fact is that it makes little difference whether mention is made about turning in advance or a little later. It must be kept in mind that any directions given in advance must be in as "neutral" and moderate a tone as possible, in order to avoid giving the impression that the Subject *must* turn the cards. Many Subjects who have no spontaneous inclination to turn the cards will, when the tone is neutral, miss the remark entirely. Any Examiner who observes that his instructions regularly have a suggestive force in this respect (possibly due to his manner of speech) does better to adhere strictly to Morgenthaler's directions.

We recommend a procedure approximately as follows: After contact has been made with the patient, we say to him, "I am going to show you a few cards (it is well to avoid saying "ink blots" or "pictures," though "figures" is permissible) and I would like you to tell me what they could be. You may tell me as much or as little as you care. You may move and turn the cards around as you please. When you have finished, return the card to me." The remark about turning may be omitted, but in that event it is necessary to act accordingly later on.

If there is no wall clock or the Examiner has no wrist watch and has lain his watch on the table, it is sometimes necessary to make a casual remark about the watch if it becomes evident that the Subject is becoming anxious. A simple remark such as "Pay no attention to the timepiece, it is there only for my personal pleasure; take all the time you want," will serve to put him at his ease.

These procedures are only points of departure. Under no circumstances should they be looked upon as fixed, magic formulas to which one must adhere rigidly.

The test cards are handed to the Subject in the $\wedge$ position. As Rorschach

---

[4]See also Klopfer and Kelley, The Rorschach Technique, New York, 1942, p. 30.
[5]Klopfer and Kelley, op. cit., p. 31.

expressly notes, they must be held no further than arm's length at most. At a greater distance, the perceptions are altered and the interpretations are not comparable. This is the reason why they are not suitable as lantern slides. The Subject must not be permitted to lay the cards down and attempt to view them from a greater distance.

Sporadic encouragement such as "Yes, yes," "very good," "fine," "my, how nicely you are doing," and the like, is permitted.

If the Subject is not getting under way satisfactorily with the first card, we take a waiting attitude, as though the experiment is a matter of small import, glancing out the window or something of the sort. If that does not do the trick, one may ask in a friendly way, "Well, what are you finding there?" It is useless to press the Subject to associate. Should there be just no success at all, one simply tries the next test card.

If the Subject wants to return the test card after a single response, or if he should make a lengthy pause, it is best first to inquire "Anything else?" or "Something more?" If this does not bring results, the thing to do is to repeat the directions. "You might like to give more responses; as I have already told you, you may give as many as you like." (It would not serve the purpose here to repeat the phrase, "or as few.")

The Subject sometimes intersperses questions intended, for the most part, to avoid the task. Morgenthaler provides many examples of this kind of procrastination (p. 225). Such questions must be ignored as long as possible. Only if nothing else works, it is necessary to bring the Subject to the task with kind words or maybe sharp ones. If the Subject begins to mention problems, he should be told to wait till "later."

The problem is different when the Subject inquires whether or not this is an intelligence test. The purpose is best served with a denial, insofar as this can be done consistent with the truth. One may say that something may well be brought out concerning the type of intelligence, but that that certainly is not the purpose or the most important aspect of the test. It can be explained that we wish only to obtain "a general insight" into his personality in order to understand him better and so be in a better position to help and advise him.

Should the questioning touch on the test factors themselves, whether in general or in particular, it is necessary to put the Subject off until after the test, explaining at that time what he wishes to know, and what is within the range of his intellect. However, one must never promise an interpretation of the test results.

If the Subject asks, "May I tell what this or that means?", referring to some detail, or to the red, the answer should be, "You may tell what anything means," or, "You may say whatever you wish."

Some Subjects who have heard something about psychoanalysis inquire whether they are to communicate their associations. If we give in to this suggestion, the subject will soon depart entirely from the stimulus of the blot. This question consequently should be answered in the negative and followed, once again, by the directions "Tell me only what this could be, tell me your immediate impression of the card." Suggestions which might tend to encourage "free associations" are to be avoided; even a formula such as "What does this remind you of?" may be hazardous. Later, following the completion of the entire test administration, when the uncertain responses are being cleared up, we have the opportunity to throw new light on individual responses and, in addition, to elicit additional free associations (a separate protocol). Sometimes it is advisable to obtain a word association test or a TAT.

It is never permissible to limit the time, although a limitation of the production of associations is occasionally unavoidable. Morgenthaler proposes that the card be taken away after eight to ten responses in the case of persons who associate endlessly. Zulliger (Bero-Test, p. 14) places the upper limit at six responses. On noticing that the Subject is not coming to any stop, we try to achieve it first with a simple "yes, well." Even a movement of the head or hand very frequently does it, causing the Subject to return the test card. When these devices fail, it is still best, for the most part, to continue to take the record, for when the subject is so possessed by his task that he does not notice the movement or the remark, something very essential is weighing down his spirit, something that should not be missed. However, when it becomes evident that the responses become stereotyped, aiming at quantity (Dd, Hd, and the like), it finally becomes necessary to take the card away and give the next one, but this fact must be entered on the record.

## TAKING THE RECORD

If one hopes afterwards to find the meaning of the record, a precise and clear protocol is essential. Personal data: the Subject's name, birthday, vocation, and possibly his address in case the Examiner should wish to speak to him again, are set down in the upper left hand corner. The date, the exact time (to the minute) when the test administration is begun, when card V is completed (half-time), and when the test is completed, are recorded at the upper right.

Because the test cards of the various editions have not come out exactly equivalent, for the purposes of comparison it is essential to state on each protocol the edition which was used, and also, of course, whether it was the original series or the Behn-Rorschach parallel series, e.g., "Ro III Ed" or "Be-Ro." Note should also be made, whether the Subject has seen the test cards previously or has otherwise obtained information concerning the method; in that case it should be noted when and how.

Whether one is to avail himself of printed forms is a matter of taste. We prefer a simple, wide pad of ruled paper, since too much printed matter can become confusing because most tests do not produce everything listed. The paper is to be ruled lengthwise into at least six or seven, possibly eight, columns. The first column is used for the number of the card, the time of presentation in minutes, and the position. The second column is used for the exact location of the response. (These first two columns can be combined into one.)

The text of the response, recorded as nearly verbatim as possible, goes into the third column. If the Subject speaks too much or too rapidly, we must content ourselves with abbreviations and, in certain instances, with cues, "by which as far as possible the most characteristic in the expression is preserved" (Morgenthaler). It requires a certain amount of experience even at this stage to be able to judge what is significant. It is better to help oneself with abbreviations and selective recording than to utilize a third person, a stenographer (so also Klopfer and Kelley, p. 36). The separate portions of the scoring formula—the signs—are entered in columns 4 through 7.

Exclamations and asides, even movements and attitudes of the Subject, must also be entered into the record (laughter, wrinkling the brow, sighing, and the like). Naturally, the nature and duration of any interruption that may take place should be recorded. The record keeping of remarks, exclamation and swearing should be carried out as unobtrusively as possible.

Each true response may be numbered (the intervening comments are not counted). It is better, although not essential, to begin numbering anew with each card; this will facilitate the identifying of particular details in any scientific treatise. If this is not done, it is recommended that the actual number of responses for each card be recorded in a narrow column before or after the scoring formulas (between columns 3 and 4 or after 7). This makes the total count and the waxing and waning of responses emerge more clearly.

Above all, a clear distinction must be made between what the Subject has said and what the Examiner has added. The latter should, for the most part, be put in parentheses, and even, when possible, recorded in some other script (Gothic, stenographic, Greek).

An explanatory remark or two in regard to the first two columns is now necessary. There are three chief ways to indicate (column 1) the position of the card and how it is held. Loosli-Usteri has suggested the use of small angles, the point of which always indicates the upper edge of the card. In this popular system, $\wedge$ is the normal position, $\vee$ is upside down, $>$ is

top to the right, and $<$ is top to the left. If the Examiner does not possess
any ability at concrete, optical imagery he can either utilize degrees: $0°$,
$90°$, $180°$, and $270°$, corresponding to the deviation of the top of the card,
when rotated clockwise in each of the four main positions. Or, following
Morgenthaler and Zulliger, he can use alphabetical signs: $a$ is the normal
position, $b$ the card on its right edge, $c$ the card upside down and $d$ the card
on its left edge. If it is in the oblique position, one can write $\nearrow$ or $a/d$.
Whenever no position is noted, always the normal one is meant. It is
especially important to indicate when the card is returned to its normal
position. The best procedure is to indicate the position for every response
once the Subject has begun to turn the card; otherwise, acute doubts often
arise, rendering precise scoring impossible. For complete turning, Klopfer's
proposed symbol Ⓢ can be used, giving it as many windings as there were
turnings of the card.[6]

Special care must be taken to locate exactly the specific part of the blot
used (column 2). The errors on this point are extensive and severe. Count-
less test records taken by beginners or by untrained assistants must be discarded because it is simply impossible to find the meaning of it. The notation "the middle," for card I, for example, is entirely insufficient since it
may mean the entire middle, the upper or lower half of the middle, the
upper horns, and perhaps even only the small humps between them. The
careful physician or anthropologist does not write, "Naevus on the left
breast," but rather, "A naevus about the size of a pea, dark brown in color,
two fingers breadth to the left and three fingers breadth below the nipple
on the left breast." The blot details in the Rorschach test, fortunately, are
decidedly easier to localize. The beginner especially must learn to be very
exact in this respect; he cannot imagine how many possibilities there are
for misunderstanding. The more unusual or the "crazier" the response is,
the more one must strive to give the exact location. When the form level
is high, it is possible to guess what is intended, but this is not the case when
the form level is low.

It must be kept in mind that the expressions "upper," "lower," "left,"
and "right" are conditioned by the position of the card. In this connection we emphatically recommend Morgenthaler's proposal (p. 227) that
if these expressions are not in parentheses, they refer to the card in the
normal, $a$, position, but if they are in parentheses, they refer to the position of the card at the time ($b$, $c$ or $d$). When confusion might occur, it
is advisable to make the meaning entirely unequivocal by the addition of
a qualifying "now" or "otherwise." With card VII it is often useful to
combine both notations (with and without parentheses) when the test

[6]Klopfer and Kelley, op. cit., p. 39.

card is held on the side. For example, "*b,* the projection in the (upper) upper third." That is, the little projection on the third which is now on top of the two otherwise top ones, in other words the projection of the left upper third of the card when in the *a* position.

If the record flows too quickly for the locations to be precisely noted, they should be noted provisionally with an abbreviation or two and recorded exactly immediately after the test record has been completed. The particular details of the blot cannot be found again later unless this is done.

With complicated percepts, it may be necessary to note the locations of individual portions, with more than the usual care, in the text of the record. Naturally, parentheses are to be employed; for example, this response to card IX, the whole blot: Two fools (the brown with the green) on a red cloud (the red). Or this one to card X, utilizing the red, the middle gray and the middle blue: Two policemen with bobbies' helmets (the middle gray) are opening a door with their crowbars (middle blue).

As far as possible, one must try to convey the location in words. When this proves impossible, or when it may easily cause confusion, one must use the sheet with the reproduced figures to mark off the response. These location charts are available in pads or as part of a complete record blank. The responses marked on the sheet must be numbered to conform to the test protocol. It is unnecessary to trace out all the responses and, because very many percepts overlap, the result is more confusing than clarifying. Sometimes it is necessary, after the conclusion of the test, to copy or to trace up the spot interpreted.

# CHAPTER III

## The Scorings

### THE CLASSICAL CATEGORIES

#### THE ELEMENTS OF THE SCORING FORMULAS

ONCE THE TEST RECORD has been obtained and the examination proper completed, every response is assigned a score. Scoring is the groundwork of the entire investigation; it is the point of departure of the study and hence is extremely important.

Scoring is an art, in German *kunst*, which comes from *können*, to know how. It is an art that demands a background of extensive experience; theory alone is not enough. Even the most adept student finds himself constantly running into new problems and difficulties. In the beginning, an expert must examine and correct the beginner's protocols time and again until his judgment has been developed. It will be useful for the beginner, once he has gathered a certain amount of experience, to review his earlier test records critically. The number of tests one should administer, or the number of years one must work in order to develop sufficiently cannot be stated in general terms. It depends on one's specific psychologic aptitude for this work, and also on the variety of material at one's disposal: healthy people from all levels and age groups of the population and the mentally disturbed of all categories. Only persistently soundly based work can achieve the purpose; quantity alone will not do it.

Still, the greatest variety of material and the widest experience are of no avail in the absence of a sure theoretic foundation. It would not be difficult to prove this point with examples from the literature. We shall endeavor, therefore, to work out the basic principles and to outline the correct approaches as clearly as possible. Mechanical scoring, which does not meet the basic requirements of the method, is demanded only by those who lack understanding of its dynamic flexibility. A completely mechanical scoring is neither possible nor desirable; it is not possible because the same response may have quite different significance with two different subjects, as they may demonstrate by their intonation, gestures or verbalizations; it is not desirable because it would destroy the essential advantages of the method, especially its great flexibility. Brosin and Fromm[1] assert, quite correctly, that it is an error to look upon scoring and evaluating as independent procedures. In order to decide with certainty the scoring of many doubtful responses, one must know the significance of the scoring for the whole personality.

[1]Henry E. Brosin and E. Fromm, Some principles of Gestalt Psychology in the Rorschach Experiment, Rorschach Research Exchange, Vol. VI, 1942, p. 2.

Every response is judged in four different ways: the *manner of approach* —the way in which the stimulus is grasped, i.e., whether as a whole, a large detail or a small detail and in what connection; the *determinants*— the psychologic experience factors which have produced the response, whether form, or other factors with or without form; the *content* of the percept—human, animal, object or other; and the *degree of originality*— the general frequency of occurrence of the association. Each of these qualities is represented in the scoring by an alphabetical sign. In the matter of frequency, however, only the very frequent and the exceptionally infrequent response receive signs.

### 1. MANNER OF APPROACH

Probably the most difficult task in the scoring is that of judging the mode of approach. Problems of Gestalt psychology play a role here, as they do also in connection with the determinants. The way in which one grasps the blot stands in close relation to the cortical processes that go on during the act of perceiving.

(a) If the test figure is interpreted as a whole, we speak of a *whole response,* and mark it W. An example of this response in the first test card would be "a bat." However, the following association is also marked W: "two witches (lateral details) are rushing upon a poor sinner (center detail)." The first response is a "simple" whole; the second is a *simultaneous-combinatory whole,* built up on details. Both, however, are *primary* wholes, arising quickly from one act of perception. Had the subject said, "Two witches (the laterals) and, in the center, a man standing; the witches are maybe rushing at the poor sinner," the response would be labeled a *successive-combinatory whole* and would belong among *secondary* wholes, i.e. those not instantly grasped in one perceptual act.

When the details are sharply perceived but their mutual relationship is not taken into account, the combination is a *confabulatory-combined* whole. These, too, are secondary wholes. In card IX, for example, the response may be "two magicians (the brown) and two children with their dolls (the green detail) are playing upon a cloud." All three details, perceived separately, are seen clearly and correctly, but the magicians were seen with the card in the normal position, while the children were seen with the card on the right or left side. These confabulated wholes are usually also connected with poor or partly confabulated form perceptions. Thus, for example, at the response of a paralytic in card III—"two gentlemen sitting in a cafe over a bottle of red wine"—it is true that the "red wine" is between the men; however, there is no table, and the men are not sitting. The red wine is confabulated from the red color.

Secondary responses also include *contaminated whole responses,* these being the condensations of schizophrenics who fuse two responses, their perception strongly suggesting a double exposure on a photographic plate. When, for example, card IV is seen as "an animal skin, with boots," the usual skin is being tied in with the boots of a man, who otherwise would be seen as a whole. (More details concerning these secondary wholes will be found in chapter 5.)

The two men in card III are technically a W, even though the red details are not included.

Rorschach intuitively followed Gestalt psychology, and he did well to do so.[1a] A frequent addition is "excluding these," as for example to the lateral end projections of the bat in card V. This response can, nevertheless, by the addition of the notation "object criticism," be scored W with confidence. There is no reason to devise such new scoring formulas for these percepts as Klopfer's "cut-off" W, since they are intended as W responses, and the subject's critical attitude can otherwise be noted. But the limit is reached when, for example, a subject, in viewing card VI, disregards the entire upper section (which is a D) and only sees the major detail as "animal skin." Such a response is better scored as D, with the P set in parentheses.

Doubt as to scoring may occur when the figures, owing to their symmetry, are seen as two halves. In general, these are W (e.g., "two men" in card III, "two women" in card VII; similarly, in card VI, if held on the left or right side, a reflection of a "ruin at the sea's edge"). When, however, one half is described separately without being related to the other, and the other is later pointed out as being the same, it is not W.

A very important group of secondary W's are the *confabulated whole responses,* which Rorschach has scored DW. In these the whole is derived from the detail. (However, confabulations are found also in the primary simple W and in detail perception, and, on the other hand, not all DW's are confabulations.) The development of the DW is as follows: The Subject perceives some detail clearly and sharply; then, from this point of departure he reaches a general conclusion regarding the entirety, without having closely inspected the rest. As a result, in most cases the form of the association suffers. Rorschach cites as an example "a crab" in card I, so perceived because the two details usually seen as "horns" (upper middle) are now "nippers." Such is the case, too, when in card VIII, a Subject, starting with the center blue, calls the entire "the chest" or "a skeleton." There are DW−, i.e., F−. When the detail is very small or uncommon these responses are DdW, e.g., a "butterfly" in card VI, where the subject is reacting to the "antennae" at the top.

[1a]See Brosin and Fromm, op. cit., p. 8.

When reality is under control, this approach may also result in good form perception. Rorschach's own example in card I is "a large bird" (because of the wings). He scored this DWF+ (p. 125). These are the more infrequent and at times very interesting DW+'s.

It is an error—which, as the literature indicates,[2] is rather widespread—to suppose that a DW must only be F–, i.e., poor form. This misunderstanding arises from a superficial reading of Rorschach's text: "Naturally, the result of DW visualization is unclear conception of form." (Psychodiagnostics, p. 38). His words are correctly understood but his meaning is not. This is apparent from the sample just cited. Then, too, the rapid, often quite hasty leap from part to whole, with the corresponding tendency to treat everything else in an offhand manner, is the essential psychologic fact. Highly endowed individuals can indulge in such liberties without notable loss in the sharpness of their observations. Either the rest may fit, or else they arrive at an interpretation in which everything except the one detail must be more or less amorphous. Thus, in the figures in card III, the "stuffed birds" for the upper portion (the head and trunk) are F–, according to Rorschach. But "two men dressed up as birds" (because of the heads) is a DW+. Another example would be "a mill on a hill" in card V. DW responses are usually given in card VI, chiefly because of a positive, sthenic overcoming of the difficulties stemming from the card's heavy darks. Examples are "a rabbit skin," because the large lateral projections are seen as "paws"; or, starting from the upper detail, "Phoenix risen out of the ashes"; or, "a sparrow that is leaving a pool drawing a wake behind him"; or, "the Lord is spreading out his arms and saying 'Let there be light.'" An example of DdW+ in card VI is "a cat skin," because of the "whiskers."

A special variety of DW is the *white-space whole response*. It is advisable to group together all the whole responses in which the white spaces play a prominent role as DsW. Following a proposal by Zulliger,[3] these responses can be subdivided into two groups: SW and WS. In scoring the protocol, a DsW may be set down first, and then SW or WS, as the case may be, above it. SW is defined as a whole response in which a very sharply perceived interpretation of the white space is the point of departure, whereas the rest is confabulated. Such responses are essentially analogues of DW–. The WS, on the other hand, is a whole response in which the white space

---

[2]The assertion is frequently made that all DW's are, as such, DW–'s. In only two writers have I found a positive assertion that there is DW+. One is in Beck's samples, in Vol. II of his text "Rorschach's Test" (p. 12) "Some DW are F+, some F—"; and in Ruth Bochner and Florence Halpern, The Clinical Application of the Rorschach Test, New York, 1942, p. 6: "Good DW or DdW responses are not impossible; and in some records may occur with considerable frequency."

[3]Zulliger, H.: Der Z-Test, Berne, 1948, pp. 22 and 34.

is worked in only secondarily, while the forms are seen more sharply; these responses are more closely related to DW+. Although a distinction between the two cannot always be made with certainty, it must be attempted because of the considerable practical importance involved. Example of a WS: card I, "a mask with eyes and mouth." Example of SW: card I, in the inverted position, "a gate." (It goes without saying that SW's are secondary wholes.)

(b) When the percept is not a W, it is in most instances a *detail response,* or D. D is common, usually on the larger details; most of the others are labeled Dd (see below). Whether or not a detail is "common" is determined not only by the frequency with which the detail is perceived by Subjects, but also by its size, form, and position. That certain laws of Gestalt psychology must thus be taken into consideration is apparent; Rorschach himself intuitively felt and hinted at this when he said (p. 39) that their delimitation from Dd rests on "factors not yet fully studied" and mainly on investigations concerning "individual sensitivity to special rhythms."[4]

The D's, as Klopfer and also Brosin and Fromm have correctly emphasized, are "sub-wholes" or "part-wholes," in the Gestalt sense;[5] they are usually either entirely or partly "insular" or "peninsular" in shape. Details that are relatively small and that have these features can be D in accordance with these principles when the form has much *Prägnanz* and, most of all, when it has an appropriate *position.* (Statistical frequency is only a consequence of these factors.) Mid-portions especially are apt to be D's. Rorschach calls attention to the black, pointed detail in card II and to the blue in the center of card VIII (p. 39). With these belong also the horn-like details in the upper center of card I; the humps, however, which in fact lie more medially, are not D since their form is less compelling. The brown dot detail in the center of card X, although not treated uniformly by Rorschach, must nevertheless be rated a D because of its isolated, insular shape and its central position, analogous in this sense to the pointed detail in card II. The best example to show how figure and ground play determining roles is provided by the center detail within the lower center green of card X. With the card in the normal position, this detail is a D when seen as "rabbit's head" with dark "eyes." With the card inverted, this portion, without the "eyes," becomes a Dd ("little figure"). This is confirmed in the statistical findings.

Generally speaking there are no great difficulties in distinguishing D

[4]It should be noted that Rorschach died in 1922, whereas Wertheimer's fundamental work on Gestalt factors was not published till 1923.

[5]Klopfer and Kelley, The Rorschach Technique, pp. 92-93; Brosin and Fromm, op. cit., p. 9.

from W. It is to be noted only that in card VI, inverted, Rorschach correctly scores a percept of "two boys" or "two masks" W, even though no attention is being paid to the projection. This response is a kind of "technical W," manifested also in card III. The percept can be scored a D only when the projection is specifically and explicitly excluded, or perhaps covered up, as was the case with the "animal skin" response.

(c) "The small-detail answers are those which remain after the statistically common D's are subtracted from the total." So states Rorschach in his original summary defining the Dd's (p. 39). But he makes some important additional comments, to the effect that the Dd's consist of three heterogeneous groups. (Some hasty critics have thrown this up to Rorschach as a reproach, but understanding psychologists will grasp his position and be grateful to him, for he has actually anticipated certain psychologic principles which we are only today beginning to understand theoretically.)[6]
The three classes of Dd responses are as follows:

1. The smallest details and parts of D. These will be either (a) the very smallest portions which, although shown independently, do not easily arrest the attention and hence are not frequently perceived (e.g., "the squirters" of card I), or (b) small projections and corners, or contours or parts of contours ("coasts," etc.). Then, too, (c) they may be details within the inner design of the large D's, provided these are not D's themselves as a consequence of *Prägnanz* or of central position (e.g., the black portion in the lower half of the center D in card I).

2. Details cut off in an unusual way (deviating from the more usual Gestalt percepts). An example of this is the "soldiers' memorial," organized from card I as follows: from the center detail the entire upper half is extracted, and with it is taken only the darker portion of the lower half. Of the lateral details only the upper half is utilized.

3. In very exceptional cases the usual D may become Dd if seen "from a quite unusual viewpoint, in peculiar relationship" (Rorschach, p. 39). Here, too, of course, Gestalt-psychology points of view manifest themselves. In card I, for example, the upper half of the lateral is seen, not as the usual animal head with the snout pointing outward, but as a donkey's or a hound's head with the snout lying in the medial edge of the details; the wings and heads of the lateral figure then become the two ears. Another example is the black pointed detail of card II, which is seen as two heads with pointed hats leaning back to back. This third class of Dd neatly demonstrates that, in judging the Gestalt factors of the manner of approach, a relationship exists between approach and the interpreted results, which is, in fact, Rorschach's own opinion.

[6]In this connection see K. W. Bash's interesting report in Rorschachiana III.

It follows from the foregoing that in respect to area a Dd can be larger than a D, as in the case of the infrequently selected upper half of card IV being seen as a chandelier. This response is Dd; the perceived image is cut off quite artificially and its lower limits are not indicated within the blot stimulus. The fact is that a Dd can be put together out of a number of D's, as we have just seen in the example of the "soldiers' memorial."

The question of D or Dd is a *Gestalt* problem. For the most important positions, however, we can rely with confidence on the tradition created by Rorschach himself. How the various principles of Gestalt psychology are weighed against one another also in this established classification is best shown by the example of the several mid-details of card VI. The black in the pedestal (the leg of a chair) is a D, owing to its position and to its form *Prägnanz*. But the mannikin above it, i.e., the black in the upper middle, is a Dd because of its less sharp contour and because it is only part of a more "pregnant" form. Correspondingly, the middle of the upper extension, with or without the "pregnant" pedestal detail (in the former case it is a bell), is a D. The uppermost part of the detail is also a D because of both its peninsular projection out of the entirety and its position in the midplane. Since in the course of the building up of the entire figure the lower part of the midline (Rorschach's "curling iron") is much less frequently attended to, it is a Dd. The entire midline can, however, quite rightly be considered a D, not only because of its size and position but because of the relative ease with which it is extracted and the *Prägnanz* of its form (e.g., "a sword," a "newspaper holder," or a "gimlet"). All these responses are, in fact, borderline cases. They can be established empirically, statistically, by experiment, and in accordance with practice, but it is also possible to understand and explain them theoretically.

Statistical frequency actually follows the classificatory principles set up by Rorschach on the basis of internal evidence. For that reason, frequency statistics can be drawn upon as an indirect line of evidence when a decision has to be made in practice. It would be a mistake, however, to follow this evidence slavishly, particularly since most of the statistics now available have been derived from material that is by no means representative.[7] The brain functions of scholars cannot be established as a standard for farm hands or ships' crews. It goes without saying that to decide on doubtful and borderline instances by the utilization of statistics alone can and must lead to untenable results, the truth of which observation is shown by, for

[7]As Arthur Guirdham correctly says, sufficiently many-sided material of normal persons is lacking: "Rorschach's cases were mostly Bernese householders, Vernon's were Yale undergraduates, and mine, nurses." (On the value of the Rorschach test, Journal of Mental Science, 1935, p. 868.) Also, most American statistics were based on high school and university students.

example, Beck's research. Nevertheless, that these frequency statistics are valuable in and of themselves can be seen in the work of Ralph R. Brown. By using them one can obtain interesting insight into the psychologic structure of certain cultural groups and of populations that are geographically differentiated. Still, for practical purposes the classification should always be made *first* on the basis of the meaning of the matter, with statistics being drawn in only secondarily.

Before concluding this section the reader should also be aware of the DdD responses, analogous to the DW. DdD's are usual details, but their selection has been determined by primary concentration on a small detail. For the most part these are good forms, in contrast to DW; for example, in card IV, the midsection seen as a "crab's head" (because of the eyes); or card VI, in which the top is seen as "cat's head" (because of the vibrissae).

(d) One particular kind of detail was originally considered by Rorschach a "special form of Dd," but has since been established as a more or less independent entity. These responses, labeled Ds, are the space forms, or perceptions of the *white spaces* either between the black or colored blot details or bordering the figures as little bays within the dark or colored details, which may be seen as solid figures themselves. These responses are classic examples of reversal of figure and ground; there are even details as the upper lateral projection of card IV, where the detail itself and a portion of the white background may actually reverse. In cards II and IX only, the white spaces are more easily perceived because of the factor of closure and their central position. For these reasons the occurrence of this detail category is comparatively rare.

When the selected space detail is unusually small or cut off in an unusual way, it is necessary to score the response Dds, analogous to Dd. This is also the case when only a portion of a larger space detail is being interpreted.

In several instances the perceived white space is combined with an adjoining detail or small detail. When these additional portions are insignificant, they may be disregarded (but see Chapter 5, "Fusion of Figure and Background"), but if they are classified as larger D or surrounding Dd with the space detail, e.g., seen as "eye," it would be better to score DsD, DsDd or, if necessary, DdsD or DdsDd.

(e) The last group of modes of approach are the *"oligophrenic Dd's"* or *Do's,* so-called because Rorschach originally thought they were typical for mental deficiency. (More will be said about this point later in describing their symptomatic significance.) A Do is a perception of a part of a human or an animal form where "normal" subjects may easily see the whole human or the whole animal. This is most easily explained in card III: instead of the whole human, a Subject may see the head, neck, or legs, that is, see them only as head, neck, or legs, and not as something else. Another example of Do is to see a "caterpillar head" for the upper lateral portion of the red detail in card X, in inverted position. (The entire red can be and frequently is seen as a whole caterpillar.) A percept of the pegs, card I upper middle, as "hands" is similarly scored Do because the entire mid-portion is often seen as a human with upraised hands; likewise, a visualization of these projections as "crab's nippers" is Do since the upper half of the middle is usually seen as a common crab. If, however, they are seen as "antlers of a roebuck," it is not Do because there is no roebuck here. Where there is justification for seeing only the indicated body part, the response is not Do. The green profiles in card IX are for this reason D, but the lateral portion of the same detail seen as "human head," with the card held with the top either to right or left, is Do, since here the entire human is to be seen.

Thus, the decisive factor in this classification is the content of the percept. Whether the selected portion would or would not, with another interpretation, be a Dd does not matter. The pegs at the upper middle of card I would otherwise be a D. The two upper red details in card II are Do when seen as heads (e.g., "with night caps on") even though this is out of proportion to the rest. (The majority of subjects imagine the white spaces to be the face of the clown.) Nevertheless, it is correct to score Do here because the association "heads" would normally lead at once to seeing the entire as whole human.

Care must be taken not to score Do if the whole human or animal has already *been* seen; an example of this would be when the men in card III have been previously perceived, and the legs selected thereafter.

Under some circumstances it cannot easily be determined whether the response is Do. Thus, when the entire is original, but the selected detail is not, Do is not to be considered. Such an example is the detail in the upper edge of card IV, "the castle," which Morgenthaler has identified as "Michel." Under no circumstances should the percept "a face" be scored a Do, even though one can very readily conceive the upper lateral portions as a body and put the two together to make an "acrobat." In fact, with the card on the right or on the left side, this detail, together with portions beneath it, can be seen as a story teller sitting with knees drawn under him, pointing a warning forefinger. These interpretations, however, would be originals, and the latter very original. It would therefore be unjustifiable to consider the face alone a Do. The situation is similar with respect to the llama or goat's head in card IX (between the green and the brown). Here, too, to see a whole animal, although not original, is infrequent enough so that the head alone is not scored as Do. This response is, on the contrary, popular.

It is different if the selected portion is itself an original but the entire body then must necessarily be seen. In this case, a Do is nevertheless to be scored. When, for example, a Subject sees the upper portion of the lateral (heads of the lateral) in card I as a "head with arm and flying hair," it is, to be sure, a very nicely seen original, but is, nevertheless, a Do. The head and arm do belong to a running girl (the profile seen lateral), but the entire girl is there. The considerations are similar with relation to the thick lateral projections in card V. If one of these is seen as a human leg, it is Do, although this portion is not original; but to see the entire "beggar lying down" would be original. Still, it is a relatively easy percept, once the leg has first been seen as such, and so the leg alone is to be scored Do.

(f) In instances in which one can establish a *tendency* to one of the modes of approach, without strictly sticking to one of the forms: a tendency to Dd, Ds, Do, etc. is noted. Such may be the case when there are indications of Dd, Ds, or Do, in elaborating a W or D response, or in inserted remarks. Of this kind would be the descriptive remark, "Here are some more small spots, but I do not know what they mean." Or the response may be a borderline Dd, Ds, or Do, although one cannot decide that the scoring is the correct one. For practical purposes it is well to note the tendency, e.g., Do, in the form of exponent. Thus, the response "boots" to the lateral details of card IV and "collar" for the neck in the men of card III are D and Dd, respectively. They are pieces of clothing and not parts of the body. "Legs" and "neck" would be Do. But in both instances Do is, so to speak, "in the air," and in most of these test records true Do are likely to be found. Should this be the case, the notation "tendency to more" is to be entered in the summary of the Do.

### 2. THE DETERMINANTS

The column for the determinants, which come second in the scoring formulas, is the most important of all. It gives information concerning the inner experience of the Subject and, at the same time, constitutes the very core of the method. Here we ascertain whether the Subject's responses were determined by form or other factors with, or in place of, form.

(a) If the form alone sets the process going, we note the percept as a *form response* and symbolize it with an F. Good forms are differentiated from poor ones by the notations F+ and F−. The "good" forms are established by findings in the average normal subject of good mental health. (Rorschach uses the term "of sound mind.") When such results are not at hand one must rely on his own judgment. Some persons may be so familiar with zoologic science that they reject the percept "butterfly" for the first card seen as a whole. Nevertheless, we must acknowledge the "common sense" of the average person; *he* thinks it is a good butterfly. As a matter of fact, this response is given by about 30 per cent of all subjects. Naturally, those that are better than these average forms are also F+.

Among the other form responses, F−, we may distinguish two groups, the *unclear F−* and the *indefinite F−*. As I have already pointed out in my treatise in Rorschachiana I,[8] the concept of form-clearness implies two differing factors: a certain definiteness of the object as named, and the resemblance of the blot to the object. The Subject's statement may be definite enough, but often the resemblance is not there. We then have unclear F−. For example, a Subject may say "a flying angel," but the indicated detail looks entirely different. If, however, the statement of the Subject is uncertain, we have an indefinite F−; this applies for example, if the response is "something anatomic" or "some sort of living thing." Here it is not at all a question of clear or unclear form, for there is no form at all and the response is amorphous. Our indefinite F− corresponds to the "noncommittal form response" in America. It is advisable to identify these indefinite F− responses with the additional notation "indef." near or over the F− sign.

As to the light-dark-determined responses, which will be discussed in the next part of this chapter, Binder[9] has described, as early as 1933, "primitive light-dark responses," in which "only a rough and vague general idea emerges." (We will learn more about these in connection with the psychopathies.) However, the appearance of these indefinite responses is not limited to the light-dark responses; they also occur in pure form responses. Some examples follow (nearly all are W for the respective test cards): "the skeleton of a vertebrate" (IV); "an object cut out in the center" (V); "prehistoric animal" (IV); "something enlarged" (IV); "animal-like" (VI); "something on which the upper figures are standing" (VII, lower third); "something of a human body" (I); "something light" (VII); "something hanging in the air" (VII); "something on which the pot is standing" (VII, lower third).

On the question whether certain individual responses are F+ or F−, there is likely to be much controversy. The subjectivity involved is nevertheless much less significant than the inexperienced student or layman might think. The doubtful instances that now and then will appear actually comprise only a small fraction of the response totals for any test record obtained by an experienced worker. If sufficiently comprehensive and variable test material is available, one may be guided by statistics in scoring such doubtful cases. But, as I have already pointed out, it is a mistake to use only statistics as a means of determining form accuracy,

[8]Der Rorschach-Test und seine Weiterentwicklung. Rorschachiana I, Berne, 1945.
[9]Binder, H.: Die Helldunkeldeutungen im psychodiagnostischen Experiment von Rorschach. Schweizer Archiv für Neurologie und Psychiatrie 30: 246, 1933.

since certain rare forms may possess a high quality of clearness while other, decidedly poor forms sometimes occur with great frequency. This may be a consequence of the wide spread of the neuroses. Statistics are primarily an *aid* to science, a fact that today seems to be greatly overlooked.

Whether or not the inaccurate (poor) anatomic forms which are frequently seen in card I are F+ or F− responses, however, is a controversial question of major importance.[10] (Example are "pelvis" and, more rarely, "thorax," etc.) Rorschach considered them F− because he regarded the poor anatomic forms as basically pathologic. Professor Harald K. Schjelderup, of Oslo, however, one of the best experts on the test, has advanced a contrary opinion, namely, that the response is so frequent among virtually healthy persons that it is even a popular response (see below) and thus cannot be scored F−. In spite of this reasoning I myself prefer to follow Rorschach's scoring, on the ground that this response discloses a trace of neurotic mechanism in virtually healthy persons too. The very fact of our living in a "neurotic age," when a large number of people show traces of neurosis, would itself be veiled if we were to judge by "statistical normality." Thus, I prefer to construe Rorschach's requirement for normality as meaning "ideal norm."

It is now increasingly becoming the practice to create a new intermediate category between F+ and F−, designated F±. Zulliger especially has followed this practice in the Bero-Test. We agree with K. W. Bash, however, when he advises against beginners using this category, since it may be misconstrued and misused. The beginner would do better in compelling himself to face the issue in every instance. The F± category can be quite useful in the hands of the more advanced examiner, however, for whom such didactic aspects are no longer so important. These scorings come under consideration (a) in truly doubtful instances, where the form is not altogether sharp but, on the other hand, is not so poor that one can readily decide it is F−; and (b) for certain group concepts which, although somewhat indefinite, are more sharply defined than the truly indefinite F−. Among the latter belong maps and groups of islands that are not identified in detail. When the response is "a country," "some group of islands," etc., which can never be entirely good or entirely poor, it is recommended that Zulliger be followed and the response scored F±. However, maps of specific countries (e.g., "France") must naturally be scored F+ or F−, depending on the clarity of the form. Thus, differences exist among the F±'s themselves—the "half unclear" and the "half indefinite" F±. But such distinctions are less important and, for practical purposes, may be disregarded, provided these responses do not appear in too great numbers.

[10]Good anatomic responses to card I also occur, e.g., "os sphenoidale."

Finally, there is the problem of the red lateral animal details in card VIII. If they are definitely seen as "wolves," "salamanders," "rats," etc., the scoring is, of course, F+. Frequently, however, subjects will only say "two animals," which conceivably could be scored F±. This, however, is not done, and for good reason. As K. W. Bash[11] maintains, this response, far from being given by persons of inferior or defective intelligence, is actually more often obtained from highly endowed individuals to whom the figures are so ordinary that they simply do not find it worthwhile to go into details. Only in those rare instances in which the Subject spontaneously thinks it over and then says he does not know what kind of animals they are, can one score F± or (following Rorschach) F−. It is best to ask the Subject at once, "But what kind of animal?" The response will then be more definite, or the Subject will simply repeat "animals," or he will say that he does not know. The latter two would then be F−.

(b) We come now to the most important, the most difficult, and the most controversial problem in Rorschach test scoring, the *movement response,* or M. The identifying of the M associations is, as Rorschach himself admits, "the most delicate problem in the entire experiment" (p. 26). Movement responses may be defined as form responses that have developed with a kinesthetic influence. They are responses in which "memory pictures of movements observed, imagined, or executed previously by the Subject have had a determining influence" (Rorschach, p. 23). Here we may be dealing with *Kinesthetic* memory pictures, also in the case of movements formerly *seen.*

Quite a number of learned articles have been written on the development of M, but the best explanation, developed long before Rorschach, is to be found in Freud's "Wit and its Relation to the Unconscious."[12] Freud writes, "I acquired the image of a given large movement while carrying it out or imitating it, and by this operation I acquired a measure of that movement in the sensations of my innervations. . . . Now then when I perceive some similar more or less large movement in another person, my most certain way of understanding it—of its apperception—is for me to imitate that movement. I can then compare and judge at which movement my own energy expenditure was the greater. Such pressure towards imitating certainly occurs on perceiving movements. Actually, however, I do not really imitate any more than I would spell out even though I once learned to read by spelling. Instead of imitating the movements with my muscles, I activate the traces of my memory imagery bound up with the energy expenditure for similar movements." He goes on to say that, as physiology

[11] Personal communication to the writer.

[12] Freud, S.: Der Witz und seine Beziehung zum Unbewussten. Wien, 1905, pp. 164-166, in Vol. VI of "Gesammelte Werke," London, 1940, pp. 218-221.

teaches us, "also in the course of the imagining, nerve impulses are transmitted to the muscles which, indeed, corresponds to only a modest excitement."[13] This is how facial expressions and expressive movements (and also M) arise; this is, in effect, the theory of M. We may say, then, with A. Weber, that the M arises out of a virtual execution of movements. (See Palagyi, Warhnehmungslehre, Leipzig, 1925.[14])

In some instances it is a matter of direct tendencies to movement that are experienced as kinesthetic sensations. The Subject says, for example, "Here are two gentlemen who are greeting each other very courteously," and he makes the corresponding gestures with hands and body. Generally speaking, ideational representations will suffice. In the field of kinesthetics, perceptions and images are especially difficult to distinguish.[15] One must be careful not to confuse kinesthetic experience with movement that is only optically perceived. As Twitmyer's investigations[16] with the Labyrinth tests have shown, optical experience is not a substitute for kinesthetic experience. Before a response can become an M, the movement must be *felt* and not simply seen. Since the subject must live what he has seen, the factor of *identification is always present.*

From this discussion, two considerations follow:

(1) *Not all described movements are M.* I can see much movement, as an optical datum, without "being in swing" with it. Ordinarily, normal persons will not identify themselves with a flying duck, a fleeing deer, or a falling vase. With regard to animals, the following rule is basic: Only anthropomorphic animals and those that have been made anthropomorphic can, in general, be seen as M; it does not follow, however, that they *must* be seen in that way. The principal anthropomorphic animals are bears, apes, sloths, and the like. It must be noted that the lateral animal details of card VIII are generally *not* M, even when they are bears climbing over something, because then their movements are not at all human-like. By animals made anthropomorphic I mean animals that, while not in them-

[13]As Alfred Goldscheider shows experimentally in his work, "Physiologie des Muskelsinns" (Leipzig, 1898), every lively image of a movement evokes at least a beginning of the act itself. (Cited according to Binder, "Die Helldunkeldeutungen im psychodiagnostischen Experiment von Rorschach. Schweiz. Arch. f. Neur. u. Psych., 30: 46, 1933.) According to David Katz, who distinguishes between "imitation reflexes" and "imitation actions," this imitation of seen movements together with the tendency to imitate linguistic sounds heard, demonstrated by Le Dantec, is the only reflex-like repetition of movements. (David Katz, Handbok i psykologi, Stockholm, 1950, pp. 281-282.)

[14]Weber, A.: Über die Bewegungsdeutungen. Zürich, 1941. Quoted Roland Kuhn, Über Maskendeutungen im Rorschach'schen Versuch. Basel, 1944, pp. 81 and 122.

[15]Woodworth, R. S.: Experimental Psychology. London, 1938, p. 45.

[16]Woodworth, R. S.: op. cit., pp. 145-146.

selves human-like, artistically are made to resemble humans and then, naturally, are experienced as such. In this connection not only the various animal creations of Walt Disney (Donald Duck, Mickey Mouse, etc.) but also Lewis Carroll's animals in "Alice in Wonderland" come to mind. Children, being more totem-minded than adults, have a wider range of anthropomorphic animal responses. In rare instances, some adults of infantile character identify with animals other than those mentioned above (see chapter 5).

Normal adults will only rarely overstep the said limit. A "leaping frog" (whole response to card IV) is no M, but an excellent F+ and an original. However, certain Subjects, chiefly artists or artistically minded persons may be so inclined to the kinesthetic that even lower forms of animals or inanimate objects may come to life for them (as in fairy tales) and be experienced as true M. But this is exceptionally rare. It is best to follow the rule: to him that has, shall be given. In other words: In attempting to determine a true M we would do well to follow Rorschach's procedure (p. 26) and make the *sure* M's our points of departure, i.e., if the subject already has eighteen certain and unequivocal M's in his record, we may without hesitation count two more doubtful responses as M. (With regard to inquiry, see below, "Inquiry.")

As Beck[17] points out, the tendency to overlook a true M is rare in the literature; if anything, the danger lies in the opposite direction—an M is frequently scored where none exists. The abuse here is widespread; everything possible and even impossible is scored as M or some subform of M. We are indebted to Beck for having denounced this practice (p. 93) and we must emphasize the dangerously fallacious aspects of this "label" psychology, as Beck terms it. Explosions, volcanoes, flashes of lightning, or objects floating around in the air are almost *never* M. Simple descriptions of a movement seen only as such, or of a position, even in humans or in anthropomorphic animals, is not sufficient to determine an M response. Even the human figures usually seen as M—card I (the middle) and cards II and III—are *not always* M. Responses such as "caricatures," "drawings," "shadows" of men, and the like, always create the suspicion that they are seen but not felt. When a Subject says, in a sleepy tone, "two men," and then perhaps moreover describes the parts ("Here is the head, the eyes, the arms and legs"), we may be sure that we are not dealing with an M. The Subject may actually go so far as to describe the bearing of the men; yet this is so obviously an "optical" perception that we may unhesitatingly dismiss any idea of kinesthetic feeling.

(2). The second conclusion derived from the tenet that M must be under-

---

[17]Beck, S. J.: Rorschach's Test, I. Basic Processes. New York, 1944, p. 92.

stood as experienced, and not only seen movement is that *a response scored as M does not itself always have to be seen in movement.* Even to feel oneself as being in a bodily posture may be a kinesthetic reaction. A catatonic schizophrenic, contemplating card V, gives the response "two Chinese who have dropped dead" (Rorschach, p. 159); this is an M, even though the Chinese are lying quite motionless. We may get similar associations of "fallen" persons from epileptics. Both these groups, the catatonics and epileptics, typically have a special understanding of the psychologic experience of the stiffened and of the fallen. A soldier standing "at attention" is a fine example of M, while a "leaping deer" is practically never so.

M may even be found in Do responses, e.g., the "upraised hands" for the middle detail in card I, when the "hands" alone are seen. Faces are often M when described in such a way as to disclose a kinesthetic factor: "the face of an angel blowing a trumpet," "someone sticking his tongue out," "a spitting face" or "a twisted face," and those that are seen with "bent" or "stretched out necks" and the like. We must be more cautious with "grinning" and "weeping" faces, where only facial expression is intended. Grinning masks, for example, are seldom M.

Distinction can usually be made between two groups of movement associations: the *extensor* and the *flexor kinesthesias,* but there are also responses in which the two are fused. (See the section on psychologic significance.)

Not all Rorschach students can learn to recognize the M response with equal facility. The ease with which one learns in this important area depends, as Rorschach noted (p. 26) on constitutionally determined kinesthetic factors. Persons at either extreme are at a disadvantage. Those who themselves produce few, if any M responses will find great difficulty in recognizing the M of other individuals, while those who produce a great many M responses do not know the limits of the "ordinary mortal." Such examiners find much more kinesthesia than is actually the case.

M responses, being *also* form responses, are also scored M+ or M−, depending on their form accuracy. The same basic rules that apply to pure form responses also apply here. Thus, M− indicates that the movement has been truly perceived, the kinesthetic factor is entirely intelligible, but the form is a poor one. An epileptic child reacting to the gray detail of card VIII says, "Here comes a dangerous witch." The threatening, expanding, striding aspect of the figure is kinesthetically intelligible, but there is not much of a witch here. In card VII the lower third may be seen as "men lying stretched out;" the detail is actually something that lies, but the form has no resemblance to men. And one more example, "someone chasing a bird," a response to the gray and yellow outer lateral details in card X, is also M−.

In those rare responses which Rorschach calls *"confabulated F-M"* and which must on principle be regarded as F, we are dealing with yet another phenomenon. Here the movement itself is confabulated, and the corresponding form, of course, likewise does not exist. An example of this, in reaction to card IX on either its left or right side, is the response "two little girls (the green) that have climbed on an object (the brown), a stump of a tree; from their faces they look like old aunts." To be sure, the girls can be seen, but not with the card in that (the normal) position, and not as if they were climbing. This response was from an old deteriorated schizophrenic. It may happen that human figures, usually seen as standing still, are confabulated into leaping or running persons. All this is confabulated F-M.

It sometimes happens that the Subject develops his association by first perceiving form and then, after further study, gradually developing a kinesthetic sense which finally comes to expression. Rorschach labels these *secondary movement responses.* (sec. M). In the primary movement associations the kinesthetic develops simultaneously with the form perception. A secondary M response would be, in card III, "Here are two men with thin legs and high collars; incidentally, it seems as if they were pulling at something, quarreling about something."

When the smallest details in a figure are seen in movement and are manifestly M, they are to be indicated as small M, i.e., *small movement response.* Here the distinction from M is only a matter of size; no other views play a part, as is true with Dd responses. Thus, we must not uncritically score every Dd that is seen kinesthetically as a small M. The larger Dd's—e.g., the black mannikin in the upper middle of card IV—are M, only the smallest Dd's— e.g., the lighter "men" in the lower center of card VII—are small M. Psychologic significance varies between the two in many respects and so they are not counted together. The objection has been made that since these associations arise "only together with a great number of M"[18] their interpretation could not be essentially different. But this view has been shown to be incorrect. There are indeed a few test records without a single M in which several small M's do occur.

In rather rare instances an M response seems to appear in some animal perceptions that are "beyond the M boundary," i.e., perceptions of animals which, although as a rule no longer capable of being identified with by adults, are nevertheless apparently experienced as movement. Loosli-Usteri[19] makes the good suggestion that such responses be scored MF, which is similar to the American FM. The fact remains, however, that this response is still to be considered a form response, the scoring symbol probably being

---

[18]Bleuler, M.: Der Rorschach'sche Formdeutversuch bei Geschwistern Zeitschr. f.d. ges. Neur. u. Psychiatrie, *118*: 384, 1929.

[19]Loosli-Usteri, M.: Persönlichkeitsdiagnostik. Rorschachiana II, Berne, 1947, p. 17.

F with an MF exponent. Some American writers, no doubt over-reacting to incidental comments by Rorschach concerning contributory kinesthesia (p. 184 and 191), have set up a special category for animal movements that are not seen in anthropomorphic pose which they score FM. As far as can be seen at the present time, this scoring has done nothing but create confusion, since every possible association that has not the slightest trace of kinesthesia is labeled "animal movement." On this point it is well to again emphasize Beck's warning (above, p. 32). In exceptional instances, of course, such scoring may be justified, but it must be practiced only with greatest caution. The sign MF should be limited to those instances in which the percept borders on an anthropomorphic tendency. If not the animal, at least the movement should have something of the human form in it and be so perceived and experienced. "A bunny is sitting on its hind paws and making bye-bye" or "A bull is advancing with lowered head for the attack" are examples of this type of response. The expression of movement must be vigorous and plastic.

This scoring category is not an absolute necessity. In the very clear instances one may just as well score M, since the M limits I have described above do not by any means constitute a hard and fast rule for everybody, it is rather a rule of thumb.

(c) After form and movement, the third great class of determinants is the *color association,* or C. Rorschach employs the sign C not only as a general identification for all color responses as a group but also as an indication of one of the subgroups. In scientific writings, it is advisable to identify the group as a whole by using the term "color interpretations."

Since some of the Rorschach test cards contain bright colors, it often happens that a response is determined by the color, either *with* form or *in the place* of form. If the response is determined by form *and* color, there may again be two cases: form may dominate, in which case we speak of a form-color response (FC), or color may dominate, in which case we have a color-form response (CF). When *only color* has been the deciding factor, we have a primary (or pure) color response (C). Generally, these discriminations present no great difficulties.

(1) The *form-color responses* (FC) are again differentiated according as the forms are good or poor; hence the signs FC+ and FC− are used. By far the greater number of such responses are FC+. Examples: In card VIII the blue detail seen as "two silk lounge pillows"; in card IX, "cooked crayfish" for the upper brown details and "a poplar" for the middle line; in card X, "caterpillars" for the green in the lower middle, "grasshoppers" for the upper lateral green, "cornflower" for the lateral blue. (But simply "flowers" here would be a CF.) Some "butterflies" are also FC, e.g., the lower red of card II in most instances. On the other hand, in card III the middle

red is usually F+. Still, "a tropical butterfly" or "a red butterfly such as in the tropics" would be FC. The expression "red butterfly" requires further inquiry; it may only be a way of identifying the detail. In card VIII a percept of the lateral details as "red polar bears" is not FC but F+, since here the color is mentioned only because "red" does not belong. "*Lucus a non lucendo.*" When the color is used only for localizing the detail as, in fact, it frequently is, the scoring is also F+ ("Yellow dogs" for the inner middle yellow of card X. When, however, this detail is seen as "lions," it is usually FC.) Similarly, the response, in card IX, "the green is two faces," where "green" serves only to identify the detail, is F+, whereas "The Green Face" (Gustav Meyrink) would be FC+. "Foxes" as a percept of the lateral animal details in card VIII is quite frequently FC+, but it is best to make further inquiry about this one after the test. (See below.)

Occasionally, FC responses may be given in reaction to black, gray, or white details. In the case of gray this response may even occur in the color figures, e.g., in card VIII, "a distant mountain" for the upper gray detail.

The FC– associations provide more difficulties. In color associations in which the form is poor, the inclination is to score CF. Here the classifications of unclear and indefinite forms again become useful. If the reaction is definite but the form percept unclear, we have an FC–. If a subject decides that a detail with a pink hue is a "crayfish"—e.g., the lateral red in card VIII —and if this form does not fit, it is a FC–; a typical FC– is the response, given by a functionally retarded (pseudodebil) neurotic, to the lower middle green of card X (the usual caterpillars): "Two parrots with heads and tails." In this sample, there is direct evidence in the verbalization that the form was the primary determinant. Other examples: in card III, the upper lateral reds seen as "two pantaloons"; in card X, the middle blue seen as "a heraldic animal." What counts in these instances is that the subject obviously *wants* to give what is primarily a form association, with color a secondary consideration; but the form accuracy does not quite succeed. With such persons it is useless to inquire for more details because intellectual functioning is so reduced that they do not grasp what is involved.

(2) *Color-form responses* (CF) are determined primarily by color and only secondarily by form. The form element in most of these instances is indefinite and "vague." Among typical CF responses are "entrails," "explosion," and, more recently, "an atom bomb," for card IX. In card VIII, similar examples are "icebergs" or "lakes" for the central blue. Responses such as "ornaments" or "wallpaper design" for the whole of cards VIII, IX and X are nearly always CF. So also, in these figures, are the indefinite "maps" and the frequent but indefinite anatomy associations. (An anatomy association for the entire card VIII is sometimes DW, if the blue in the center is the point of departure.) Rorschach had originally scored cer-

tain special responses as CF–. Later, he evidently gave this practice up. It might occasionally be necessary to score an extremely poor CF as original–.

(3) The *primary color responses* (C) are determined by color only, and they are more nearly related to the free colors described by Katz. This may especially be seen in the response "sky" to any of the blue details. Among other typical C associations are "blood" or "tomato sauce" (for red), "water" (for blue), "forest" (for green), and the like. If a form element emerges, the response must be scored CF as, for example, "a stain of blood," "squirts of blood," "forest on a map," "color on a painter's palette," this last being a response to the whole of card X.

If the subject simply mentions or enumerates colors, we have *color naming* ("that is red," "black and red," "three colors," "five colors"). A number of students score CN here, but this is not essential. The scoring D C Color (or W C, as the case may be) suffices. However, in adding up the summary in these instances the examiner must note color namings separately and evaluate them as such. Under no circumstances can color naming be put into the same category with the rest of the color responses. They have a psychologic significance of their own. There are times, however, when they can be distinguished from the purely descriptive comments only with great difficulty. "And now we have colors" is *not* a color naming. (For more on this subject, see chapter 5.)

(d) In rare instances both *M and C together* determine a response. Here we must first inquire whether one or the other component is the predominant or the primary one. Thus, if in card II the "dancing clowns" are seen first, and only later perceived as having "red caps," the response is to be scored M. If "red caps" emerges later as a response on its own, it is scored DFC+. It is much rarer to have the converse of this, which Rorschach illustrates by the example of the response "cardinal purple" being given to the large red details of card X and, a little later, the response "two cardinals are striding towards each other" being developed. In such a case it is preferable to score two responses: the first C, the second M. MC is to be scored only in the rare instances where both factors appear to be contributing simultaneously. "Witches' sabbath" for card IX is an example, as is also (inverted position) "a stout lady decked out in colors bestriding the ballroom in all her glory." (This last was presented in the form of a quotation from a Swedish poet.)

The scoring symbol MFC+ should be used only in exceptional cases, as in this response to card VIII (inverted): "A couple of persons (white space detail between lateral red and the middle) are sitting at a table (blue) with a lamp on it" (center red). The scoring is DsD MFC+ Scene, O+, the essential thing being the M in the persons who are sitting down. The form is so good that it would be unfair, from the point of view of form scoring, to leave it MC. (As will be seen in discussion of summarizing, the color assessment in the MC scoring formulas is CF.) If we were to disregard the color altogether, the lampshade would be missing. To break up the response is hardly advisable, because the essential factors here are the organizing of the DsD and the fusing of figure and background. Another example where it would be proper to score MFC+ is the following: "A big funny wizard, who is ashamed because he has a red head and large ears." The response was given to the whole of card IX in the inverted position. (Concerning MLD, see the next portion of this chapter.)

(e) The most important determinants are form, movement, color, and light-dark-determined associations (described below). Two other determinants are found in schizophrenics, in schizoid individuals, and in children, namely, the idea of using the *number* of blot details as association determinants—e.g., two spots called "father and mother," "six faces" in card VII and "Kullman and Guest" for two tiny details, these responses being obtained from one of our schizophrenics—and the so-called *"position" responses*, the latter seemingly determined chiefly by positions seen. (Example: "Heart," because the detail seen is in the center of the figure.) Although the great majority of such percepts are anatomic in nature, there are also some that are not anatomic. A fine example is reported by Beck[20]: the two gray details at the top of card VIII seen as "the North Pole."

### 3. THE CONTENT

To classify content is the simplest task in the entire test technique. Abbreviations have been established for the most important categories: H for the whole human figure; Hd (human detail) for a portion of a human; A for an entire animal; Ad (animal detail) for a portion of an animal; Anat for anatomy; Sex; Bt for botanical; Ls for landscape (or N for nature); Oj for objects (inanimate); Arch for architecture; Orn for ornamental; Map, not only for maps but also for anything geographical; and Ab for abstracts. All other content is set down unabbreviated. Among these are "food," "scene," "picture," (the monosyllabic German *bild* is sometimes more convenient), "blood," "fire," "water," "clouds," etc.

Like Peer Gynt, we make no distinction in the Rorschach test between "troll" and "man." Trolls, ghosts, gnomes, and the like, despite their occasionally having an animal attribute, e.g., tail, belong basically among the human-form responses. Indeed, such percepts are frequently direct parent images. In any event, both the content and the special features in these responses are nearly always derived from the human element in the Subject's environment.

[20]Beck, S. J.: Rorschach's Test. Basic Processes. New York, 1944, p. 150.

"Masks," to be sure, are recorded as such (see chapter 5), but they are to be counted among the Hd responses rather than as a separate category. This becomes important in establishing what amounts to a stereotype around the face which might easily be overlooked, since nearly always a few masks will be found among them.

Animal skins are considered by Rorschach as A and not Oj. He is certainly correct, for when the interpretation is "skin from a beast of prey," "a goat's hide," or "animal rug," for cards IV and VI, what is essential is that almost always the form is animal-like, the lateral projections assuming the shape of legs. Rorschach also counts an actual "animal skin" response as A and not Ad. This is to be kept in mind, since his findings depend on these scorings. Animals in anthropomorphic pose and animals in human movement are, naturally, A.

Abstract associations are real responses containing an abstract idea: "eternity," "love," "loyalty," "friendship," "liberty," "iron dictatorship," and the like. But such associations as "spring," "summer," and so on are doubtful; they probably belong to the so-called "impressions." One must be on guard against counting as responses and then labeling as Ab certain expressions which are not responses at all. Among these are symmetry, impressions, descriptions, and evaluating remarks. Comments such as "These two are exactly alike"; "here are two halves"; "beautiful curve, I like it"; "this gives me a sense of movement"; "I can't stand red"; "Oh what colors!" are not Ab.

### 4. ORIGINALITY

Certain responses are scored P, popular, or Orig, original, depending on their frequency at one or the other extreme.

(a) Rorschach himself introduced the *"popular"* concept relatively late. At first he had scored only originals. If the same response "was given by approximately every third normal Subject" he considered it a P (p. 184). But, as has already been pointed out in the discussion of the anatomy responses to card I, the innocent word "normal" can present quite a problem. The fact of the matter is that popular responses are less frequent than Rorschach indicates. In the United States some students count with every sixth, rather than every third, Subject[21]; the actual frequency may well be somewhere in between.

Since P responses are determined in considerable measure by factors of environment and by the so-called folk mentality (the national character), they are, to a certain extent, subject to local differences. The clowns of card II, for example, scored W M+, are P in Switzerland and probably

[21]Mary Ford: The Application of the Rorschach Test to Young Children. Minneapolis, 1946, p. 101.

also in other European countries. Native Americans, however, see them only rarely.[22] While in Denmark the middle red of card III seen as "butterfly" is a P, confirming experience in Switzerland, we get the popular "a bow tie" (Swedish: "en rosett") in neighboring Sweden.

Oberholzer correctly claims that there are only about nine P responses that are in any measure international: "bat" or "butterfly" to card I as a whole; "clowns" and the like to card II (W); "two men" and the like to card III (W); "animal skin" to cards IV and VI (W); "bat" or "butterfly" to card V; "human head," "woman's head," etc. to card VII, upper 2/3; "bear head" or "elephant head" to the middle third of card VII; and various animals for the laterals of card VIII. (It will be observed that the two variations "bat" and "butterfly" are applicable to both cards I and V.)

It may happen that the popular response undergoes some essential variation, either in the percept or in the determinant, in which case it is advisable to set the P in parentheses. For example, if, in card VI, the large lower detail, rather than the whole, is seen as "animal fur," the score is (P). This is also true of the "shadow of a bat" in cards I or V, or the two men in card III seen as film figures with birds' heads, in which case, depending on the way it is said, the response may be M or F. Other examples of (P) are, in card IV, "animal skin with ends bent over" or (which happens only rarely) the bat in card V seen as such because "it has sort of hooks (the leg detail) with which to hold on" (DW).

(b) *Original responses* (Orig) are the opposite of popular. Rorschach's position is that a response is original "if given approximately once in one hundred tests of normal Subjects" (p. 45). Since, however, this cannot always be established by statistics, the scoring of "Orig" is also a matter of judgment. Like the P responses, Originals are to be scored according to the frequency of the *response*, not of the blot detail that has been selected. Otherwise many Dd's which are seldom perceived would *eo ipso* be scored originals, which they are not, as for example the many far-fetched small "faces" that one sometimes gets.

Originals are also classified as Orig+ and Orig−, the distinction generally in accordance with the form quality of the response.[23] Originals that are CF or C are usually Orig−. Only with an F± response is it necessary to decide whether it is Orig+ or Orig−, and this decision is generally always easy to make. The classification Orig± is not recommended, since the problem here is not one of quantification, as in regard to F+ per cent,

[22]Brosin and Fromm: Some Principles of Gestalt Psychology in the Rorschach Experiment. Rorschach Exchange, Vol. VI. 1942, p. 10.

[23]Only two exceptions to this rule are found in all Rorschach's illustrations, on his pages 147 and 149.

but solely a question of how really creative or misguided the idea is. It is the originality, in other words, and not the form that is essential.

In order to estimate endowment qualitatively, it is useful, apart from observing the distribution of the originals on the various modes of approach, to undertake an additional *division of the originals.* Zulliger was the first to follow this procedure when, in connection with the Bero-Test, he introduced a classification of interpretation and apprehension originals. It has since become evident that this classification still does not cover all the theoretical features that have proved valuable. Following a proposal by Dr. K. W. Bash, he, Zulliger and the present writer have agreed on the following classification of originals:

1. *Interpretation originals.* These "usual" originals consist of two subgroups: *motif originals,* which bring new contents into the W, D, usual Dd or Ds and *elaboration originals,* which are new arrangements, embellishments, or supplements of a not very original theme. They "develop thorough elaboration on a blot detail the Gestalt of which is not a new one" (Bash).

2. *Apprehension originals.* The originality of these lies less in the content or its elaboration than in the selection of the area responded to, "which is grasped in an unusual way that deviates from the ordinary rules of Gestalt perception" (Bash). It is not an absolute necessity to introduce new scoring formulas here. One can satisfy the needs by writing "Ap" over the scoring of the "apprehension originals," those that, so to speak, "fall out of the row."

In the case of the motif originals, it is necessary to observe whether any of them and, if so, how many are "vocational" originals, that is, originals whose content stems from the Subject's occupation. The great majority of these originals are Orig+.

In elaboration originals it may happen that the same response can be scored both Orig + and P. In cards II and III, for example, the respective responses can be "two persons praying over a sacred fire" and "two persons each with his purse; they are tugging symbolically at the skeleton of the sacrifice (lower gray, middle) which is on their conscience." In evaluating such double scores, the P is usually the more important factor. When the summary is computed each of these categories is counted once.

In the apprehension originals we see striking departures from the usual Gestalt apprehension and figure-ground perceptions. All fusions of figure and background belong here (see chapter 5), as do also many other combinations of white spaces with adjacent details. An example would be, in card III, inverted, the large center white space together with the middle black being seen as "the Via Appia (the white); here are two trees (the middle black); and it ends at a wrought-iron gate" (gray). This association is no fusion of figure and background; yet it is an apperception original because of the unusual breakup and re-combining of the blot details. Should a Subject see in card VI of the Bero series a "scene with a sculpture of gods in the background (the entire) and in the middle (the black) a person coming to sacrifice," two figures are actually being perceived simultaneously. This mode of perception, because it does not consider the middle as figure and the entire as background, is so unusual that it too is scored an apprehension original.

Poor apperception originals are also found. A case in point would be the following response to card X: "A misshaped woman (the whole); the neck bones (mid-gray), her breasts (mid-blue), the uterus (mid-green)." This response was given by a well endowed young person in a neurosis related to puberty.

There are instances in which apprehension originals may at the same time be P. Such is the case when the men in card III are wearing "white aprons" (the white space between the legs and the middle black).

(c) Finally, there are the *individualized originals* (Ind), which Rorschach describes as "percepts that are given only by this one subject" (p. 189). It stands to reason that only the experienced investigators are in a position to score Ind; others had better be content with simply an Orig. But when the investigator of wide experience feels confident that "no one else will ever hit on this association," then the scoring Ind is in order. Examples: in card III, inverted, a response of "an egg from which two baby chicks are slipping out" to the center white space together with the torso of the man; in card V, the whole seen as "the rounding of a berry, with humps," enlarged. In the case of the former percept the association is at the same time an apprehension original. The individualized responses are of course counted among the originals.

PSYCHOLOGICAL VALUES OF THE SCORING SYMBOLS

As shall be repeatedly pointed out, the Rorschach test is anything but a mechanical procedure. Its scoring formulas, the basic principles of which have now been outlined, are not to be taken as the catchwords of "Egyptian dreambooks." Nor does the scientific literature on dreams provide such "translations." To avoid the pitfall of mechanical dreambook technique the student should note Rapaport's caution: "The examiner will be able to avoid the dreambook type of interpretation, the mechanical attitude toward the test, and the idolizing of scoring, only if he has a sound background of psychological and psychiatric theory."[24]

Each separate scoring element has in fact its psychologic significance in each individual case. But this is not a rigid or an unalterable finding; it

[24]Rapaport, D.: Diagnostic Psychological Testing, Vol. II. Chicago, 1945, p. 89.

varies from case to case with the picture as a whole. As several writers[25] have correctly pointed out, the Rorschach protocol represents an entire "Gestalt." We cannot extract the separate ingredients and observe them detached from the whole. Some psychologists of mechanistic mind, finding it too difficult to achieve a painstaking analysis of a structure as a unit designate the test as "unscientific," on the theory that only that is "scientific" which can be established with the mathematical precision of physics. In psychology one cannot think in terms of physics.

Although there are in the scoring formulas of the Rorschach test as a result no hard and fast psychologic meanings valid for all cases, nevertheless psychologic interpretation follows certain main principles. Such basic meanings of the individual test factors, however, are to be understood as only theoretical elucidation; they cannot be used the way one would use a dictionary for the purpose of a "translation." In the present chapter we must be content with a sketchy outline of the basic psychologic meanings, since any thorough discussion would anticipate the problems which will be treated in part Three of this book. Moreover, it is didactically much more advantageous to discuss the psychologic meanings of the separate response categories, relative and ramified as they are, within the framework of the interpretation of a whole test.

### 1. MANNER OF APPROACH

The manner of approach by and large projects the procedural "set" or "mental approach" of the Subject.

(a) W corresponds in general to the ability to obtain an over-all view. It is the grasp of the larger unit and has a relation therefore to the theoretical intelligence as well as to systematic thinking. However, not all W's are evidence of higher theoretical intelligence. A necessary first condition is that the majority of the W's be sharply perceived forms. Many inaccurate W's are found, for example, in deteriorated organics; many indefinite ones in unstable psychopaths. In these responses there is an identifiable quality concerning which more will be said below. But not even all W+ responses are evidence of an especial, theoretical endowment. When they are mostly or, as often happens, all P, the Subject is capable of grasping only the most ordinary concepts. In a more positive sense, W+ P may be considered the expression of "common sense." In persons who have a truly superior theoretical intelligence, many of the W's are not the ordinary ones; and

[25]Kuhn, Roland: Über Rorschach's Psychologie und die psychologischen Grundlagen des Formdeutversuches. In: Psychiatrie und Rorschach'scher Formdeutversuch. Zurich, 1944, p. 41. Also Bochner, R. and Halpern, F.: The Clinical Application of the Rorschach Test. New York, 1942, p. 17.

at least a small percentage of them are quite original. Children are subject to somewhat different rules, as will be seen in chapter 14.

W's are related not only to theoretical interests, however, but are expressions of affective drive for intellectual achievement; a W *is,* in fact, such an expression. Rorschach speaks in this connection of "energy available for associational productivity" (p. 54). For this reason they are evidence of mental interest. If a Subject who exerts excessive effort to attain W, in extreme instances, the pure W+ type who produces only ten responses, all W+, it is considered ambition for quality achievement. (For more on this point see the discussion of qualitative evaluation, under Intelligence.) But such ambition is not always connected with endowment; some subjects with mistaken love of knowledge reveal themselves by their heavy accent on W, the form quality of which is in some cases poor (W±). When the emphasis on W is marked and there is an accent on poor forms (W∓), the clinical picture is likely to be that of the psychopath with a need for self assertion.

In connection with W one may also speak[26] of "formative power," but this interpretation should rest at least in part on the positive correlation between W and M. In any event, it is applicable only with greatest caution; the correlation with M and, of course, the quality of W must be noted, and we must make sure that they are not, to any considerable extent, P.

For DW— the basic psychologic meaning is the tendency to confabulation and unreliability in the thinking and in recall. DW+, on the other hand, could point to a certain kind of constructive thinking.

DW's which are F+ or M+ (mostly in records which have many M's) are found also in artistically endowed daydreamers. In these cases they are indicative of an inhibition in the productive ability that prevents the Subject from using his artistic endowment constructively in the manner of persons with the combinatory W M+, who see all portions in equally sharp form quality.

For DdW the psychologic significance is similar to that of DW; such responses, however, are found more frequently in children and schizophrenics.

DsW usually reflects a tension between subject and his environment (vocation, family), indicating what Zulliger (Bero, p. 57) calls a "central dissatisfaction" which may go to the point of obstinacy. When the response is SW, the source of the tension usually lies deeply embedded in the neurotic traits of the subject himself, while in WS we are dealing with actual environmental irritations where the struggle may be related to political

[26]Fuchs, C.: Hohe Intelligenz. Versuch ihrer experimentellen Erfassung mit dem Rorschach Test. Zeitschrift f. Psychologie, *152*: 1942.

interests, ideology, or the fight for an idea, or also be related to reasonable self-dissatisfaction.[27]

In so-called "difficult" children, DsW may occasionally be the differential diagnostic indicator of traumas effected by the milieu.[28] Accordingly, Bochner and Halpern[29] have often found the DsW in children and young people with insufficiency and insecurity feelings whose parents are divorced (broken homes).

Concerning the rest of the secondary W see chapter 5.

(b) and (c) The D responses of a Rorschach test record indicate a grasp of the near at hand, the immediate, the simple, the practical, and are therefore related to practical intelligence. Correspondingly, the Dd's represent sensitivity to trifles—the minute, the irrelevant, the sophisticated, the far-fetched. In the positive sense they represent the keen power of observation.

To a certain extent the D's are also indicative of social contact. This becomes clearest when, considering the opposite type, we find a marked increase of Dd at expense of D without exception in persons whose social contact is either reduced or impaired as a result of various factors: depression, compulsion-neuroses, compulsive character, and occasionally schizophrenia. Among autistic schizophrenics D will frequently be at a minimum. The "nagger" or the "caviller," with his many Dd's, is a person disappointed in his environment. "He is himself unhappy, otherwise he would not offend you," Friedrich Rückert correctly noted.

A certain anal aggression is also characteristic of the depressives, the compulsion neurotics, the compulsive characters, and the naggers. (In the melancholy, too, as is known, a portion of aggression is hidden.)[30] In addition, the Dd's are naturally favored by persons whose intellectual limitations cause them to restrict themselves to a narrow horizon (few W). As Bochner and Halpern neatly put it, "They are the people who in order to feel important must be big frogs in small ponds."[31] This, too, implies a certain provocative attitude. For similar reasons an increase in Dd appears mostly in feeble-minded persons.

(d) Partly because of their relative rarity, the white space responses are among the most important and the most informative in a Rorschach test record. "They always betray some kind of opposition tendency," Rorschach says, and he notes that even more than one white space response is sufficient to suggest a suspicion. Several writers have criticized this conten-

[27]Zulliger, H.: Der Z-Test. Berne, 1948, p. 34.
[28]Reistrup, H.: Der Rorschach-Test als Hilfsmittel bei der Diagnostizierung von Milieureaktionen. Acta Psychiatrica et Neurologica 21: 687-697, 1946.
[29]Bochner and Halpern, op. cit., p. 30.
[30]Abraham, K.: Versuch einer Entwicklungsgeschichte der Libido. Wien, 1924.
[31]Bochner and Halpern, op. cit., p. 28.

tion (Ernst Schneider and Furrer, among others) on the erroneous supposition that such opposition would always have to be overt—completely misunderstanding Rorschach's opinion. His real comprehension of the significance of the space details is one of the truly original observations of this creative genius.

Simply put, the white spaces are an expression of *aggression*. It must be recalled, however, that there are other aggression indicators in the test, e.g., the anal aggressive Dd and certain complex determined responses in phallic individuals which we will study more closely in the chapter on the neuroses. In the second place, aggression is not always overtly manifest and outwardly directed. The case, then, may be stated as follows: the number of space D responses is an approximate measure of the strength of the aggression. The other aggression indicators (Dd and the "complex" responses, that is, those determined by a neurotic complex) fill in the picture. Hence it is quite natural to find a greater tendency to space details in children and young people than in adults.[32] But where the aggression is located and, most important, against what it is directed, depend on experience balance factors. Thus, the white spaces are an example par excellence of this often overlooked fact: one element of the test cannot be evaluated separately from the other elements, because the result would be a false interpretation. Likewise, only the test as a whole can establish whether the aggression is primarily positive or negative behavior. This depends first on the level of the test—the quality of the individual factors, including content —and second on the degree and structure of possible neurotic or other pathologic findings. In addition, a Ds factor is frequently determined in several ways, i.e., it can simultaneously be both positive and negative, stemming, for example, from an unpleasant character trait in an individual who has highly critical attitudes, one who is "sharp and smart." This factor is of special interest in the study of so-called national traits.

The basic rule for such distinctions is that white spaces together with color-determined responses go with externalized aggression, whereas white spaces together with M responses point to aggression that has been introverted, that is, directed against the person himself. The latter is the so-called inhibited aggression which leads to depression in some cases, to shyness and exaggerated politeness in others, but always to feelings of inferiority and self-mistrust, i.e., insecurity. When overt and externalized aggression is found on a high level, with stabilized emotions, well developed brakefactors, and relatively mild neurotic traits, it may be mainly a matter of criticism against others; if, on the other hand, the aggression is inhibited, it may be indicative of self criticism. Should the record contain both move-

[32]Zulliger, H.: Einführung in den Behn-Rorschach Test, pp. 59-60, and Enke, W.: Die Konstitutionstypen im Rorschach'schen Experiment. Zeitschrift für die ges. Neur. und Psychiatrie *108*: 673, 1937.

ment and color determinants, both of the above attitudes are present, and if the M and the color values are in approximate balance, we have a person with painful inability to make up his mind, of excessive thoroughness, and wrapped in pessimistic doubt. (See my tables in Rorschach's Psychodiagnostik, p. 260.) In coarcted experience balance, in which there is either no M or C or, at the most, one or two, we must inspect the F+ per cent and the W+. If the score is unusually high in both these factors, and the white space count increases, repressed aggression is again indicated.

That this Janus-like character of the white spaces has practical importance for applied psychology, especially in the prevention of delinquency and the psychological prevention of accidents, becomes readily apparent when we consider Arthur Kielholz's statement that "a crime stems from the unconscious guilt sense when the destructive tendencies in the id are directed against the external world; when, however, this destructive tendency is directed primarily against the individual himself, he will have an accident. . . . It is still necessary to develop diagnostic methods for early recognition of this destructive liability to accidents."[33] Here then we have just such a diagnostic potential. In persons with many white space details and a dominantly extratensive experience balance—assuming the other necessary factors are present—we may expect an overt tendency toward destructiveness (see "Antisocial psychopathy"). When a record contains many white spaces with a dominantly introversive experience balance (repressed aggression), a high accident proneness is to be expected (see also "Characterogenic depressions").

(e) As the name indicates, the Do association was originally understood to be typical of mental deficiency. It became clear later that *some* feeble-minded persons are, it is true, inclined to produce these associations. More important, however, is the fact that also normals and even the highly endowed can respond with a Do here and there, occasionally in considerable numbers. By and large it can be stated that when Do's are found together with many F−'s, they are evidence of intellectual deficiency, including the lower grades. When the record, besides the Do, includes many F+ responses the condition is one of anxiety and inhibition. These Do responses arise out of restriction of the psychic—not the physiologic—visual field, which is frequently present in anxiety and depression.

Finally, attention should be directed to a valuable hint by Zulliger, (Bero, p. 106), to the effect that the elements of the approach type also have a correlation with the levels of the libido development. Thus, W corresponds to orality, D to genitality, and Dd to anality. Zulliger, too, correlates the Ds with aggressivity.

[33]Kielholz, A.: Verhütung von Verbrechen bei Psychosen. In: Meng: Die Prophylaxe des Verbrechens. Basel, 1948, p. 146.

## 2. THE DETERMINANTS

(a) The general psychological value of the *form response* naturally varies directly wtih its quality. F+ is evidence of ability to observe accurately. The person who does not habitually observe correctly does not possess clear memory impressions and consequently is unable to recall such impressions during the test. Good form perception also depends upon the ability to concentrate on the test and to maintain an attention span.

Correspondingly, *unclear forms* will be found either in persons of low intellectual caliber because of an inferior capacity for observation, or in the event of disturbance of concentration, especially in nervous persons.

The *indefinite* F− is a sign of inhibition of formative power or inability of formation, both of which are found in combinations with other test factors in diverse conditions. A tentative review of our findings gives the following conditions for the occurrence of the indefinite F−:

1. In anal retentive characters and in depressives with inferiority feelings, along with general evidence of holding back, i.e., few responses, rejections, and the like.

2. With H lacking together with increased anatomy responses (the introspective) Do (anxiety and holding back), and with an extratensive experience balance in which the color values are labile, in secondary narcissism, that means a kind of rupture of diplomatic relations with the environment. These persons have "gotten lost from the world," to use an expression of Friedrich Rückert. (See chapter 10 for other combinations of factors to indicate narcissism.)

3. With F+ per cent lowered and possibly anatomy as anxiety symptom in case of neurotic restriction on the thinking. When with extratensive experience balance and anatomy associations, we have a hysteric pseudo-deficiency. When the experience balance is introversive, or ambiequal, and Do is present (and in instances also anatomy) we have the compulsive neurotic's constriction of thinking.

4. In organics as either (a) a symptom of the loss of the ability to concentrate in hypomanic-like restlessness of organic etiology (post-encephalitic or post-traumatic conditions, and so on); or (b) organic disturbance of recall (the loss of the ability to grasp the concrete).

5. Occasionally in endogenous depressions of specifically anxious coloring.

6. As a sign of torpidity in the abulic schizophrenic, or as a symptom of the schizophrenic's "interpretation difficulty," also abulic (as described by Wolfgang Binswanger).

7. Together with object criticism in psychasthenics who are afraid of contact or responsibility and who suffer from anxious excess caution and

from inability to make up their minds. (This egocentricity of the psychasthenics, based on a wish to avoid expenditure of energy, is not to be confused with the above noted narcissism.)

8. A simple indication of shock, especially dark shock, i.e., as a symptom of a partial stupor.

9. In fatigue, as a symptom of disturbance in recall, on a physiologic basis. (They may then appear, together with occasional perseveration, in persons who are not original.) E.g., the tired night-clerk who reports, "Mr. What's-his-name has been here."

10. In so-called laziness—torpid conditions of unknown causation.

(b) *The movement response* represents first of all the wealth of inner living. The remarkable fact is that it is not the overtly active persons who produce the most M's but rather those whose motor trends are stabilized, the quiet, "innerly living" individuals (Rorschach, p. 25). Thus, just as externalized motor expression interferes with dreaming (Freud), so it is the *constraint* on activity which favors production of M. Besides, the imagination of the very introversive individual shows more orientation toward the kinesthetic than the visual. In E. R. Jaensch's system the person with many M responses and a corresponding lack of color associations belongs in the $I_3$ orJi types, that is, they integrate entirely by turning inward. These persons, in fact, as Rohracher puts it, have "replaced the visual images which hold a certain degree of coherence with the external world, with content which is for the most part kinesthetic and dynamic."[34]

For reasons as yet unknown, the M response is correlated with the creative powers of the personality and also with religious experience. That the M's are the most general indication of productivity has been empirically established beyond doubt; Walther Rathenau, the great author and philosopher, very clearly perceived this relationship between inner living and creative power when he said, "Dreams held in rein by will power and kept down to earth—that is the secret of all production" (*Von kommenden Dingen*).

A consequence of the introversive character of the M is the fact that, as Piotrowski has shown, the feeling of being unloved leads to an increase of M.[35] Besides, WM+ H responses were observed (Friedemann, A. Weber) in children who saw death.[36]

Within this realm of the creative life, however, two tendencies are again to be distinguished. One is a fantasy still based in reality, which, in the last analysis, is directed toward refashioning the outer world; the other is a fantasy alien to reality, an escape or flight from the world. Only the former

[34]Rohracher, H.: Kleine Einführung in die Charakterkunde. Leipzig, 1934, p. 64.
[35]Piotrowski, Z. A.: A Rorschach Compendium, revised and enlarged, pp. 26-27.
[36]Kuhn, R.: Grundlegende statistische und psychologische Aspekte des Rorschach'schen Formdeutversuches. Rorschachiana I: 327, 1952.

is the form Rathenau had in mind when a little before the passage cited above he said, "The most real productivity is the visionary one." Thus we can agree with Meili-Dworetzki[37] when she defines: "Rorschach's introversity would to us be the tendency to cast the ego in imagined situations, actions, or roles, and to apply the psychic energy not preponderantly to adjustment to the outer reality and its digestion, but to a life in one's own world of imagination. This tendency may lead to mere fantasies and daydreaming but, if combined with adjustment to reality, may also lead to creative realization." To determine which of these alternatives is given in a Rorschach test, in the first line the experience balance[38] is decisive, and in the second line the syndrome of sense of reality (see chapter on "Intelligence").

Both these kinds of inner living are also represented in the Rorschach test by two kinds of kinesthesia: the *extensor movements*, which project the urge to move toward the world, whether with friendship and cooperation or with hate and aggression, and the *flexor kinesthesias*, or tendency to flee from the world. These poses correspond to what the anthropologist designates "warm" and "cold" attitudes: the individual presents either the greatest or the least possible body surface to the environment. The symbol of the first pose (but only for the positive variety) is embodied in the phrase "Ye millions, embrace!", while the symbol of the second pose is a hedgehog in a rolled up position. The flexor kinesthesias increase with age.[39]

Normal individuals hardly ever give the M− response. Epileptics and manics produce them rather often. They also occur in the Korsakoff syn-

[37]In: Versuch einer Analyse der Bewegungsdeutungen im Rorschach-Test nach genetischen Gesichtspunkten, Schweiz. Zeitschr. f. Psychologie, Vol. XI, 1952, p. 281.

[38]The connection between the M and creativity has been rejected by some American authors (David C. McClelland, Anne Roe and others). The differing results of the investigations in question are due to the facts that 1) these authors have been working with an entirely changed M-conception (Klopfer's), and 2) they have neglected to treat the M factor in connection with the experience balance. Creativity and creative output are two different things. Creativity is only one precondition of creative output. Another precondition is that libido is fixated to this creative endowment, that the Subject is interested in his endowment. This fixation of libido cannot be ascertained solely from the Rorschach test (Zulliger, personal communication). That, on the other hand, there are artists who must be characterized as "noncreative" (e.g., the copyists) is a hackneyed fact with which Rorschach himself dealt in detail. Nevertheless these passages by Rorschach are not mentioned either by McClelland or by B. Klopfer. The entire debate would have been superfluous if they had read Rorschach and used his original method.

[39]Meschieri, L.: Humeur et interprétations des mouvements d'extension et de flexion au test de Rorschach. Contributi d. Istit. Nazion. Psicologia d. Consiglio nazion. Ricerche: Rome, 1950, as cited by Rizzo, C.: The Rorschach Method in Italy. Rorschachiana I: 310-311, 1952.

drome and in schizophrenia, and are the sign of a productivity which disregards reality and goes beyond its control. It has a similar symptom value as the confabulations. The occasional M– found in neurotics are generally carriers of important complex-determined thought content.

The *confabulated FM* and the *secondary M* are likewise basically pathologic. The confabulated FM is found in delirious conditions and also occasionally in the feeble minded and schizophrenics. Secondary M, which is not at all rare, is found principally in epilepsy and at times in ixothymic character structure related to epilepsy. According to Rorschach it also occurs in manics, but it is much more difficult to pin the response down in that group because of the latter's tendency to sudden production.

The *small M* response obviously stands in special relation to the "urge to invent." Like the M it is thus also an expression of the creative talent, but it has a more specific significance. It is found in productive paranoids and in animated confabulating Korsakoff patients; it also occurs among normals, especially those endowed with formative and literary artistic powers. Finally, it is found in those Subjects who possess a talent for teaching, the connection being their good storytelling ability (Zulliger).

(c) The *color response,* in its several categories, is an index to the affectivity. Owing to its extraordinary importance it will be considered in a chapter by itself; here we shall content ourselves with a few remarks.

(1) The FC+ response projects those feelings which involve a regard for the object of the feelings and which at the same time are held under the certain control of reason. The psychologic significance of FC+ responses is therefore twofold: first, such a response shows an affective contact, the capacity for rapport, the binding to "the other," the emotional adaptation to the situation and to the needs of the object; second, it shows rational control (self-control) which holds the feelings within limits.

The FC– is found in individuals who indeed also endeavor to attain adaptation, but, owing to intellectual shortcomings, do so with only doubtful success. This response category is a warning to us to keep in mind that not only does the affectivity influence the thought processes, but that our thinking also influences the affectivity. (Concerning the black, white, and gray responses as FC see chapter 5, "Black and White as Colors.")

(2) In the CF responses we have a measure of the labile affectivity in which there is still a striving for contact, but without success in establishing a stable relation with the object of the feelings. The libidinal urges here may be identified as stimulus search[40]: hormone secretions have created driving restlessness. "The cerebrospinal apparatus of orientation" has been

[40]Brun, R.: Die Raumorientierung der Ameisen. Jena, 1914. Also: Allgemeine Neurosenlehre, Basel, 1948 and Über biologische Psychologie. Schweiz. Ztschr. f. Psychologie *8*: 3.

activated, but the object of the search has not yet been found. It cannot be known from this response alone whether the object simply has not been physiologically attained, as in puberty (the primary stimulus search), whether neurotic difficulties exist (secondary stimulus search), or whether the emotional unrest is of organic origin. The unrest in this stimulus search is an appetence behavior,[41] a strain condition, consisting fundamentally of pressure toward releasing an instinctive action, which persists until such action becomes possible. In the human psychopathology such a condition can become a lasting one; hence, in neurotic maladaptations one can very well use the paradoxical label "a lasting temporary condition."

(3) The pure C responses are signs of pure emotional discharge, of impulsivity which serves only for the discharge of the feelings and in which the question of adaptation no longer exists. Strictly speaking, the C responses are an expression only of the *pressure* for such discharge; whether it actually occurs depends on other factors.

(d) Only individuals of very high ability, especially persons of artistic bent, produce the MC response, although it does appear occasionally in schizophrenics.

(e) The psychologic significance of MF, "number" and position responses, for practical reasons will be dealt with in chapter 5.

## 3. THE CONTENT

The content of the responses, in general, permits a survey not only of the individual's horizon but possibly also of his more special interests. However, beyond this, the separate classifications also have special meanings.

In the number of *human* responses we have to a certain extent a point of departure from which to judge the roles played by social and human interests in the life of our Subject. (See more on this point in chapter 8.)

The *animal* classification provides by far the largest number of responses. Partly because of the symmetry of the test figues and partly because of the actual forms of the ink blots, animals are the most easily perceived forms, and therefore constitute the main measure of stereotype or "boresomeness" of the Subject. (See under "Summary.")

Regarding the *anatomy* responses, Rorschach noted that they have a special relation to the "intelligence complex" when produced by non-medical Subjects. Eugen Bleuler[42] interprets the term "intelligence complex" to mean the need in certain individuals "to show that they are not so stupid." Aside from compensating for actual feelings of intellectual inferiority, whether or not they are warranted, this response appears to have

---

[41]Lorenz, K.: Über den Begriff der Instinkthandlung, Folia Biotheoretica, II, 1937, cited from David Katz, Mensch und Tier, Zürich, 1948, p. 220.

[42]Bleuler, E.: Lehrbuch der Psychiatrie. Berlin, 1937, p. 412.

some relation to hypochondriacal tendencies (Rorschach); in any event, they are found generally together with a "narcissistic investment of the body image."[43] Even in physicians and nurses a rather large number of anatomy percepts, if they are *poor* forms, are usually indicative of tendencies to neurotic hypochondriasis. Here the response may actually be considered vocational original minus. Naturally, anatomy content of good form quality does not have this significance in persons of these vocations. (See chapter 5 for anatomy as stereotype.)

That *sex* responses, if produced in excess, have their source in neurotically impelled behavior is obvious. In most cases these percepts are then also seen where they are *not* present, in which case the form frequently is poor. On the other hand, a few scattered good-form sex responses are entirely normal, since several of the test cards contain one or more genital-like shapes, namely, II, IV, VI, VII and IX. Some individuals, because of almost Victorian propriety, neurotic inhibition, or inhibition through the sexual situation with regard to the Examiner, produce no sex responses at all; in most such cases, however, the neurotic inhibition reveals itself through either symbolic or disguised sexual responses ("female pelvis" and the like). Occasionally a subject will even go into a sexual symbol stupor (see chapter 5).

Rorschach points out the many *botanical* responses he observed in six- to eight-year-old children and adults of senile deterioration, the former group corresponding fully to the results obtained with the English Mosaics Test. In the latter especially girls in the prepubertal years showed a pre-dilection for flowers.

The technician's or artisan's interests are naturally more frequently projected in *inanimate objects*. In conjunction with architectural, decorative, and art responses, such percepts often yield a very good picture of the Subject's general education. According to Loepfe, children have a tendency to see many inanimate objects; hence, when adults who are in nontechnical vocations produce a great number of such responses, it is at times an indication of infantilism.

When *architectural* responses appear in notably large quantity, or when they are seen in perspective—even though not in increased number—it is in many instances an indication of an inner insecurity for which the person is attempting to compensate. The phenomenon is a common one in history, going back to some of the Caesars and other historic rulers: Caligula, Louis II of Bavaria, William II. Such men could never build enough to be satisfied. In modern times, of course, there is the example of Adolf Hitler.

[43]Mahler-Schoenberger, M. and Silberpfennig, J.: Der Rorschach'sche Form-deutversuch als Hilfsmittel zum Verständnis der Psychologie Hirnkranker. Schweiz. Arch. f. Neur. und Psychiatrie 40: 325-326, 1937.

*Geographic* or *map* responses are either avoidance responses (unnamed islands, countries, etc.), without significance, or, when a name is used, indications of a quantitative school-ambition in individuals lacking self-reliance. Even as adults such persons still have in them something of the "good schoolboy." Should these responses seem especially forced (far-fetched geographical parts, etc.), they are to be regarded like the anatomy associations (with which they are often found) as signs of "intelligence complex." These responses are not infrequent in boastful psychopaths who have need for self-assertion (the bragging type). All this, naturally, does not hold for professional geographers who, especially when they also have a tendency to be one-track specialists, can produce astonishing numbers of such responses.

Other content themes are of particular interest because of their relation to complexes, e.g., caves, explosions, fires, scenes, and, most of all, the rather infrequent food responses: ham, steak, chicken, cake and the like. The latter usually permit inference of a heightened orality, as do also alcoholic topics: carousing men, wine bottles, whiskey bottles, and the like. Nevertheless, caution must be exercised in connection with the food responses. An investigation in America has shown that hungry persons give food responses with notably greater frequency than those who have satisfied their appetite.[44] In young children food responses are relatively frequent.[45]

Mention should also be made here of the "pars-pro-toto" responses given by children. Frequently, according to Zulliger's observation, they report whole animals though only a head is present. This class of response has been observed also in infantile and confabulating adults.

### 4. ORIGINALITY

(a) The *P response* is a measure of the degree to which the person is in intellectual contact, i.e., "his participation in the concepts of his community" (Rorschach). It is particularly the measure of the Subject's ability to understand and be understood by "the man on the street." (See chapter 8.)

(b) *Originals,* especially the motif-originals proper, are naturally a measure of the original imagination and are therefore especially frequent among the artistically endowed. Moreover, they provide a rather good picture of the individual's interest trends and his general cultivation. Vocation-determined originals naturally abound in vocation-bound individuals, while persons of many-sided education produce originals from the most varied fields. The vocationally toned "original minus" are very rare and

---

[44]Personal communication from Professor Olav Gardebring, Salt Lake City, Utah.
[45]Beck, Samuel J.: Rorschach's Test, II, p. 221.

nearly always point to a neurotic attitude by the Subject toward his calling or to conflicts in connection with it.

Animals that are "original plus" are rather infrequent. The conclusion from them is nearly always that the Subject has an unusual love for and observation of animals.

Good elaboration originals usually point to literary talent, even though this may amount to no more than letter writing, an art which is not too widespread today.

The apprehension originals to date have not been widely investigated, but one positive psychologic significance in them is a high structural lability of the thought processes. They may also have a negative value, a lowering of the regard for reality. This is true not only for the subgroup of figure-background fusion but for the whole group as well, also if form perception is good. (It should be kept in mind that the usual perception of a Gestalt is the perception of a *thing*.) The lowered sense of the real is therefore the more plausible interpretation, since the response is usually found with a general increase in per cent of originals and a lowered percentage of P. In an especially striking case of this kind, a graphologist who was carrying on a control investigation established the inadequate sense of reality as the most outstanding trait. Apprehension originals, especially the poor ones, are consequently found in disturbances of control over reality in neurotics, organics, or schizophrenics.

In general it may be noted that "original minus" scores occur with a wide variety of qualities. Some with "weak" form (neurotics, feeble-minded) still remain intelligible; unintelligible, "horrible," bizarre responses are found in schizophrenics and organics. Any diagnostic procedure resting on purely formal "Orig–" can easily lead to misunderstandings and misdiagnoses.

Finally, it is worth mentioning here, as Manfred Bleuler[46] has shown, that siblings frequently give the same originals. This is especially apparent in twins; for example, each of a pair of girl twins gave the very rare response "a core" (of an apple) in reaction to the lower half of the large white space detail in card IX. Marriage partners may also occasionally give the same originals. A systematic study of such observations might well adduce valuable material pertinent to Szondi's hypothesis of the Genotropism.

(c) The purely *individualized* responses have the same psychologic value as the originals in general, their content being for the most part complex-determined and thus making possible important inferences concerning the deeper levels of the personality.

[46]Bleuler, M.: Der Rorschach'sche Formdeutversuch bei Geschwistern. Zeitschrift f. Neurologie *118*: 1929.

## BINDER'S SHADING AND LIGHT-DARK RESPONSES

We have so far by-passed a large class of determinants because their scoring to some extent stands apart from the classical scoring in that it generally follows principles of classification formulated not by Rorschach but by Binder, after the former's death. Rorschach was familiar with this response group, having already correctly penetrated to its basic psychological value; what we are referring to here is that large field of shading and light-dark responses which he treated as a common group, scoring F(C).* Depending on whether the form element was more or less clear-cut,[47] Rorschach discriminated between F(C) and (C)F responses, describing the psychologic significance of both as "an anxious, cautious, unfree kind of affective adaptation" and "a tendency to a fundamentally depressive mood" (p. 193). He had also already established that perspective is frequently stressed in these responses and that there is a tendency in some of them to be associated with space details (pp. 185, 199).

Binder devoted a very comprehensive study to this problem.[48] He makes a major distinction between the F(C) percepts (now generally designated *shading responses*) and the LD (light-dark) determined associations, thus narrowing the sphere of the F(C). For, as he himself emphasizes, he uses this scoring sign in a "much more precisely limited" range (Binder, p. 27). Scientific publications must therefore state whether they are using the formulas F(C) in the older, broader sense, which was Rorschach's, or the newer, narrower one, which is Binder's.

Oberholzer[49] still uses the sign F(C) in Rorschach's broader sense, without subclassifying. We, too, find it advisable not to abandon the original collecting of all these in a single group. The simplest thing is to retain the older F(C) scoring and to use Binder's classification as subgroups. (See chapter 4.)

Other subgroups have been proposed within this modality, notably Klopfer and Kelley's in America. Binder's classification is preferable to Klopfer's since it develops organically the Rorschach test categories; the Klopfer method, on the other hand, follows the principle of attention to the object immediately apparent (surface, depth, etc.) and veils what is psychologically essential. Besides, this classification is mixed in with the factor of tridimensionality which were better treated by itself (see chapter 5 under EQa).

---

*In view of the various American scoring signs for the shading determinants, confusion will be best avoided by retaining the German forms, i.e., (C), F(C), etc. (translator's note).

[47]Zulliger, H.: Einführung in den Behn-Rorschach-Test, p. 65.

[48]Binder, H.: Die Helldunkeldeutungen im psychodiagnostischen Experiment von Rorschach. Schweiz. Arch. f. Neurologie u. Psychiatrie *30*: 1-67, 233-286.

[49]*In*: Du Bois, C.: The People of Alor. Minneapolis, 1944.

Even though tridimensional responses are often shading or light-dark determined, this is by no means always the case. It is therefore best to avoid mixing the two categories. We thus follow Binder's work. The principles by which he classifies and their psychologic significance are presented here briefly for the reader's consideration.

## Delimiting the Light-Dark Responses

It is necessary first to delimit the entire sphere of the light-dark and the shading responses from such borderline cases as the following, which do not belong to this category and must be distinguished from them:

1. Responses determined by the white as such. Here Binder further distinguishes between (a) pronounced primary white responses, e.g., "snowman" to the white space in card IX (this is best evaluated as Ds FC+ Obj Orig+) and (b) secondary white responses, e.g., "lampshade of white porcelain" to the white space in card II or "white stag" to the space between the blue and the gray of card VIII. These responses are best scored as Ds F+.

2. Details perceived only according to the contour produced by the shading, without regard for the light-dark quality. In Binder's words these are "responses in which the outlines between darker and lighter shadings enter merely as a form element in the interpretation; the light value itself in the shaded detail plays no role in the percept as developed." In card IV, inverted, for example, the black within the "boot" seen as "Jutland." These are pure form responses.

3. Responses in which only the elaborations are determined by the dark tone, e.g., the "men" in card III wearing black suits; the "bat" in card V having such a dark color (Binder). These associations are also pure form responses. The influence of the light-dark factor may be indicated by the symbol FLD → F+* (Zulliger).

4. Binder's "intellectual light-dark responses," i.e., responses which, in contrast to the naive reaction, develop the light-dark element intellectually, to which the average person is in the habit of reacting with his feelings while neglecting the form element which ordinarily is the focus of the

---

*(Translator's note.) In his *"Helldunkel"* "classification, Binder accents certain aspects of the light-determined responses that do not precisely correspond to classifications in American usage. The nearest equivalents are Klopfer's K and Beck's Y, with the usual F modulations. But, rather than use symbols which may not precisely correspond to Binder's intent, the translators are identifying the Helldunkel associations simply by the initials LD, translating directly "light-dark." This usage is followed throughout the present English version. The designation "light-dark," used here, is identical with "chiaroscuro" as introduced in the American literature by M. Rickers Ovsiankina. Thus FLD=FCH, LDF=ChF, and LD=Ch.

intellectual activity. Binder recognizes three subgroups of the intellectualized light-dark responses:

(a) "Light-dark naming"—almost entirely identical with the light-dark descriptions (see chapter 5). Examples: "An impression of much shading" or "as in the art of carbon drawing." It is best to use no scoring formulas here but simply to note description (see chapter 5). However, a scoring formula is warranted for the not infrequent association, "One can see the screen here" (Dd F– indef. Screen).

(b) "Scientific" reminiscences. Example: "The clouding as two chemical fluids are being mixed," "the transparent shadings of infusoria under the microscope."

(c) Descriptions of light-dark symbols. Example: card I, "the bright islands of Fortune (the white spaces) within the dark ocean of Misfortune"; card II, "Helvetia (the inner white space) as the white symbol of innocence and the dark round about are the belligerent countries."

The associations in these latter two subgroups can perhaps be formally evaluated as light-dark determined responses—LDF. In the summary, however, they must be separately counted, exactly as is done in color namings.

CLASSIFICATION OF THE LIGHT-DARK RESPONSES

For lack of a general symbol for the shading responses as one group, we follow Binder in using the term "light-dark determined" to include both the shading responses and those specifically determined by light-dark values. But Binder, as already mentioned, correctly makes a sharp distinction between those two principal groups: the shading detail responses and the light-dark responses proper.

1. The (C) *interpretation,* i.e., the shading responses, are for the most part either D or Dd. They are "identified by the subject's focusing on each and every more striking shading element within the blot area which he has selected. Furthermore, he directs his attention first to the form contours of the individual shadings, and second to their light values." Binder then stresses all this again, as follows: "Several individual shading elements must be interpreted in every F(C) response, and moreover each one individually interpreted. These different shading elements within the selected blot area must be tonally distinguished and clearly differentiated from one another." It is important to note this carefully, in order not to be led into making misinterpretations.

Very frequently these percepts are seen in perspective, but it does not follow that they must always be seen so. Some are seen combined with white space details, partly as a perspective percept, partly in the ordinary way. Since such combinations are always seen in various shaded elements, it is not necessary when using the symbol Ds F(C), or DsD F(C) to indicate this Binder group especially—all these responses automatically belong to this group of percepts. Only in responses involving the black-gray shading detail is it recommended that the symbol F(C) be written twice, one over the other (see chapter 4). Examples: card II, "A roadway in a park in bright sunshine (white space detail) surrounded by dark, over-hanging trees (the black). The road narrows toward the back into a small path in the distance (the gray in the upper pointed detail) which is in the shadow because there is a rough stone balustrade on both sides. The road leads to a little pagoda-like house in the garden (the pointed detail)"; abstract of a response scored Ds F(C)+ Perspective Na. Card VI, the upper projection: "A fountain with a triton of black marble, the water is flowing down (the gray next to the black). Behind it there is a Roman bowl made of light, clouded marble with strange gargoyles (the ends of the wing detail)"; abstract, scored D F(C)+ Arch Orig+. Card II, the black pointed mid-detail: "A little fir tree; the trunk stands out brightly from the meadow behind it. And above it is its crown with the dark stripes of the branches," D F(C)+ Bt Orig+.

Interpretation of shading may be found also in the colored figures, as in Rorschach's example referring to card IX (the medial edge of the brown with the shaded parts considered as mountains): "This is just like the Norwegian coast," Dd F(C)+ Geo Orig+.

2. The light-dark responses are in the main given to the whole figure or the major details. They are "characterized by the fact that no separate shading detail is especially selected." Here we are dealing with "a diffuse general impression of the light-dark values relevant to the entire test figure (Binder, p. 28). By analogy with the color associations, Binder groups the light-dark determined ones as follows:

(a) *FLD+* or *FLD− responses.* In these the outlines are clearly per-ceived, and are of first importance while the light-dark impression plays only a secondary role (Binder, p. 29). If the form is good, we have FLD+; if not, it becomes FLD−. Examples: card IV, "a scarecrow with dark draperies hanging from it," W FLD+ Obj Orig+. Card VI (side position, upper half), "silhouette of a castle ruin upon a rock," D FLD+ Na Orig+. Card II, the black, "a large raven in flight" (lateral details are the wings, center pointed detail is the head), D FLD− A Orig−.

The animal skins in cards IV and VI are seldom scored FLD+. Nearly always the correct scoring is F+. Only when the woolly quality of the ani-mal skin is especially described or the pattern of the hide much accented (as, for example, in card VI) is the scoring FLD+. It is the same in those rare instances in which the Subject expressly remarks that the corners of the hide (in card IV) are turned over (the lighter portion of the boots).

(b) *The LDF* responses. In these an indefinite light-dark factor is the primary while contours are perceived only weakly and unclearly. Examples: card VII, "storm clouds," W LDF Clouds. Card IV, "X-ray of an animal," W LDF A (possibly anatomy). Card V, "a mountain slope heavily wooded, a sort of mountain range," W LDF Na Orig–.

"Clouds" and "x-ray photographs" are nearly always LDF. X-ray photographs are FLD+ only in the case of specific assertion, for example, when an expert in the field describes precisely the x-ray of a specific bone section, but this is very rare.

Birds' eye views, i.e., photographs taken from airplanes, etc., are for the most part LDF. Only when the subject speaks of a particular outline are they FLD. But this is rare because in those instances they are usually described as F. In addition, airplane views and mountain top panoramas are, when LDF, mostly to be thought of as seen from "a distant locality" (see chapter 5 under "intrapsychic inhibition").

(c) *The Pure LD responses.* In these the form determinant is entirely lacking. Only the pure, diffuse light-dark factor remains. Examples: card IV, "a stormy mood," W LD Na Orig–; or "like a nightmare," W LD Abs Orig–. Card I, on the right, "the play of the waves," D LD Na Orig–.

Certain LD responses which Binder designated "primitive LD interpretations" play an especial role (they are for the most part LDF, but some are also FLD–). They stand in close relationship to our indefinite F–, the only difference being that the light-dark value here plays a dominant role. The content in these associations stems from circumstances which "do not have distinct or clearly defined forms in reality as well." Binder gives the following examples: card I, "stalactites," W LDF Na Orig–; "marshland full of holes," DsW LDF Na Orig–. Card IV, "cinders or something crystal-like," W LDF Obj Orig–. Card VI, "rocks, or perhaps a mass of ruins," W FLD– Na; "quite decayed, deteriorated goods," W LDF Obj Orig–. Card VII, "slimy creatures out of the ocean," W FLD– A Orig–; "just like baked stuffs," W FLD– Obj Orig–. As especially typical examples of this type we might also add "dirty snow," card VII; or "splashed-about dirt from the street," card VI.

Finally, we should mention the rare MLD responses, which in many respects represent a parallel to the MC. As an example: card IV inverted, the black in the boot seen as "two women in black veils hurrying towards each other," Dd MFLD+ H Orig+. These responses, like the MC, are usually found in the artistically endowed. This leads us to our next section.

## THE PSYCHOLOGICAL VALUES OF THE LIGHT-DARK RESPONSES

Here the same limitations and reservations apply as have been indicated in reference to the psychologic values of the classical scoring formulas. That is, we are offering theoretic leads, and not "interpretations."

Binder takes the position that the lively colors more readily affect the peripheral single feelings. The light-dark values, on the contrary, influence the mood, that is, the central reactive feeling-tone as a whole. But to this may be added something else. As long ago as 1923, Hans Christoffel,[50] in the volume in honor of Eugen Bleuler, showed that achromatic shaded or black-white visions were typical of anxiety conditions and pointed out also that a constant relation exists between black and masculine and white and feminine. This relation holds for our own western culture, and not for the East, as is indicated by the Taoist symbolism for Yang and Yin, where white stands for the masculine Yang, and black for the feminine Yin.

With this as a starting point, Binder found the following psychologic meaning for his several response categories:

1. *In shading responses,* the intellect is always dominant. In addition, these responses disclose a finer degree of emotional adaptation, besides the general capacity for rapport shown in the FC responses.

The fine nuances projected in the F(C) associations are variously evaluated, depending on the Subject's experience balance. In predominantly extratensive individuals, but particularly those with many FC, it has a "plus" valuation. For the ability to empathize has been developed in them to a general delicacy of feeling. It is different with the color-prone individuals who accent the pure C response. (See chapter 11, the discussion of the schizoid.) In introversive persons, already shy in their contacts with others, the F(C) associations point to oversensitivity, lack of self-assurance and the capacity for being easily hurt. What in the extratensive is a strong point, in them becomes a weak point. The F(C) responses represent the tender spot of the introversive.

According to Binder, the more precise psychologic value of these shading responses derives from the kind of shade selected. The dark element is preferred by anxiously depressed, cautiously measured personalities, whereas the passive clinging character who finds pleasure in tenderness is apt to emphasize the lighter elements.

When white space details are organized with shaded percepts, i.e., Ds F(C), they contain for the most part important complex-determined material, expressed as wish fulfilments. Rorschach himself had already established this point in his Psychodiagnostics (p. 199).

2. The *light-dark responses* are, on the contrary, expressions of a central mood, for the most part dysphoric.

(a) FLD+ responses go with good conscious control over mood reactions. (Binder calls this "sophropsychic," that is, intrapsychic, control.) This regulation of feelings and impulses is achieved through a process of selection rather than one of repression.

[50]Christoffel, H.: Affektivität und Farben, speziell Angst und Helldunkelerscheinungen. Ztschr. f. Neur. u. Psychiat. *82:* 46-52, 1923.

(b) FLD– responses point to an inner effort at self-control and adaptivity, but one which is not always successful, owing to an undifferentiated intelligence.

(c) LDF responses, on the contrary, are evidence of an insufficient effort at mood control. When several LDF responses are present, this is an indication of strong dysphoric trends.

(d) Pure LD responses, finally, betray a complete lack of the ability to control mood.

According to Zulliger, the MLD always indicate an inclination to fear, mostly in connection with persecution ideas.[51] One may well say, following Ernst Schneider,[52] that the CF responses correspond to the tensions involved in the effort to adapt to the outer world, the LD associations to the tensions resulting from a vain effort to adapt to the world within.

## WHAT IS A RESPONSE?

Up to now, we have not answered the question of how the limits of individual responses should be fixed.

### "Responses" that are Not Responses

1. *Peripheral comments* of an emotional, evaluative, or descriptive kind— exclamations, criticisms, remarks about the symmetry or similarities of the figures—are not scorable responses. This should be obvious. Unfortunately, experience shows that this is not always the case, and this is why we mention the matter here. But we do not intend to digress any further here and will go into more detail in chapter 5.

The only real difficulties develop in distinguishing between simple side comments and color naming. To make this distinction requires unusual sensitivity and a capacity for empathy; what counts is whether what is uttered is *meant* as a response or not. "There are many colors here" is for the most part no response at all, but a common remark caused by color shock. The Subject is merely trying to gain time and is filling in the pause with an aside. "Four colors" could perhaps still be considered description. But this assertion is usually followed by an enumeration of the colors and then it is indeed a color naming (W C Color). The simplest form of color naming would be, "This is red," (D C Color). Color naming is in fact a transition phenomenon between simple description and a scorable response.

"Inkblots" are for the most part regular responses (LDF or CF). It is

[51]Hans Zulliger, Angst in der Spiegelung des Tafeln-Z-Tests. Ztschr. f. diagn. Psychologie, vol. II, 1954, pp. 58-59.

[52]Schneider, E.: Psychodiagnostisches Praktikum für Psychologen und Pädagogen. Leipzig, 1936, p. 56.

simple description only when the subject, instead of interpreting the figures, exclaims, "Oh, now I know. These are only ink blots that have been folded together and opened up again."

2. The question becomes a bit more difficult when the distinction to be made is between simple elaboration or completion of a response on the one hand and an independent response on the other. This, too, can be done only on the basis of experience and a certain amount of intuition. Should the Subject perceive the men of card III and then point to the heads and legs to complete the response, these usually are not independent responses. The Subject only thinks that we do not perceive his men, and he wants to delineate them accurately. Similarly, for the response "two men salute each other, here are their hats," or "two waiters are carrying a tub," a W scoring will usually suffice. It is different when separate details are lifted out, especially if, as often happens, this is done later, after several other responses have intervened. It is best to treat such a selected detail, with its special interest for the Subject, as a separate response. Thus the Subject may say, "Two gentlemen, in a queer, somewhat bent position," and then after reflection add, "they are dragging something around, it appears to be a kettle." This added association should certainly be given a separate score.

This question arises especially frequently in regard to card X. The first response to this figure may be a simple "sea animals," "sea plants," "on the floor of the ocean," or "a flower garden," and then examples will be given. It is quite correct to treat these examples as separate responses and to score a W first and then several D. It will frequently happen that the examples are FC (e.g., cornflower), while the W is for the most part CF.

BREAK-UP OF RESPONSES

A much more difficult problem is how to break up responses that are given as units. As we see from Rorschach's examples, we are now and then compelled to break complex-determined associations apart in order to bring into the open all the important scoring components. Thus a schizophrenic in response to card VIII produces the contamination, "The resurrection of the colossal, coloric, red, brownish and blue venous tumors of the head." Rorschach breaks this up as follows: DW CF– Abstr Orig–, for the entire response; DM+ A for the resurrection of the red animals; DC Color for the color naming; Dd CF– Anat Orig– for the tumor of the veins in the head (the veins being pointed out at various points).

This breaking up of condensed responses usually causes great difficulties to the beginner, for it is necessary to think here *e juvantibus*. That is, one must consider the consequence of each scoring possibility, something which is beyond the scope of a beginner. The rule itself is not as difficult as its practical application: A response must be broken down into as many formulas as are necessary to cover all its essential components. Let us illustrate this with a few examples.

The first is taken from Zulliger's textbook on the Z-Test (p. 45). The response, which might just as well have been given to card III of the Rorschach test, is "Two men are struggling over a butterfly." The entire combination is scored W M+ H P and the score D F+ A P is given to the butterfly alone. The first formula serves principally to account for the W and the M factors. The second one is necessary in order to point out the double emphasis on the P factor.

Not infrequently, cautious persons reacting to card VI will first see the larger detail as "animal skin" and then "set the response right" by noting that the upper projection could also belong to it. Were a single formula to be used here, this would amount to ignoring an essential factor, namely, the sequence. The correct scoring is D F+ A (P) ; W F+ A P.

The problem of breaking up a response naturally arises with special frequency in combinatory and contaminated wholes. These are to be separated only if they contain heterogeneous scoring components: "Two men fight over a woman," (card I) need not be broken down, since all the components are M, and the formula W M+ H includes all the essential factors. A different case is represented by the following samples of simultaneous combinations, all three of which were obtained from the same test record. To card VIII held on the right side, the response was given, "A chameleon is walking over a cliff, and below is a stream in which it is reflected." The formulas are, W FC+ Ls, for the whole; D F+ A P for the chameleon; D F± Ls for the cliff; and D CF Ls for the stream and the reflection. This subject had produced many color associations and had seen this scene too in color, but her color emphasis was not the same in each component of her response. Color dominated in the "reflection" because the "stream" was determined by the blue. In the percept as a whole this influence retreated, and the form became primary, hence FC. The chameleon is chiefly F, for though this animal takes on numerous colors, it is never red. To card IX the response was, "Elves on a hill," spontaneously elucidated as follows: the red is "the red-hot poles," the green is "the hill," and the brown shows "how they are attempting to dress up as elves." The scoring formulas: W MC Scene Orig+, for the whole; D CF Fire for the red-hot poles, D FC+ Ls for the hill, and D M+ H for the elves. Had the subject not produced all this elaboration herself, we could easily be content here with an MC. The same figure in the inverted position was perceived as "two frogs sitting on the ground and eating a mushroom." As a whole this is certainly FC, even though one of the components—the ground— has no form whatever. The scoring formulas: W FC+ Scene Orig+; then D FC+ A for the frogs (the green) ; D FC+ Bt for the mushroom (the

red) ; and D C Ground for the ground. The separate scorings are necessary here partly because of the determinants, and partly because of the
varied content.

The following response to card VI is an example of a contamination,
in this instance given by a person who was only schizoid: "A turtle with a
head like a snake and a cat's whiskers; it also has gills like a tadpole." The
scoring formula: W(cont)* F+ A for the whole (it is F+ because the
principal form as well as the majority of the details are good forms) ; D F+
Ad for the head; Dd F+ Ad for the whiskers; and for the gills, D F− Ad
Orig−. The modes of approach are varied here, a jumble of D and Dd.
The form accuracy fluctuates. Only one of the embellishments is original
minus. The entire thing could, to be sure, be scored original minus, but
this would be an unnecessarily crude handling of the data, for we are dealing here with a contamination that is still under control of reality. It is
a borderline example of the so-called "borderline contaminations" (see
chapter 11 under Schizoid).

Finally, here are two other examples which seem to be quite similar, but
which deviate from one another in an important nuance. Responding to
card II held on right side, a psychopath says, "A decapitated animal, with
blood puddle; reflected." Scoring formulas are: for the whole, W FC+ A;
but, in addition, D CF Blood. Had only the decapitated animal been
named, the single FC+ would have been adequate (the color for the bloody
neck), but so strong is the color-determined element in the added "blood
puddle" that the first scoring alone would not have been enough. On the
other hand, CF for the figure as a whole would not be correct, for that
would be to undervalue the form in the animal percept, the achievement
of a combination, and the grasp of symmetry, all of which are form elements. Quite different, however, is the following example, "a lamp, and
the light rays are indicated," in response to the white space and the middle
red of card II. Here the scoring formula, DsD FC+ Obj, is sufficient. The
light-ray alone would otherwise be CF. But to score it thus here would be
inaccurate, for the very reason that it is the achievement of a combination
which has brought "form order" into the colored detail. The psychopath
also attempted this with his blood puddle but did not succeed.

Finally, let us emphasize once more how important it is not to go too
far in breaking up responses and to use this method only when it is indispensable. The net effect is always to inflate the response total and thus
reduce the percentages. It must be recommended, therefore, in the case of
short protocols, that the percentages be fixed on the basis of the total after
the additional responses have been deducted.

*i.e., contaminated.

## THE INQUIRY INTO DOUBTFUL RESPONSES

### THE NEED FOR INQUIRY

At times it is not possible to decide on the correct scoring without asking the Subject. The special conditions under which the test is administered usually prohibit carrying on such an inquiry during the test period. Should the uncertainty concern the location of a perceived detail, the examiner may indeed ask to have it pointed out during the test itself. A casual "Where, please?" usually is enough to obtain the information. But at times even the description of an unclear location must be postponed until after the recording has been done because any lengthy discussion in the course of the examination itself would influence the time factor. In particular, any inquiry concerning the determinants or modes of approach during the test administration is strictly prohibited, for even a single question in these areas would be suggestive, and seriously compromise the free association. Should one ask, for example, "Do you mean the entire figure or only some particular detail?" the Subject might be influenced then to look for details, although he might not have done so spontaneously. It goes without saying that to inquire about color, shading, or even movement is still more dangerous, aside from the fact that by going into long discussions, the time factor would again be distorted.

This is the dilemma: the need to obtain information on the one hand, and on the other the restriction against doing so during the test administration. Hence the necessity for carefully going over all uncertainties following the recording of the protocol. That is the so-called "inquiry," the clearing up of doubtful responses so the riddles do not appear afterwards. When a test is taken under strictly "blind" conditions, the inquiry must naturally be made by the person who administered the record. This in turn presumes full control over technique and much psychologic insight, and precludes the use of inexperienced assistants.

### TECHNIQUE OF INQUIRY

The most important basic rule in making the inquiry is, as at the investigation of a crime, the absolute avoidance of suggestive questions. The questions must be either deliberately vague, or suggest alternatives. We do not say, "You no doubt are referring to this detail?" but, "Do you mean the figure as a whole or some specific detail?" In general, clarifying the modes of approach presents no serious difficulties.

Among the determinants, we are chiefly concerned with color or movement. Naturally, we must here be even more alert to guard against suggestion. But neither should we ask questions that cannot be understood.

Most persons have so little psychologic understanding, are so inexperienced in introspection, that it serves no purpose to present the problem to them in theoretical form. Hence it is useless to question them directly about colors. In a case when it is unclear as to whether we are dealing with F or FC, it is hazardous to inquire. "Do you think that the color is a contributing factor here?" Experience shows that most persons see this question as a problem of "form or color." Of little use, too, are complicated explanations about the difference between FC and CF. Simple persons often do not understand them at all. For this reason, it is easy to get wrong replies to direct questions about color participation. It is better to bring the matter up indirectly. If, for example, a butterfly is seen, one may ask "Could it also be some moth or night moth?" Should the Subject deny this, one may ask, "Why?" Some remarks about the colors then usually come out spontaneously. Or one may simply ask, "Why did you just say crab?" and as a rule the desired information follows. Cultured individuals, especially artists and scientists, may be told directly what we are driving at. The Subject may then decide for himself what the answer is.

It is the questionable M that provides the chief difficulties in the inquiry. Here the greatest possible caution is in order. As Rorschach warned (pp. 25-26) under no circumstances must any question be put during the test administration relating to M. But there are also snags to asking it after the performance. It is best to have the doubtful percept explained in detail, and if the Subject answers the question, "Can you describe it in greater detail?" by going into much description of formal and static elements, detailing the extremities and other body parts, an M can be excluded with confidence. On the other hand, if after the performance of the test a movement is demonstrated, this does not furnish absolute evidence of an M. The Subject sees a flying duck and makes a little motion with the hands. This is no proof of empathic identification. As Rorschach expressly emphasizes (p. 25), there are associative recollections of movement which are not felt but only designated. The decision can be reached only on the basis of the general impression given by the use of language and by the Subject's entire conduct. For example, responding to card IV, a person may say "a bear," and nothing more. He is requested to describe it further, and perhaps the response is obtained, "Don't you see how he is staggering toward us with his gigantic claws, his broad gait, threatening?" This is an M response. The Subject may say, however, "I was thinking about these odd things here (the upper lateral extensions) that reminded me of bear's claws, and then perhaps also, the fur, it seems so shaggy." This is no M (and need not be FLD). The way the Subject acts is naturally taken into account. This kind of reaction has most significance in connection with humans and human-like animals.

These indirect questions may, however, not achieve their purpose, and the Subject's statements may continue to be unclear and ambiguous; then, with intelligent persons with intuitive insight, the attempt may occasionally be made to explain what it is all about. In doing this, it is best to compare the ambiguous M response with other, unambiguous M responses made by the Subject, or, if there are none, to make comparisons with other kinesthetic reactions that come easily to him. The experimenter says, for example, "Imagine that you are sitting in a Vienna cafe listening to a lively Vienna waltz, and being carried away by the beat of the music. Or imagine that you are watching a circus; an acrobat is doing his act, revolving around and around a horizontal bar when suddenly he seems to be tying his legs into knots. Quite involuntarily you curl up on yourself as though you were trying to find out how he does this." And then the problem of the interpretation in question can be explained.

However, not only may the responses themselves present uncertainties which must be cleared up but doubtful points are also found in the test's other productions. In fact, three of these always require an inquiry: the inverse interpretations, the repetitions, and the pars-pro-toto responses.

If it is suspected that the percept is inverted, seen upside down, the Subject is asked to point to it. This may be done during the test administration, but in any event following the close of the testing. For example, a person says "Two trees," for the outer red of card III. He is asked, "Show how, please." Or, if necessary, he is asked directly, "Where is the trunk and where are the branches?" Should the Subject then indicate the trunk above and the branches below, with the card in normal position, we have an inverse interpretation. A caution to be made here is that some Subjects as a matter of courtesy will turn the card when they are pointing something out. This must always be prevented. They must be told, "Please keep the card exactly as you see it; I am familiar with it and will easily find what you're looking at."

The Subject may repeat a percept. For example, his second association to card X may be "Two cornflowers," and then his seventh response to the same card may be the same answer. He is then asked at once—since we are concerned with recent memory—and in an even tone of voice, "But have you not already said that?" This is not a suggestive but a contrasuggestive question. The even tone is intended to screen the fact that we are "on the scent," and to simulate an uncertainty on the part of the examiner. If the Subject's reply is "No," we may be quite sure that we are dealing with a real repetition, i.e., a disturbance of recent memory (most often on an organic basis). If this is not the case, the response is usually, "Yes, but I was not certain whether you had already written that down."

The pars-pro-toto responses also always need ascertaining. Often these are not "genuine," but are merely due to inexactness in the manner of expression or carelessness.[53]

Should new responses emerge during the talk following the test administration, these are to be noted down separately and kept strictly apart from the examination proper. In the evaluation of the record, these associations can be drawn upon as supplementary evidence; as in helping answer questions which the protocol proper leaves open. Since these responses were not produced spontaneously during the performance itself, but were given under totally new conditions, they can under no circumstances be included in the summary. Doing so would lead to totally erroneous results.

## THE LESS, THE BETTER

So much for the heart of the matter. However, we do not live in a theoretic vacuum, and it is necessary to point out also the ways in which all this can be taken too far.

Many psychologists manifest a tendency to "busybody" in their testing, which can jeopardize the success of the entire experiment. They can never do enough about making the investigation complete, claiming that this is in the interest of more precision, but risk missing out on the main thing. In line with this tendency, a proposal has been made that all details of the protocol be gone over with the Subject after the test in order to evoke new ideas; and that these post festum ideas be recorded all together. Such a procedure is not only superfluous, but actually harmful. To ascertain which of the response categories are accented and which disregarded, is the object of the evaluation. By encouraging certain percepts, the experimenter can only divert himself from a correct understanding of the protocol. "Schematization and standardization of an investigation does not make it more objective; the objectivity is only apparent." The words are those of the Swedish neurologist Tore Broman[54] in connection with an investigation of the question technique in obtaining neurologic anamnesis. This warning is an important one, applying also to the technique of our inquiry.

As a general rule a supplement recording responses made after the test is unnecessary. The situation is so different that these responses would have to be evaluated by quite different criteria. Among persons who reject a great part of the cards, the test may be repeated in full, but only in exceptional cases. The critical results are still based on the analysis of the distribution of the rejections obtained in the first protocol. The supplementary responses,

[53]Zulliger, H.: Über symbolische Diebstähle von Kindern und Jugendlichen. Institut für Psychohygiene, Biel, 1951, p. 11.

[54]Broman, T.: Frågetekniken vid upptagningen av neurologisk anamnes. Nordisk Medicin 41: 361, 1949.

even when freely given, must under no circumstances be made part of the first test record.

In addition, experiments intended to fill gaps in the test findings ("testing the limits") are indicated in rare instances only. Complete absence of some response category—M, C, H or P—during the test proper has its significance. Eliciting responses to these categories may have interest from a research viewpoint, but hardly ever diagnostic significance. Only if it is suspected that the Subject has misunderstood the instructions thinking, perhaps, that he is supposed to see only anatomical content because the experimenter happens to be a physician, or that he is supposed to keep entirely to free association, should the instructions be restated correctly and the experiment repeated.

Unnecessary supplementary investigations are not only time-consuming, they actually breed errors. If the Subject is quite unnecessarily made to describe all the parts of a very simple percept, in order to make sure that some little "disturbing" detail has not also been included, this may result in a a totally wrong scoring. In card II, the response "two clowns," spontaneously produced, remains W M+ H P even if the subject should suddenly discover, under the very different conditions of a later interview that the middle red does not belong to the percept.

In America, too, where a general inquiry after the test is the usual thing, Beck agrees that it is better to be guided by experience than to stimulate the cautious "retrospective" responses in what is after all a new situation. He says[55] that, "universal experience in these responses can be more heavily weighted than S's testimony, so far as technique of scoring goes." We are also in full agreement with Rapaport when he insists that in the test technique, "time-consuming, complicated inquiry had to be avoided as much as possible."[56]

Only when real doubt obtains, must we "ascertain" the response, but this must by all means be avoided wherever possible; the less the better.

[55]Beck, S. J.: Rorschach's Test, I. Basic Processes. New York, 1944, p. 17.
[56]Rapaport, D.: Diagnostic Psychological Testing, Vol. II. Chicago, 1946, p. 88.

# CHAPTER IV
# *The Summary*

## THE TOTAL COUNT

ONCE ALL THE scoring formulas have been determined, all their components are counted, and the totals drawn up for the entire protocol—this is the so-called summary.

### THE RESPONSE TOTAL AND THE TIME

First the *number of responses* is figured out. The response totals already noted in the protocol for the individual test cards serve this purpose best. Should there be suspicion of color shock it is well to add up the response total for the last three cards separately, as Zulliger does. The way to write this is, therefore, "R 34 (VIII-X 12)."

Next comes the *time*, in minutes, required for the entire test. Here it is advisable, following Morgenthaler's proposal, to record the time spent on two halves of the test in parenthesis, the time from the presentation of the first card till the conclusion of the fifth, and the time spent on the rest, for example, "time—40 minutes (22/18)."

These factors permit us to calculate the *time per response*. This average reaction time is to be distinguished from the reaction time proper. It is the average per association, "the response time," derived as a ratio of the duration of the whole experiment to the response total, while "reaction time" is the time which elapses from the presentation of each card until the first response is given. Only the latter is designated reaction time in the United States. In general it is unnecessary to do this timing with a stopwatch; that may even be very disturbing to a nervous Subject. It is sufficient to note the exceptionally long pauses following the presentation of a given test card (e.g., card VI, after about 1½ minutes, "Perhaps an animal skin"). The time per response is naturally influenced by the reaction time, and in general all that is necessary is to compute the response time.

The average number of responses, according to Rorschach, is 15-30 responses in 20-30 minutes, which means a response time of one minute or a little more.

Friedemann[1] advises a time analysis which will differentiate between the time spent on the color cards and that spent on the black ones. It seems, however, even more profitable to focus on all three categories of the test cards and, following a suggestion by the Swedish doctor, Ann Marie

[1] Adolf Friedemann: Bemerkungen zu Rorschach's Psychodiagnostik, Rorschachiana II, p. 58.

71

Broman[2] to count the response time in four figures. First we obtain the response time for the entire test, and then the corresponding figure for the black alone, the black-red alone, and the color cards, each to the second decimal point. It is sufficient for our purpose to score with half-minutes. We have in recent years been obtaining this data by routine, but have so far been unable to process the results statistically. Yet we have the impression that some very interesting regularities can be patterned out. The average response time for the black-red and the color cards as a rule produce opposite results, although the reasons for this have not been adequately investigated. When one is shorter, the other is longer, and vice versa.

Friedemann[3] makes the suggestion that the response times for associations to the angular and the closed-in forms be compared to those for the round and open ones, and this also appears to be worth considering.

### THE TOTALING OF THE ELEMENTS IN THE FORMULAS

The individual elements of the formulas are now added together according to type and set down in four columns corresponding to the four divisions of the formula.

(a) *The approach.* W here comes first, then D, then Dd, then Ds, then Dds and finally, Do. It is best to set down Dds as a separate group analogous to Dd. But to set up the various secondary W, as well as the DdD and the DsD, as independent groups in addition to the others, makes it hard to get a picture of the total count. The DW, DdW, and DsW *are* W and if we wish to see at a glance how many W the subject has perceived, we are not interested in first counting the several sub-groups. It is consequently advisable to enclose these sub-totals under their main groups in parentheses as Rorschach himself did. Above all, it is necessary to indicate how many of the W are accurate forms, thus: W 11 (8+) (2 DW+, 1 DsW+). All accurate forms count as W+ without regard to whether they are F, M, F(C), FLD or FC. LDF, LD, CF and C responses are as a matter of principle W− and naturally also poor forms.

In evaluating the Ds it is not only necessary to take into account the "pure" Ds and Dds but also the related combinations (DsW, DsD, DdsD, etc.). If in addition to two Ds and one Dds, the W responses include two DsW, and if there is a DsD among the D and two DdsDd among the Dd, this distribution still has the same symptom significance as would 5 Ds and 3 Dds.

It may be that only a tendency regarding some of these categories ap-

[2]Ann Marie Broman: Personal communication.
[3]Op. cit. p. 57.

pears, in which case we note "tendency" (e.g., Do=tendency). Should these responses appear and other responses and comments show a trend toward them as well, we write down "tendency to more" (e.g., Do 2, tendency to more).

(b) *The determinants.* In this row it is best to begin with M, as Rorschach himself always did; and to do so even when none appears (M=0). It is essential to see at once from the total whether there are any M and how many. In the other categories we need to include only what actually appears. We must not forget to state in parentheses whether all the M are good forms or whether some of them are M−; e.g., M=8 (+), or M=6 (1−). The MC, MLD (or MFLD, MLDF) and the very rare confabulated FM, are separately listed as are also the small M, which are similarly to be marked with a plus or a minus. It is not advisable to treat these very rare and highly significant blends (the MC and MLD) as sub-groups (similar to the DW). The fact is that they belong to *two* groups and hence have to be counted in twice. The opposite procedure to that used in the modes of approach is here the clearest.

Following the several M categories, we set down the F. The number of F− and of F± are included in parentheses and it should possibly be noted whether any of these are indefinite F−, e.g., F 12 (3−, and of these 1 indef, 2±).

The several light-dark and shading determined responses may either be listed separately in accordance with the Binder classification, or the several categories can be put together in the summary as a whole (following Rorschach's original practice), with the Binder classifications set next, separately. For purposes of scientific investigation the latter is preferable, partly because these groups have a certain symptom value in common, in spite of their individual peculiarities. They are entirely lacking in persons of rugged character.

Finally we have the three kinds of color responses: FC, CF, and C. Only in relation to FC is it still customary to indicate a plus or a minus in parentheses; e.g., FC=4 (1−) or FC=5 (+). If the pure color responses include color namings, this is to be noted, e.g., C=3 (2 color namings).

(c) *The content.* This offers no unusual difficulties apart from the fact that it is here that mistakes are most easily made in the totaling. It is recommended that a permanent standard order be adopted for the most important content categories, e.g., H, Hd, A, Ad, An, Sex, Bt, Ls, Oj, Ar, Ornament, Map and then the more infrequent ones such as Food, Scene, Painting, Blood, Fire, Cloud and the like (in any order) and, finally, Abstracts. In the main groups there thus is a transition from the organic to the inorganic. It has been found very useful to separate out various edible objects from other objects under the topic "food." The first four categories, H, Hd, A, Ad, are always to be set down, even when the finding is zero. The fact of their presence or absence is important in making a qualitative judgment relating to the individual's intelligence as well as to his capacity for social contact and his mood.

(d) *The frequency row* consists in general only of the P and the Original responses, since the unique responses are extremely rare. Should some of the P be in parentheses it is best to put down two totals, e.g., P=6 (8?) ; in other words 6 "usual" P and two of borderline quality have been found.

Next, the plus or minus sign must be added on to the Orig, and it should also be noted whether any of these responses and how many have a vocational source. So far as the three sub-groups of the originals are concerned, it suffices to note the rare but important apprehension originals separately as "Ap," e.g., Orig=26 (3-), (4 Voc+, 5 Ap, 1-).

PERCENTAGES AND TYPES

Finally, a series of ratios and of "types" will be given. In general only the following four categories are computed by percentage; the accurate forms, animal content, the P and the original responses.

(a) F+ per cent—*the per cent of clearly perceived forms*—is the ratio of accurate form percepts to all form responses. In contrast to W+ we are here dealing only with pure form responses. M, F(C), FLD, and FC are not included. The indefinite F- are treated as unclear forms and F± are counted half and half, e.g., F = 40 (8-, including 4 indef, 4±), F+ =

$$\left( \frac{30 \times 100}{40} \right) = 75 \text{ per cent.}$$

The indefinite F- are treated as ordinary F- in calculating the F+% but notice must be taken of them when the whole picture is being evaluated. If the indefinite F- were to be subtracted from the rest and we then calculated the F+ per cent—something which Rorschach did not do—a quite misleading picture would result. For the inability to produce a clear-cut response, whatever the reason, always betrays a deficiency in intellectual achievement. It was therefore unwise of some psychologists to put these indefinite responses at the zero point (together with the pure color and light-dark responses) and so set up a form-level scale at that center.[4]

(b) The A (*animal*) *per cent* is the ratio of the sum of animal and animal detail percepts (A plus Ad) to the response total for the entire test. If, for example, in 40 responses 15 are A and 5 are Ad, the A per cent is 50.

(c) The P per cent (*popular response per cent*) is the ratio of the P responses to the total test productivity. When (P) responses appear, the rule is to calculate two percentages.

[4]See 1946 Supplement of Klopfer's and Kelley's "The Rorschach Technique."

(d) The *Orig per cent*, finally, is the ratio of original responses to the response total for the test. It is not necessary to calculate a separate Orig+ per cent, but it is well to state in parentheses what the distribution of the quality of the originals is. If all the Orig are good ones we write (+), otherwise (±) or (∓), depending on whether the good or poor ones predominate. When, among very many good originals, isolated poor ones appear or the reverse, we write (+_+) or (_+_) after the original percentage.

(e) To calculate *any other percentages* of W, W+, D, Ds, Do, M, C, Bt, Oj, and the like, is generally unnecessary for diagnostic purposes because the examiner's experience should make it possible to draw appropriate conclusions from the absolute numbers themselves. Percentage figures of this kind may possibly facilitate matters in the kind of scientific investigations in which the findings of the several groups are to be compared with one another, but to compute a W per cent would in general be devoid of meaning, since the W, as Kuhn[5] has demonstrated by comprehensive statistical investigations, does not correlate with the response total but can be evaluated only on the basis of absolute number.

The anatomy responses are, however, an exception to this rule. Where these appear in great numbers (and this applies also to sex associations) so as to exceed a percentage of 12, it is desirable to calculate the anatomy per cent, enabling us to obtain an index to this special kind of stereotyping. Anatomy and sexual associations can with confidence be counted together for this purpose. An anatomy per cent of zero to 12 generally has slight significance and therefore may be disregarded—except, of course, when highly specialized complex responses appear, as when a singer's only two anatomy responses refer to the throat. The 12 per cent limit is Zulliger's and has proven its worth in practice.

(f) The mutual ratio of the modes of approach in any one test protocol was called *the approach type* (Ap) by Rorschach. He uses as his point of departure a normal average of 8 W, 23 D, 2 Dd, and 1 Ds in 34 responses. He calls this average type W-D. It is possible that his 8 W is pegged too high for the normal average. Still, the mean for the normal can hardly be below 6.[6] Depending on which is emphasized, W or D, this letter is underlined.* If the emphasis is in the direction of Dd or Ds, or if more than

[5] Communication on the 2nd International Rorschach Congress in Berne, 1952.

[6] See Samuel J. Beck, Rorschach's Test, I. Basic Processes, New York, 1944, pp. 83-84.

*Because it is difficult to underline in type, notations that would be underlined in the Examiner's record will be set in italic type throughout. Boldface italic will indicate extra emphasis which the Examiner might mark in his records with a double underline.

one Do appears, these classifications are also to be noted in the Ap, in parentheses if their number is rather small. A few examples will best demonstrate this.

10 W, 18 D, 1 Dd = Ap $W$ — D
 5 W, 26 D, 3 Dd = Ap W — $D$
 8 W, 30 D, 4 Dd = Ap W — $D$ — (Dd)
 6 W, 25 D, 5 Dd = Ap W — $D$ — Dd
 8 W, 15 D, 6 Dd, 3 Ds = Ap $W$ — D — Dd — Ds
 4 W, 28 D, 6 Dd, 4 Ds, 2 Do = Ap (W) — $D$ — Dd — Ds — (Do)
 4 W, 16 D, 14 Dd, 9 Ds, 1 Dds, 4 Do = Ap (W) — $D$ — $Dd$ — Ds — Do
 2 W, 18 D, 12 Dd, 4 Ds, 3 Do = Ap D — $Dd$ — Ds — Do

Pure D or Dd types are never found in Rorschach's published material, and they probably are extremely rare. Pure W types, on the other hand, are by no means rare. A distinction is to be made between the W+ type, where ten or approximately 10 W responses with predominantly good forms are produced, as against a W– type in which 10 or almost 10 W responses are given, but with predominantly poor forms. The latter Ap is occasionally found in torpid schizophrenics.

(g) By the term *sequence (seq)*, Rorschach refers to the order in which the modes of approach follow one another in the individual test cards. The general practise is first to make a survey of the entire test figure, and only then to turn to the details. Naturally the D attract the attention before the Dd or Ds, and hence the "normal" sequence would be W, D, Dd, with now and then a Ds, in most of the cards, but with occasional minor deviations. When the Subject always makes the effort to perceive a W before turning to a D, and if he never produces a Dd before a D, the sequence is designated as rigid. Such cases are exceptionally rare. In the main, a W response is not produced for every card; now and then there may be an irregularity in the order of detail, and a belated W may follow. This sequence is the "optimal controlled" variety, that is, orderly. If several obvious irregularities appear, as when W follows the D percept more than once (and in these records there are usually still other irregularities), the sequence must be looked upon as loose. When the lack of orderliness is so pronounced that no visible rule is followed at all, it is a confused sequence. In instances when the Subject starts most of the cards with a Dd or a Do, and then proceeds by way of the D to the W percepts, we designate the sequence as inverted.

In actual practice there are naturally borderline instances which may be indicated as: "moderately loose," "severely loose," "loose tending to confusion," "partly inverted."

At times the sequence cannot be established because only a single response is given to each test card, or because several responses to the same card only occur a very few times. It is best then to write: "sequence?"

A sample of a confused sequence follows:

| Card | I | II | III | IV | V | VI | VII | VIII | IX | X |
|---|---|---|---|---|---|---|---|---|---|---|
| | D | Dd | W | Dd | — | W | Dd | D | — | Dd |
| | W | | W | Dd | | Do | D | Dd | | D |
| | | | W | Do | | Dd | D | D | | |
| | | | | W | | D | | Dd | | |
| | | | | D | | | | | | |

(h) The most important ratio in the entire summary is the *experience balance* (EB). Rorschach uses this term to designate the relation between the movement and the color responses.

The computation is very simple. Each M counts as one. On the color side, CF counts as a unit, and so one CF is 1.0, one FC is 0.5, and one C is 1.5. In MC responses, one point is scored for each side; in MLD, one point for the M side only. (Only in the very rare cases of MFC may a half point be scored on the color side.) The small M are not added to the EB. Thus, 4 M, 1 MC, 1 MLDF, 3 small M, 4 FC, 3 CF and 1 C, makes an EB of 6/7.5 (4 + 1 + 1 + 0 over 2 + 3 + 1 (for the MC) + 1.5). The sum of the M responses is always put on the left side and the sum of the color responses on the right. When color naming appears, it is best to figure two EB, one with and one without the color naming. But the full symptom value goes only to the EB without the color naming.

According to Rorschach, five kinds of EB are to be distinguished. It is "constricted" ("coarctated") when the figures on both sides are zero or one (i.e., when they are 0/0, 1/0, 0/1, an 1/1). When the total is no more than 3 on each side, the EB is called "constrictive" ("coarctative"). Any EB whose two sides approximately balance each other, and possess higher counts than 3 (e.g., 5/6, 8/8, 9/11), are ambiequal. If M notably predominates, Rorschach calls the EB introversive (e.g., 5/2), and if the color values are heavier, it is an extratensive EB (e.g., 3/8). (We do not agree with the claims made by some authors, such as Enke and Binder, for "introversive color responses.") In determining the introversive and extratensive types, it is necessary to discriminate between those in which the smaller side of the balance merely shows fewer of the responses in question and those in which it shows none. If one or the other side is entirely lacking, Rorschach speaks respectively of an "extratension-lacking introversive" (values ranging from 2 M/0 C to x M/0 C) or of an "egocentric extratensive" (values from 0 M/ 2 C to 0 M/x C).

(i) *Color type.* Naturally, the significance depends upon which elements make up the color side. In an EB of 6/6 there is a real difference depending on whether the color values were derived predominantly from FC or from CF or even C responses. As we have seen, a person's inner control over his affects and his ability to stabilize them is indicated by the distribution of his color responses. Hence the need for some special phrase which can identify the several possible combinations. K. W. Bash has proposed the concepts of "left type," "middle type," and "right type" for the color values. The reason for this is that one usually notes the FC first (i.e., on the left) and then the CF, finally passing to the C. Since we are utilizing these expressions in the following pages, they are here stated with Bash's own examples:

|            |                  |
|------------|------------------|
|            | 12 FC, 0 CF, 0 C |
| Left type  | 10 FC, 1 CF, 0 C |
|            | 8 FC, 2 CF, 0 C  |
|            | 5 FC, 2 CF, 1 C  |
| Middle type| 4 FC, 4 CF, 0 C  |
|            | 3 FC, 3 CF, 1 C  |
|            | 2 FC, 2 CF, 2 C  |
| Right type | 1 FC, 1 CF, 3 C  |
|            | 0 FC, 0 CF, 4 C  |

All the examples add up to a total value of 6 color units in the EB.

(j) *Attitudinal index:* The experience balance with its double polarity (constriction-dilatation, introversion-extraversion) presents some difficulties for statistical treatment. In order to overcome these difficulties, K. W. Bash[7] has proposed the following novel method of evaluation.

When the two components of the experience balance are divided one by the other (M : sum C) a number results that Bash has called the experience quotient (EQ). All extratensive values of this EQ lie between 0 and 1, the ambiequal EQ is 1, and the introversive values lie between 1 and $\infty$. This corresponds to the behavior of the tangent function. The inverse tangents of the experience quotients would thus give a linear expression of the introversion-extratension scale, in which at the same time the factor of constriction or dilatation is eliminated. The corresponding value, the attitudinal index (abbreviated EW from the German *Einstellungswert*) is therefore determined by the basic formula: EW = arc tang $(\Sigma M/\Sigma C)$. It follows from this that the experience balance 0:X (including introversionless or egocentric extratensives) has an EW = 0; the extratensive experience types have an EW that lies between 0 and 45; an EW = 45 would designate ambiequality; and the introversive experience types have an EW between 45 and 90. The extratensionless introversives (experience balance X:0) finally have an EW of 90. The EW of 0 and 90

[7]Bash, K. W. Über die Bestimmung und statistische Verteilung der Introversion und Extratension im Rorschach-Versuch. *Rorschachiana-J*, I. pp. 333-343 (1953).— Idem: Einstellungstypus and Erlebnistypus: C. G. Jung and Hermann Rorschach (English). *Journal of Projective Techniques* Vol. 19, No. 3, pp. 236-242 (1955).

would thus be the extreme values. The absolutely constricted experience
balance (0:0) could not be represented in this notation.

By means of the attitudinal index, the distribution of introversion and
extratension in the population can be determined with relative ease. The
EW gives in general a distribution that suggests bimodality. Furthermore,
K. W. Bash was able to show by means of this method that men tend more
to extratension, women more to introversion (loc. cit. p. 338), at least in
a Swiss population.

(k) A number of other indices and types have in the course of time
been set up for the Rorschach test. They are in the main superfluous and
further testing has proved several to be actually misleading. Usually the
reason for this kind of elaboration is a wish to simplify something complicated, but we cannot do violence to psychologic structure any more than
to other natural phenomena.

Of course, there are ratios that really have a significance, and which can
be of great value in scientific investigation. One such example is the color
index of Van Der Waals (Amsterdam). This is relatively unnecessary for
purposes of diagnosis but quite useful in statistical comparison. It is the
ratio of the response total to the color cards over the total to the black
cards alone, thus:

$$\frac{\Sigma \ R \ (II, \ III, \ VIII, \ IX, \ X)}{\Sigma \ R \ ( \ I, \ IV, \ V \ \ VI, \ VII)}$$

### FORMS AND CHARTS

Many kinds of Rorschach test forms (tabulation sheets) have been
developed and some with many elaborations. Whether one cares to use
these forms is a matter of taste and habits. They do not improve the quality
of the psychological work and, with regard to their aid to clearness, opinions
differ. One gets the strong feeling from much of this that the piling-up
of technical finesse at times is supposed to stand in direct relation to psychologic value. Clearness, to be sure, has a great value, but the simplest presentation is for the most part also the clearest.

For purposes of scientific clearness, the best way to record the essential
data of the "raw material" is by means of files. As a matter of space economy
it is not expedient to have every possible scoring category and other test
phenomenon printed in advance, but rather to avoid any form that is
altogether too large and impractical. Actually, only a portion of all the
possibilities appear in one test protocol, and the fact remains that the clearest
way is to write down only that which is actually produced, though of course
always in accordance with the same pattern and in the same column order.
An optimal measure of clarity will thus be attained. A very simple chart
is therefore quite adequate. Using a punch card system, one may mark

out the observed topics on the edges of the cards and very easily sort out the cards of any particular category for purposes of a correlation study. A brief summary of the evaluation can be entered on the back of the cards together with a synopsis of the clinical data and the diagnosis.

## II. THE SYMPTOMATIC SIGNIFICANCES

The summary brings to light certain new quantities whose basic symptomatic values we have not yet dealt with and which will be described below. It is to be understood, however, that it is not possible to extract the separate symptomatic meaning of any individual finding, since this meaning is a function of all the factors as a unit.

1. *The content.* In addition to the absolute quantities and their distribution (as an index to interests, cultural level), the relative quantities of the first four categories are also of significance. In the well-endowed normal person, H is generally greater than Hd. An inversion of this ratio (Hd greater than H) indicates either a lower intelligence achievement (due to lack of ability or to inhibition of the intellect) or a depressed mood or an anxiety.

The ratio of A:Ad normally results in A being greater than Ad. The inversion of this usual ratio has a symptomatic significance similar to the corresponding inversion of the human responses: either intelligence is lower, or we are dealing with depression or affective inhibition. Here, too, the hampering of the intelligence is related to achievement only, and appears to operate primarily in terms of practical intellectual life, since the animal associations, as with the D responses, stem from concrete-mindedness. Conclusions as to the Subject's innate and possibly richer potentialities can be drawn only from the interrelation of all the test factors.

2. *F+ per cent* is important for judging intelligence and is particularly related to clearness of observation and the ability to concentrate. The unintelligent score a low F+ per cent since they do not observe clearly. Nervous individuals often do so owing to the disturbance of concentration. All this is far from saying that a reduction of F+ per cent found together with indications of originally high endowment always indicates a disturbance of concentration. The capacity for recall may be impaired while the memory traces themselves are sharp. This can in turn be due to disturbance of recent memory or disturbance of memory for past events. Such interferences are found in several organic conditions as well as in the functional disturbances of the capacity for recall in pseudo-mental debility.

3. The *A percentage* is the general indicator of stereotypy, according to specific conditions set up by the test. This percentage shows how easy it is or how difficult for the person to free his associative processes from their

dependence on a previously established mental set. The lower the A percentage, the more mobile the thought processes; the higher the A percentage, the more inert they are. The tendency to stereotypy (high animal per cent) may be due to the greatest variety of causes: lack of intelligence, inertia, conventionality, a stiff adhesion to vocational thinking in persons of normal intelligence (somewhat in line with Szondi's "vocational ego"), advanced age ( A per cent increases with age), depressive mood, anxiety, schizophrenic or organic deterioration. The reduction of mental alertness with advanced age has been strikingly confirmed by recent investigations. The forming of new associations becomes difficult with age, much more so than routine memory.[8]

When the A per cent is low, we must not overlook the fact that some other response category may be taking over the role of stereotypy indicator, such as anatomy, stones, branches, flowers, and the like, sometimes also vocationally influenced responses, e.g., coastal stretches and islands in the case of geographers, histologic preparations with medical persons, etc. Otherwise, a lowered A per cent in the normal individual points to mobility in thinking, due to training or artistic endowment, and also to freedom from vocational biases. (At the same time it is a remarkable fact that epileptics have in most cases a rather low A per cent.)

4. The *P percentage* (aside from the absolute quantity of P, since there is a limit to their total number) is for the most part an index to the social adaptivity of a person's thinking. In the feeble-minded and mentally ill, this finding often makes it possible to draw worthwhile conclusions as to the patient's capacity for adjustment and contact; while in the psychopathic personality it is a valuable prognostic index—the higher the P percentage, the more favorable the outlook.

5. The *Original percentage* is naturally a direct indicator of the originality of the individual's thinking. At the same time it gives us an insight into his general education or his vocational thought habits, depending on the relative distribution of the originals. It is of the first importance, naturally, to observe whether the originals are for the most part good or poor. When poor originals predominate, they are always a sign of neurotic or psychotic disturbance. Furthermore, for purposes of correct interpretation, it is important to notice the distribution of these responses among the various modes of approach and among the various kinds of original responses, (whether motif or elaboration or apprehension originals).

[8]See among others, J. G. Gilbert, Mental Efficiency in Senescence (Archives of Psychology, No. 188, 1935); and: Memory Loss in Senescence (Journal of Abnormal and Social Psychology, Vol. 36, 1941, pp. 73-86), here quoted according to Samuel Granick, Studies in the Psychology of Senility. A survey (Journal of Gerontology, Vol. 5, No. 1, January 1950).

6.  The *Ap type* is principally used for a qualitative evaluation of intelligence. Here the W factor is evidence of the capacity for taking an overall view, for thinking systematically and theoretically; the D factor indicates practical intelligence; and Dd is characteristic of a love of detailed work, diligence, and persistence. The more Ap approaches a pure W+ type, the greater is the drive for qualitative achievement; while the drive for quantitative achievement is more often indicated by a tendency toward increased Dd. But a displacement towards Dd may also have a depressive mood as its source, or may stem from a compulsive meticulousness, or from anal aggression.

7.  The *sequence* is the index to orderliness of thought, degree of logical training and discipline. A rigid sequence is found in persons whose thinking is "held in a vise," that is among pedants, the "school marm" type and bureaucrats. Persons of average endowment, moderately clear in their thinking, as well as the scientifically minded, provided they are not at the same time somewhat neurotic, are orderly; neurotics, persons of imagination, artists, and persons in a state of exultation, show a loose sequence. Confused sequence is found almost exclusively in schizophrenics or in marked schizoids.

It is quite understandable that when a Subject can produce no more D responses he will, in his effort to give as many responses as possible, turn to the Dd. It is quite another matter, however, when the Dd responses are the first to appear to a test card, and when the Subject only later turns to the D and finally to the W. These are instances of inverted sequence. This is always a sign of an anxiety-laden cautiousness, a fear of being directly concerned with the major task or at least the one immediately at hand. Persons who respond in this way are compelled to feel out a situation before they become confident enough to "come out of themselves."

A more modified tendency to turn from the D to the W percepts is frequently found in persons who are constructive thinkers, inductive intellects who progress from empirical observations to the basic facts and their interrelations, and also in persons with artistic talent.

Zulliger,[9] working on the basis of ideas already developed by Rorschach, maintains the importance of still another variety of sequence. He claims that it makes a difference whether the Subject turns from lateral details to middle ones or conversely from the middle to the laterals. The lateral to middle approach is found in practical minded opportunists, persons with a good grasp of the concrete, the "handy" and hobby-minded people. The middle to lateral approach is found in persons who are rather more determined, who act out of deliberation, persons who are unsure of themselves but go about their work systematically. When there is a cramped

⁹Hans Zulliger, Einführung in den Behn-Rorschach-Test, Berne, 1941, pp. 105/106.

emphasis on the middle details this reflects an attitude of uncertainty and anxiety.

8. If we were to attempt anything like a complete survey of the symptomatic significance of the *experience balance,* we would have to reproduce about half of Rorschach's "Psychodiagnostics," for his concept of the EB is the core of the entire experiment. It is only within this framework that the other factors come to life and become intelligible.

The EB mirrors the personality's basic attitude toward the ego and the environment. It has been established that the M responses represent the individual's intimate inner life, while the color responses as a whole correspond to the more external side of his mental life, his reaction to the environment. Theoretically, this makes sense when we consider that the kinesthetic experience and imagery that underlie the M responses belong among the proprioceptive sensations (Sherrington), while the world of colors is mediated not only through the exteroceptive sense of vision, but also has a direct relationship to the affect which is being externalized.

But all this is only true in a general manner of speaking. As we have already seen, the trends "towards the world" and "away from the world" are to be found in the different kinds of M. Similar tendencies are found in the color responses. Goldstein and Rosenthal[10] have shown in their interesting researches on certain color effects that:

"red activates a tendency towards externalizing movement, green towards internalizing movement . . . We must therefore suppose that the attraction to the external world is stronger in the case of red and yellow than it is in green and blue. And that the latter colors in fact activate an adduction, a removal from the stimulus, a withdrawal of the organism towards his own inner sphere."

Leaning on Jung's terminology, Rorschach has chosen the expression "introversive" and "extratensive" to designate these basic relations to the inner world and the environment. But he expressly states that his concept of introversion "has almost nothing except the name in common with Jung's" (p. 77). Rorschach maintains that the introversion in the M response is "a universal human characteristic," that it is in fact a tendency, a process, but not a condition (p. 77). The same holds for its opposite, and for that reason he calls it extratension, not extravertedness. As K. W. Bash has stated in his article, "Einstellungstypus and Erlebnistypus: C. G. Jung and Hermann Rorschach,"[11] Jung's conception of his own typology has since the publication of the "Psychologische Typen" (1921) developed in the

[10]K. Goldstein and O. Rosenthal: Zum Problem der Wirkung der Farben auf den Organismus, Schweizer Arch. f. Neurologie und Psychiatrie, Vol. 26, 1930, pp. 10 and 23.

[11]In "C. G. Jung and Projective Techniques" special issue of the "Journal of Projective Techniques" (1955).

same direction as Rorschach's so that there is no longer any essential difference between their views.

The EB thus permits us to see which of the two tendencies predominates, or whether both are developed to an equal degree. Where the EB is ambiequal the two tendencies alternate. Persons in this category tend to need to draw back into themselves for the "creative pause" when they have expended themselves over an extended period of time. Then when they have withdrawn for a time long enough to develop new impulses, they react again to the pressure towards renewed activity in the external world. Rorschach has correctly seen that this is the way in which genius works. We find the same opinion more recently in the historical writings of Arnold J. Toynbee[12] who looks upon this need to withdraw before accomplishing an act (withdrawal and return) as the essential sign of the creative person.

The introversive EB, that which emphasizes the M side, is said by Rorschach (p. 73) to represent a more differentiated intelligence, more originality in their productivity, more inner living, more stabilized affectivity, a rapport which is more intense, rather than diffused (the individual's circle of friends is smaller but more intimate), a measured and more stabilized motility, less ability to adapt to reality and, finally, as a result can also represent an awkward, clumsy kind of person.

The extratensive EB, emphasizing the color side, is characterized by a more stereotyped intelligence, more reproductivity, a more externalized way of life, more labile affectivity, a rapport which is scattered rather than intense (a large circle of friends but rather superficial ties), lively, more labile motility, a rather large contact with the environment (capacity for adaptation to reality) and related to this a certain adroitness and dexterity.

The coarctated and coarctative EB's, finally, are found in persons who are rather stiff, dry, with a tendency to pedantry, possessing rather less originality in their productivity, but also less emotionally responsive. Their capacity for reproductive intelligence may result in important achievements, and they are mostly valued for their dependability. Aside from such "normals," it is among depressives that this EB is frequently found, also among compulsive neurotics, compulsive characters and recovered schizophrenics.

The question of correlating the EB's with the psychologic imagery types (the visual, auditory, motor, haptic, and indifferent types) is as yet unanswered. It will be a difficult question to answer, too, since the various types are not the same within all the imagery spheres. While Charcot and the older investigators like Fechner, Galton and Taine believed that the imagery type characterized the entire manner of imagining, later evidence has shown that this is not the case. It is possible for a person's speech imagery to be quite acoustic-motor in type and yet for his imagery of objects and of numbers to be visual. The majority of people belong in fact to a

[12]Arnold J. Toynbee, A Study of History.

"mixed" type. Rorschach (p. 100) clearly recognized these difficulties and refers in this connection to William Stern's "Differential Psychology."

The EB is not, however, a fixed, unchangeable quantity. Alcohol and drugs can produce transitory changes, alcohol usually in the extratensive direction. Stauder[13] reports that intoxication caused by either alcohol or sedatives has a dilating effect on the EB, and incidentally also produces perseveration. The animated mood broadens (dilates), the depressive mood or fatigue narrows (coarctates) the EB, but without altering the qualitative relationships. A displacement in the introversive direction is caused by a cheerful mood or highly concentrated creative work (inspiration), while the enjoyment of external stimuli has an extratensive effect.

Correspondingly, typical alterations are found in the several age phases. The EB of very small children is dilated (ambiequal or extratensive), but at school age it becomes for the most part coarctated or coarctative, and begins to dilate again only during adolescence. Boys are more introversive during adolescence, according to Behn-Eschenburg[14] (productive, self-reliant, original), and possess greater coarctation ability (abstractness, objectivity) with less emotionality. Girls, on the other hand, are more extratensive (reproductive in their intelligence), more adaptive emotionally, more capable of affective contact and more lively. After full maturity has been attained, at about the age of 30, there is a trend to introversion, and then comes the age of the greatest variability. Only after the age of forty does the capacity for introversion decline, and a slow coarctation begins to set in, which usually progresses until after the age of sixty, often well into the advanced years. In senile dementia, however, a renewed extratensiveness is released. As we will see later, this is not the only infantile reaction of the senile.

[13]Karl Heinz Stauder, Konstitution und Wesensänderung der Epileptiker, Leipzig, 1938, p. 93.

[14]Hans Behn-Eschenburg. Psychische Schüleruntersuchungen mit dem Formdeutversuch, Berne, 1921, p. 52.

# CHAPTER V

# Special Phenomena

WE HAVE NOW brought together all the purely formal aspects of the "raw material" of the test. We might begin the interpretation at this point. However, on this basis alone we should still not get very far in understanding protocols obtained in cases of mental illness. The fact is that the Rorschach test, besides, contains a great number of factors which cannot be counted or weighed quantitatively. These may well be called the "imponderables." But these very factors are of the greatest importance for the correct interpretation of the test. We shall consider them in this chapter under the heading of special phenomena and will first summarize them in a list.

This summary has been developed through practice and experience. Even the most sophisticated test expert cannot keep his mind on all the noteworthy and salient points of a protocol at once. For the less experienced this is even more difficult. Time after time it may happen that something important is overlooked. The necessity for a standard reference list seems quite obvious. Such a list can be gone through after the scoring in order to check all important diagnostic points. Furthermore, it is helpful if some infrequent but important response categories are included in this list, for example, M-, secondary movement, perspective, "number" and position responses.

This list is then a memory aid. It can be gone through step by step in order to establish which of the named reactions occur in the protocol at hand. The phenomena in question can then be specified in the same order after the scoring. In connection with this, it is strongly recommended that any observations indicating the presence of shock be noted, such as, special comment in reaction to card II, the first response in VIII, the sequence in IX, and so forth. At any rate, it is necessary in the case of phenomena where dots are added ( . . . . . ) to specify the card at which the phenomenon occurred, as proper conclusions can be drawn only from notes specified in this way. The simple notation "colorshock," is meaningless unless the card is identified and the degree of shock is known. This is especially important for examiners who keep a card index, since the protocol itself cannot be seen in them.

A great number of the phenomena mentioned were observed by Rorschach himself and described by him. Others stem from the work of later investigators. For quick reference these have been listed with the names of their authors. From my own observations, the kinetic descriptions, the pseudo-color response, and the auditory associations, indeed, have not yet been published, and the sexual symbol stupor has previously been mentioned only with specific reference to the point detail in card II.

The sequence of the list is in part, but not entirely, arbitrary. The attempt has been made to proceed from the general to the specific, and also to group similar phenomena together, such as shocks, stereotyping, and infrequent types of responses. Since there are protocols in which a dozen or more of these reactions appear together, it will be useful always to note them in the same order so that it may be seen at a glance which are and which are not present.

After we have gone through the list and noted all the special phenomena after the scoring summary (and in part also given the reasons for them) the "stock taking" is complete. Only then can the interpretation proper be made.

We present here the standard list. We shall then go through it point by point, and discuss each in greater detail.

### List of the special phenomena

(.... indicates that the card where the phenomenon occurs must be mentioned.)

1. Rejection ( .... )
2. Interpretation awareness (heightened, lowered or annulled)
3. Subject and object criticism (Fränkel and Benjamin)
4. Color shock ( .... ), sometimes with attraction to color
5. Delayed color shock ( .... ) (Zulliger)
6. Overcompensated color shock (Bohm)
7. Red shock ( .... )
8. Red attraction (Zulliger)
9. Dark shock ( .... ) sometimes dark attraction (Binder)
10. Overcompensated dark shock ( .... ) (Bohm)
11. Interference phenomenon (IV or VIII) (sometimes double interference phenomenon) (Bohm)
12. Blue shock (Bohm)
13. Brown shock (Salomon)
14. White shock ( .... ) (Bohm)
15. Void shock ( .... ) (Orr)
16. Kinesthetic shock (Loosli-Usteri)
17. Simultaneous and successive combinations
18. Descriptions ( .... ) (sometimes light-dark descriptions)
19. Kinetic descriptions (Bohm)
20. Pseudo-color responses (Bohm)
21. Color naming
22. Intellectualized light-dark responses (Binder)
       Light-dark naming
       "Scientific" reminiscences
       Light-dark symbolism
23. Intrapsychic inhibitions (Binder)
24. Impressions ( .... ) (Zulliger)

25. Symmetry (....)
26. "Or" answers (Zulliger)
27. Perspective responses
28. Pedantic formulations
29. Confabulations (or confabulatory combinations)
30. Contaminations
31. Secondary movement (or confabulated F-M)
32. Suppressed movement (sometimes small-movement) (Bohm)
33. M responses with double meaning (Zulliger)
34. Movement-color blend with bodily sensation (Zulliger)
35. Perseveration
    Gross perseveration
    Sticking to a basic theme (Bovet)
    Ruminating type (Bohm)
    Perceptional perseveration (Guirdham)
    Perseveration of the perceived area (Bohm)
36. Anatomical stereotypy (possibly with perseveration)
37. Body part stereotypy
38. Face stereotypy
39. Infantile responses (content) (Loepfe)
40. Inverse interpretations (infantile in form) (Weber)
41. Infantile abstractions (Zulliger)
42. Repetitions
43. Evaluating remarks
44. Self reference
45. Number responses
46. Position (possibly anatomical position responses)
47. Black and white as colors
48. Color denial (Piotrowski)
49. Chromatic responses to achromatic cards (Piotrowski)
50. EQa responses (Guirdham)
51. EQe responses (Guirdham)
52. MF responses (Klopfer, Piotrowski)
53. m responses (Klopfer)
54. Lack of subjective clearness in the manner of approach (Pfister)
55. Emphasis on the middle; emphasis on sides (Zulliger)
56. Acoustic associations
57. Initial test inhibition (Bohm)
58. Illusion of similarity (....) (Bohm)
59. Disavowal (....) (Bohm)
60. Denial (possibly responses in question form) (....)
61. Fusion of figure and background (....) (Bohm)
62. Censorship (initial and final) (Bohm)
63. Sexual symbol stupor (hole in the middle of I; the pointed detail in II;
    middle in red of II; peg in III; the point in IV; the point in VI; notch
    in VI; eggs in VI; middle of VII; projections in VII; slit in IX) (Bohm)
64. Mask responses (Groups I, II and III) (Kuhn)
65. Amnestic word-finding difficulties
66. Aggravation (possibly other clinical findings)
67. Complex-determined responses

1. REJECTION. The most general and also the grossest disturbance of psychological functioning during the test emerges as rejection. It manifests itself in a sudden interruption of the interpretation of some particular card, an inability to face or incipient difficulties in meeting the task of interpretation. This rejection is usually the result of a stupor, an inhibition or blocking of the flow of thought; in rare cases it is perhaps also due to an absence or to either an epileptiform or psychasthenic splitting of consciousness, as in a twilight state.

In purely depressive inhibition, however, a response usually appears spontaneously. Thus this condition does not usually lead to a true rejection. In order to determine whether it is a matter of a mild or serious blockage, the examiner should, without getting impatient, say "Come on; try it; cautious persuasion. If the Subject wants to give up, and pushes the cards away with the words "No, I can't do this," or "I can't see anything here," the examiner should, without getting impatient, say "Come on; try it; take your time, you'll get it," "People always see something there," or "take it easy," and the like. He should then wait for a while, and if this does not help, abandon his efforts. If the stupor cannot be overcome, especially where there is a very definite and brusque rejection of a card, there is a certain suspicion of schizophrenia. However, this is by no means a sure indication for differential diagnosis, for in the first place schizophrenics often manifest only mild inhibitions and, secondly, the blockage of neurotics (affect stupor) may be very severe and quite insurmountable. In cases of true absences or short twilight states, the subject does not react at all when addressed, and usually the short episode entails a retograde amnesia.

It is important to note at which card the rejection occurs. According to the experience of most Rorschach experts, it occurs mainly in connection with cards II, IV, VI, and IX. That this should be so is quite understandable. Card II is the first card that contains red, which can cause not only color shock but also red shock. The massively dark cards IV and VI most easily give rise to dark shock. Usually card IX causes the most marked color shock and it is, besides this, not easy to respond to. Schizophrenics often reject the "easier" cards III and V, while in many cases they do best on the more difficult ones.

Rejection is only a shock symptom in most cases, and offers an index to neurosis or psychopathology. Often it results from an intelligence complex. In psychosis it appears most frequently among schizophrenics and organic conditions.

2. THE INTERPRETATION AWARENESS. According to Rorschach, "interpretation" of the figures, that is, the conscious intrapsychic perceiving, "the relating of what is seen to the engram," is actually only a "special kind of

perception" (p. 18). For this type of comparison occurs in the perception of any object. Only when the discrepancy is so great between the thing seen (the ink blot) and the engram that the comparison is just recognizable, do we speak of "interpretation." Where this is not the case, the pictures are not interpreted but determined.

The consciousness that interpretation is taking place is normal behavior in Rorschach testing, even when it is not expressly stated that the cards are not supposed to represent something definite. In some cases, this consciousness of interpretation is sharper than usual (heightened) and the Subject will spontaneously assert and repeat that, of course, the card does not represent that, it only looks that way, reminds one of that, has a certain similarity, and the like. These expressions appear mainly among depressives, pedants, and psychasthenics with feelings of alienation.

Opposite to this is the lowered awareness of interpretation. Only in relatively few cases, mostly among schizophrenics or feele-minded, is this awareness entirely annulled. Such persons are fully convinced that they have correctly determined the "pictures." The feeble-minded frequently have a real feeling of victory even in regard to the poorest perceptions. They have a strong certainty that they have at last found the "right" answer. Mildly lowered interpretation awareness appears far more frequently. The Subject makes it understood that he is not entirely clear about the interpretation process. Questions like "Is this right?" or "Will you tell me afterwards what it really is?" betray the Subject's belief that there are several possibilities, but he is basically convinced that this is a question of determining, a kind of identification, or at least of classification, something like an examination in botany.

This uncertainty occurs, according to Rorschach, in most organic psychoses, epilepsy, manic cases, and in feeble-mindedness; also in many schizophrenics, people in moods of elation, as well as many persons "of sound mind." Also young children (below five) will often determine their responses.

By applying the above-mentioned technique of reticence (that is, the Subject is not told at the outset that the inkblots have no definite meaning), it will soon be discovered that an amazing number of "normal" Subjects react with this lowered interpretation awareness. This manifests itself not only in scattered comments of the kind noted above, but also in their verbalization. Basically, as Kuhn[1] has correctly pointed out, the interpretation becomes a simple sense perception when the Subject says, "this *is* such and such" instead of "this *might be* such and such." Now the little word "is" may not always be meant as finally as this would imply, and

[1] Roland Kuhn, Über Maskendeutungen im Rorschachschen Versuch, Basel, 1944, p. 52.

we must here say, "C'est le ton qui fait la musique." Referring to Erwin Strauss, who speaks of sensual certainty, Kuhn says (p. 54): "whether a response in the Rorschach sense is to be considered an interpretation or simply a percept, is primarily a question of the sensual certainty with which the Subject experiences the percept. The greater this certainty, the more justified we are in speaking of perceiving in the Rorschach sense."

In the final analysis, this is the same as what is customarily called evidence consciousness, an idea which has been woven into the history of philosophy from the time of the "cataleptic fantasy" of the Stoics down to the phenomenologists. Anybody who is interested in this theoretic problem may learn about it in any textbook of logic. It has no great practical diagnostic value.

3. SUBJECT AND OBJECT CRITICISM. In their article, "Criticism by the Subject in the Rorschach Test," Fränkel and Benjamin[2] differentiate between the two as follows. Subject criticism, the critical attitude of the Subject towards himself, appears usually in statements like, "My imagination does not suffice," or "Imagination was never one of my strong points," "To do this I should have studied anatomy," "One should have read a lot of books about animals and plants to do well on this," or quite directly, "I'm too stupid for this." This type of comment is always a sign of feelings of inferiority and inner uncertainty, and often occurs among psychasthenics, phobic persons, anxiety neurotics, insecure psychopaths, and occasionally in incipient schizophrenics. In organic psychoses it may appear side by side with object criticism.

Object criticism, a critical attitude directed toward the interpretation, or the card to be interpreted, often goes hand in hand with a heightened interpretation awareness. The most usual kind of object criticism is that directed toward the form ("If this were only omitted," or "These ears don't go with that," and the like). All this signifies caution, restraint, and anxiety and is found not only in people who lack imagination and in pedants, but especially in psychasthenics, who are known for their excess caution and pedantry, and in organic conditions. Fränkel and Benjamin also refer to color criticism and to "primary aesthetic value judgments," but color criticism might be thought of mainly as an expression of color shock, possibly in the form of an artistic impression. The value judgments, on the other hand, are best dealt with as an independent phenomenon on evaluating remarks, since they contain an element of "point-giving," and do not signify the same things as form criticism, which might be considered

[2]Fritz Fränkel and Dora Benjamin, Die Kritik der Versuchsperson beim Rorschach'schen Formdeutversuch. Schweizer Archiv. f. Neur. u. Psychiatrie, Vol. 33, 1934, pp. 9-14.

object criticism par excellence. In the CF response, there is no criticism of form. Nor have these writers ever observed criticism in relation to movement, and we can confirm this.

Responses in the form of questions and stated in the negative carry in them an element of criticism. But it is advisable to treat this phenomenon in a category by itself.

4. COLOR SHOCK is the most frequent and probably in practice the most significant phenomenon in the Rorschach test. It consists of a stuporous behavior of a less severe kind than rejection, and is a reaction to the emotional effect of the colors. In some cases the stupor becomes so severe that it does lead to rejection. Thus rejection is often, though not always, a type of color shock. However, the milder forms are much more common and may occur in many different variations. Any distinct disturbance of the smooth flow of associations in response to presentation of a colored card (and in part also to a black and red one) is a sign of color shock.

The most simple and definite expression of this mechanism is, naturally, some kind of emotional objection, either in the form of an interjection like "Oh," or "Brr," or "The devil," or "Frightening," "Horrible," "Sickening," or, more politely, "Those are unbelievable colors," or "Such a tasteless color arrangement," or "Dear me, how those colors clash," or, without directly mentioning the colors, "That is certainly an ugly card," "Now it's becoming difficult," etc. There are Subjects who describe the symptom directly, "The colors confuse me so that I can't think clearly," or "If there weren't any colors, I could see things more easily."

Many people are able to intercept the color shock in the process of formation. These manifest the so-called assimilated color shock which is betrayed by the very fact of favorable affect reactions. Outbursts like "Oh, how beautiful," "Oh, what a delightful color arrangement" are in most cases no less symptoms of color shock than a direct objection. It may seem odd that the disturbing effect of the colors should be indicated in this way and yet it is a matter of experience that this apparently enthusiastic facade masks embarrassment, as may easily be ascertained by the rest of the Subject's conduct. Only in very rare exceptions are statements (not only positive but sometimes even negative ones such as remarks about the "bad taste of the color arrangement") not due to a color shock. Such reactions tend to occur mostly among artists or artistically oriented persons. But also if this is the case, it must be understood that the pattern of perception for the several colored or black and red cards must conform, qualitatively and quantitatively, to the standard of the others. But, as previously noted, this will be a very rare occurrence.

However, the cases in which the Subject takes one glance at the colored cards and blurts something out, are by no means characteristic of the majority of color shock reactions. Far more frequent are the different forms of so-called disguised color shock. These are found among the many mild neurotic character traits which in our day must almost be said to be "normal." But more severe neuroses can also manifest themselves in this manner (as is established from the other symptoms).

The most important sign of a disguised color shock is a delayed reaction time at one or several of the color cards. This usually happens in response to the first one if no interference-phenomenon exists. The Subject stands perplexed and does not know what to say. That a stopwatch is not needed, has already been stated. But another thing is important. The delayed reaction time following a color shock can also be covered up by "filling in" talk. The Subject suddenly makes side remarks, like "Oh, so we have colors," "Are there many more cards?" "These are all very interesting ink blots," and the like. These remarks need not necessarily relate to the colors themselves. Anything is put in to gain time until the Subject can collect his thoughts. Most Subjects will use this mechanism quite unconsciously.

The most important other forms of disguised color shock are treated by Zulliger, partly in the Bero-book (pp. 68-72), partly in a study in the Zeitschrift für Kinderpsychiatrie."[3]

The rules set down by Brosin and Fromm[4] agree with those of Zulliger in all important respects. The following rules for the diagnosis of color shock may be compiled from Zulliger's two works.

*Varieties of Color Shock*

I. *Manifest color shock:*
 1. Unassimilated: negative emotions expressed directly in words.
 2. Assimilated: favorable emotional expression stated in words.

II. *Disguised color shock:*
 1. Prolonged reaction time on presentation of the first color card.
 2. Negative or embarrassed gestures or facial expressions (sighs, hand movement, raising of eyebrows, shaking of head, and the like).
 3. Changing the sequence, especially avoiding colors in favor of space details (e.g., space detail given as the first response to cards II, VIII, and IX).
 4. Suspension of movement responses, although such had been given previously (e.g., color form or color is the first response to card II, or a light-dark response to II instead of an M and only later a movement response. According to Rorschach this is also true if movement responses have appeared

[3]Hans Zulliger, Einführung in den Behn-Rorschach-Test, pp. 68-72, and: Erscheinungsformen und Bedeutung des Farbschocks beim Rorschach'schen Formdeutversuch, Zeitschr. f. Kinderpsychiatrie, Vol. 4, 1938, pp. 145-152.

[4]H. W. Brosin and E. O. Fromm, Rorschach and Color Blindness, Rorschach Research Exchange vol. 4, 1940, pp. 39-70, as cited by Klopfer and Kelley, The Rorschach Technique, pp. 386-387.

before card VIII, and then suddenly cease or if they only appear later than the fourth or fifth response).

5. Incipient rejection.
6. Isolated sexual association as first response to card II (e.g., "menstruation," "bleeding vagina") or screened sexual response (e.g., "bloody pelvis").
7. If for card VIII an animal response is not the first one (either alone or included in a more comprehensive one).
8. Sudden lapse in previous sharpness of form responses.
9. Significant reduction in the number of responses to the colored cards (less than a third of the response total).
10. Embarrassed utterances at II or III (e.g., "That is some kind of bloody matter" or "blood spots," "blood," with the tone or facial expression of something unpleasant).

As a supplement to this list, it should be expressly stated that although the customary animal response appearing immediately upon presentation of card VIII would in general testify against color shock, there may still be color shock in such cases. Color shock may then manifest itself in other ways, either in statements, outcries, acts, poor anatomical answers, disturbance in sequence, perseveration (when this has not occurred before) etc. And naturally it is without question color shock if the Subject's first response, even though it is the lateral animals, occurs only after some lapse of time.

So far as the symptom value of color shock is concerned, it is the most general symptom of neurosis. Unfortunately, it cannot be used, although Rorschach believed it could, for differential diagnosis between the neuroses and the psychoses or mental deficiencies, since there are undoubtedly cases of psychosis, particularly schizophrenia, displaying color shock often in a severe form. Color shock is also often found in psychopathic cases which are, as we know, not only constitutional, and it is often apparent in mild cases of feeble-mindedness, when these are neuroticized. In general it seems that among the severely feeble-minded there is no color shock. This is probably due to the fact that the milder evidences of color shock are obliterated by the symptoms of oligophrenia. In particular, a qualitative deterioration of the associative processes in such cases cannot be established.

We shall discuss several variations of color shock elsewhere. Only one type will be mentioned here, an adhesion to color, or *color attraction*. It is betrayed by a very large number of responses to cards VIII – X, and among these many F–, CF and C. This type of color shock with color attraction appears, according to Zulliger, in persons who try to counteract an affective stupor by copious talking and in general have a highly nervous urge to speak. Readers who still remember the parts played by the lovely film actress Ida Wüst will immediately recognize this type.

It has been found useful to note the presence of the color shock to a particular card by a red mark on the left side of the protocol where the card number is given.

5. DELAYED COLOR SHOCK. Zulliger in his Bero-book (pp. 71 and 104) also mentions a delayed color shock, which first makes its appearance in reaction to card IX or X. A large number of these instances come under the heading of "interference phenomenon at VIII." However, there is no doubt that color shock can appear first in IX and X without any dark shock being present. It is advisable therefore to retain the concept of the delayed color shock, but to make use of it only in the absence of dark shock. It appears mainly in cases of extensively elaborated character neuroses (personal communication from Zulliger).

6. OVERCOMPENSATED COLOR SHOCK. This is a rather rare but very interesting manifestation. There are cases in which color shock spurs the Subject on to qualitatively better performance. There is evidence for this when most of the good, original associations are lumped together in the color cards. Sometimes all the good original responses may appear in the color cards. But it must really be a strikingly *one-sided* distribution. A protocol in which much originality is shown in nearly all of the cards does not indeed preclude an overcompensated color shock, but is usually a sign of the contrary.

That it is really color shock is indicated by other signs. Either there is a strikingly long artificial pause before the fireworks of original associations begin, or there are disturbances in sequence, Do answers, a sudden and striking accent on space details, or other marks of associative difficulties. At times the Subject may make a direct remark to the effect that a card is horrible. The decision as to whether or not overcompensated color shock is present is subject to rigid limitations. It is only when there are clear signs of color shock and when, in addition, the original associations are confined to the shock-producing color cards, that this reaction can be said to exist.

Concerning the symptom-value of overcompensated color shock, the whole story has not yet been told. It seems to occur among people with a sthenic character component which leads them to disregard their inner conflicts. When disturbances begin, they are tempted to "run past the signals." Consequently, when there is environmental stress, these persons are in danger of a "nervous breakdown," a psychogenic psychosis. At any rate, this reaction appears in Subjects who have actually experienced a psychogenic psychosis. But it is also found among schizoid characters even though they may lack the tendency to suffer psychogenic reactions. As to whether or not this can be said to support the theory of borderline psychoses, we offer no opinion.

7. RED SHOCK. Besides color shock, there is also a specifically red shock; ascertaining this may cause some difficulty if it occurs together with color

shock; nevertheless it is often possible. The best rule is the following: if shock symptoms appear in response to the black-red and also to the color cards (II, III, VIII, IX, X), providing that the red is not singled out as especially disturbing, interpret simply as color shock. If these disturbances appear only in cards II and/or III, while reactions to VIII – X proceed smoothly and well, then red shock alone is present. If color shock is found (disturbance only or also at cards VIII – X) and should the red cause a particular disturbance either at these three cards or, even more importantly, at II and III, it is best to interpret as color shock together with red shock. Only very rarely does it happen that red shock alone is associated with dysfunction in response to all five cards. But there must be a certain "method in the madness," so that no other conclusion can be drawn. For example, a subject says about card II, "I can't find anything at all here" and then sees the black details successively as "stones which have been dug out of the ground," "dark clouds," "a fallow field," in other words three light-dark form responses. Upon presentation of card III, first the men are seen, then the Subject starts and says "the red," then, after a pause, "an ink blot" (CF); then three anatomical responses follow, among these one poor one to the red in the middle, and one good and one poor to the black. At card VIII, the Subject does not begin by perceiving the animals, but starts with the gray (a mountain); next come the animals and then, in response to the red middle, "stones" (F-). This is, moreover, a perseveration response to the "stone" of card II. Two more poor responses follow, and finally an F+ to the red in the middle (calf's head). Card IX begins with the "camel's head," and then the Subject tries to respond to the brownish red, but the idea "eludes" her again. It finally becomes a "coral reef" (F±). Then pointing to the brilliant red underneath, the Subject says, "The last one I can't do." To card X, seven good responses are given (only one is ±); however, the sequence of the selected details is as follows: middle gray, middle blue, lateral gray, lateral green, green middle, lateral blue, and last of all the large red detail (caterpillar), and this only after the Subject had turned the card <. In this example the difficulty is so clearly a result of the red in *every* color card, that red shock *without* color shock (but in conjunction with dark shock in this case) is indicated.

The symptom value of red shock has not yet been made clear. Apparently it has neither a single basic cause nor a single symptom value; since red can be as easily associated with libidinous images (love, heart, glow), as with aggressive and sadistic ones (blood, war). Among epileptics, it may have some connection with aura (color vision). Nor is it without significance to ask whether red shock occurs in isolation or in combination with other shocks, and in the latter case, whether with color or dark shock or both. But for the present, nothing definite can be said. On the whole, red shock is more closely connected with repression of aggression than with repression of libido. In this connection, M. Loosli-Usteri, too, refers red shock back to repressed aggression.[5]

8. RED ATTRACTION. This is the opposite of red shock. It is related to color attraction, mentioned above, but not identical with it. Here the Subject shows a tendency to prefer the red blots in what he selects, and to give them especially "juicy" meanings. Zulliger cites as an example "steaks" and "ham slices," (Bero, p. 71). In some cases the two upper red spots in card II are perceived as "two juicy cutlets." Flower responses may also belong here, like "poppy," "red roses," or "peonies." Red attraction usually accompanies other symptoms as a typical ingredient of the "instinct ridden character." Perhaps other symptom values will be found to exist in other combinations of red attraction with various factors.

9. DARK SHOCK was a concept first introduced into literature by Binder.[6] It consists, according to him, of a sudden disturbance of the intellectual process, a stupor manifesting itself upon the presentation of a dark card, especially IV. The disturbance takes the form of either rejection or other inhibition phenomena. Binder himself typified the following: "Dd and Do answers, poor forms, banal stereotypies, breaks in sequence, abnormal ways of perceiving the picture, etc." The contents of these responses are not always complex-determined, on the contrary, there is often a certain "flight into the conventional."

If to cards IV and VI the first response is a P (popular), dark shock is very unlikely, unless there are definite signs of it. In doubtful cases it can then be confidently ruled out. This phenomenon of dark shock, as we shall soon see, is unlike color shock in that it is in most cases bound up with anxiety. Therefore, a mere remark without the formal reaction is not enough to establish the presence of dark shock. There are persons who are for other reasons accustomed to using strong expressions, and it sometimes happens that such people make the same remarks about the dark cards as they do about the others, saying that they are "crazy" or "nasty" or words to that effect, but nevertheless they will gladly proceed to give a popular or some other good response without the slightest inhibition. This is definitely not dark shock.

According to Oberholzer[7] who had the opportunity of noticing many

[5]Marguerite Loosli-Usteri. Le test de Rorschach, Internationale Zeitschrift für Erziehungswissenschaft, Vol. 5, p. 304.

[6]Hans Binder, Die Helldunkeldeutungen im psychodiagnostischen Experiment von Rorschach. Schweizer Archiv f. Neurologie und Psychiatrie, Vol. 30, 1933, p. 279.

[7]In Cora Du Bois, The People of Alor, Minneapolis 1944, p. 595.

instances of dark shock among the Alorese, one of the Indonesian island peoples, dark shock may appear either in reaction to all the dark cards or only to individual ones. All the black cards may evoke it. It may appear in the same strength in response to all of the different black cards or reach a climax in regard to a particular one. The order of frequency of the appearance of dark shocks in response to the individual cards is IV, VI, VII, I, V.

That dark shock is much rarer than color shock, as Binder[8] has maintained, is at any rate not applicable to Scandinavians; it has not been found notably less frequent among them.

The symptom value of dark shock, according to Oberholzer[9] is generally "anxiety about anxiety," but it is also caused by anxiety about the unknown and about the new. Oberholzer maintains that dark shock which derives from anxiety about new things may also appear in response to card I alone. To us it seems a little unclear whether we are really dealing with dark shock in these instances, or whether the appearance of a disturbance in reaction to card I alone may not have some other cause. We make the neutral notation "initial test inhibition" in these instances.

By means of skin temperature measurements taken in the course of the Rorschach test, we have verified the fact that dark shock is actually equivalent to a minor attack of anxiety. However, apart from a relatively small number of cases, we are here dealing with a physiological reaction only, one which remains below the threshold of consciousness.

Corresponding to its basic significance as anxiety about anxiety, dark shock is found mainly among anxiety neurotics, phobics (anxiety hysterics), and (in a certain form together with color shock) among psychasthenics.

The psychological background for dark shock may vary. Often, but not always, it is a carry-over from a childhood fear of the dark. However, many other trends may be connected with it. Peter Mohr[10] who has devoted an excellent study to this question, tries to explain dark shock in terms of the symbolism of black, "the opposite of the life-bringing light." The Prometheus legend has a deep meaning. "The conquest of nature has, in spite of all, left in mankind a fear of nature," a feeling of guilt, apprehension about the revenge of the Gods. The gift of fire was accepted, but the donor was damned—"sacrificed to the wrath of the Gods." Man has now transferred this fear of powerful forces to blackness, the darkness of night which reminds him of it. "The darkness of night is sinister to mankind." Already

[8]Op. cit. p. 279.
[9]Op. cit. p. 595.
[10]Peter Mohr, Die schwarze und sehr dunkle Tönung der Rorschach'schen Tafeln und ihre Bedeutung für den Versuch, in "Psychiatrie und Rorschach'scher Formdeutversuch," Zürich, 1944, pp. 122-133.

Wertheimer[11] has pointed out that the dark has a directly sinister impression. Devils, demons, thieves, murderers and robbers go about in the night. On the positive side, according to Mohr, blackness signifies firmness, the immutable, the solemn (evening dress), the symbol of authority (the majesty of death, the god-like). On the negative side it connotes guilt, rebellion, anxiety, and judgment. Since the first authority is the father, and the first guilt stems from revolt against his authority, it is understandable that Mohr found that Subjects who were in conflict with their fathers sensed an "unpleasant, sinister, and anxious mood" in card I, IV, and VI. Subjects who did not have this conflict reacted to these cards "with moods of security and calm."[12] In a later work Mohr[13] supplements this reasoning by adding that not only are childhood conflicts with the father brought to the surface by the effect of the black, but, among girls, a conflict with a man is also often manifested (p. 29). For black also symbolizes the masculine in its evil, negative aspects (p. 31, 35). (We may recall here Christoffel's point, mentioned above, concerning the sexual symbolism in the white-black dichotomy, and also the fact that this applies to our own culture only.) Thus anxiety in reaction to black may often be sexual anxiety insofar as black is equated with maleness. Such cases usually display red shock plus dark shock; the case mentioned above in the section on red shock, for instance, belongs here.

In the same way that the red mark in the margin can be used for color shock (also red shock), dark shock might be indicated by a blue mark in the margin for each card in which it appears.

Analogous to color and red attraction there is also *dark attraction*. Binder mentions this in his treatise.[14] Among chronically depressed subjects, there is usually a perseverative tendency toward light-dark responses. If this tendency is operative but not strong enough to call forth a series of LD responses, it may work as follows. The Subject "shows a tendency to select only the dark details of the picture, even though the darkness-value of the detail is disregarded in the way the figure is perceived, and consequently does not appear in the interpretation, which for this reason cannot be scored as LD" (Binder). These subjects, too, are usually anxious, chronically depressed persons.

10. OVERCOMPENSATED DARK SHOCK is analogous to overcompensated color shock, but it is considerably more frequent. Here, also, two different

[11]David Katz, Gestaltpsychologie, Basel 1944 (p. 96 of the Swedish edition of 1942).
[12]Op. cit. p. 130, 133.
[13]Peter Mohr, Die schwarze und dunkle Farbe der Rorschach-Tafeln, Rorschachiana II, Berne, 1947, pp. 24-36.
[14]Op. cit. p. 242.

conditions are required: clear signs of dark shock, and a special clustering of good, original answers to these cards.

This is not, however, what Binder[15] meant by overcompensation of a primarily experienced mood by means of "intrapsychic inhibition." Binder is describing the repression of a dysphoric *mood;* here, in our overcompensated dark shock, we are dealing with the repression of an *anxiety.* To be sure, both manifestations are closely related and often appear together in the same protocol. The presence of a sthenic character component is common to both. Binder, too, speaks of "Subjects with rather sthenic character trends." They are persons whose anxiety spurs them to activity, and who probably achieve outstanding performances when they are placed under pressure.

11. THE INTERFERENCE PHENOMENON. In some cases (by no means all) of the simultaneous occurrence of color and dark shock in the same protocol, we see the peculiar phenomenon that each shock effect interferes with the other. We have called this reaction the interference phenomenon.[16] A quite natural after-effect of the dark shock is that the appearance of the colors comes as a relief. The nightmare of the dark colors is over, the subject once more "sees the road clear ahead," and the responses again flow easily. This after-effect may at times be so strong that it inhibits or suspends the color shock which, instead of manifesting itself at card VIII does not make its appearance till card IX or even X. This effect is the interference phenomenon with the response to card VIII. It is not necessary that dark shock be displayed in reaction to all of the dark cards; it need not even be apparent at card VII. It is sufficient if, for example, there is a clear indication of dark shock at card IV. The interference phenomenon in instances may be so strong that the Subject only notices the colors for the first time in card IX. Thus a phobic woman, on seeing card IX, says, "Now it begins to be more colored," or an insecure man remarks, "Now we have color" upon the presentation of card IX.

The converse may also appear. Thus a severe red or color shock may inhibit the dark shock accompanying card IV. This is the interference phenomenon at card IV. This is a rarer phenomenon. Now and again the interference phenomenon may appear in response to both cards. This would be double interference (for cards IV and VIII).

Technically, the presence of the interference phenomenon is ascertained by the fact that dark or color shock is not found in the cards in question (IV or VIII), whereas it is found in the following ones. The extreme form,

---

[15]Op. cit. pp. 255-256.

[16]Ewald Bohm, Der Rorschach-Test und seine Weiterentwicklung. Rorschachiana I. Berne, 1945.

which is not at all rare, would be that in case of interference phenomenon at card VIII, for instance, one or several normal responses (F+ or FC or even M+) have been made to that card, while cards IX and X have been rejected. Sometimes the preceding dark shock has been so severe as to cause the rejection also of one or all of cards IV-VII. There are instances (although few) in which responses are given only to cards II and VIII. On the other hand, there are transition cases with signs of color shock at card VIII (e.g., an unfavorable remark, or the fact that the lateral animals are not the first response, as noted above), but in which the shock symptoms become so much stronger at cards IX and possibly also X (rejections or poor forms following good ones for VIII) that an interference phenomenon can barely be recognized. We have found it useful to note this as, "interference suggested." On the protocol, it should always be mentioned in parentheses among the special phenomena, whether the interference appears at card IV or VIII, or both.

It may happen that a particularly intellectual Subject introspectively describes the whole process. Thus a woman psychologist with a mixed neurosis responded as follows to card II: "Blood-stains," then subjective criticism, description, and symmetry and finally, "a female pelvis—by a stretch of imagination." To card III: "That's certainly an odd figure," then again, "pelvic region," followed by four other responses, among which the lateral red was seen as "ink blots." Card IV elicited dark shock, with a deep sigh and reversal of the succession (D, W, W). To card VI: "Here at first I can see nothing at all" (dark shock again): after which she responded "tortoise." Then to card VIII: "Those are gay colors. The others reminded me of bloodstains, but this one is cheerful. But then it is an entirely different kind of red." Animal perceptions to the lateral came as first response, then three other responses. The last of these, it is true, was to the central blue figure which she called "a mathematical figure, a triangle," (Orig–). On presentation of card IX, however, the Subject remarked immediately, "This is again something that I don't like, somewhat sad and blurred"; then, "again the blood color," and went on to interpret the green as "thunderclouds." Only then did she continue with more "normal" responses. To card X: "This is gay again, but not so pronounced as the first one. If this red color didn't have so much violet in it, I would like it very much." These introspective meditations show very clearly how in spite of a mild shock, the colors in card VIII are perceived quite differently (as a relief) than they are in the other color cards.

In order to understand the psychic mechanism of the interference phenomenon, we must borrow from biology. As Sherrington has shown in his studies of the collision of incompatible reflexes, there is a "prepotence of the so-called nociceptive reflexes," that is, the reflexes which serve to protect the total organism from injury.[17] For example, in the cat, the Goltz scratch reflex of the back leg may first be evoked by tickling. This scratching should stop the itch sensation. Should the other hind paw be stimulated with a needle prick before the scratch reflex has stopped, the latter will be inhibited, since the flight reflex, which the pain has called forth, now sets going a tonic stretching of the back leg. This is only a special case of "the law of primacy of the phylogenetically younger drive:" since the nociceptive reflexes which serve the welfare for the total organism represent a higher level of integration than the purely local scratch reflex. This relationship may reverse itself if the scratch reflex is particularly urgent. In such instances a reflex on a higher integration level can be set aside. Thus it might be said that the law of urgency supersedes the law of the primacy of the phylogenetically younger drive.

But what happens to the scratch reflex after the flight reflex has run its course? It appears as an after discharge, i.e., the previously inhibited scratch reflex once again appears, until it has also run its course.[18] However, should the itch sensation of the scratch stimulus be operative during and after its inhibition, a constantly generating excitation is stored up, upon which a stronger discharge follows.

In the interference phenomenon we have an entirely analogous state of affairs. What conclusion can be derived from this analogy to the collision of reflexes? The delayed appearance of color shock at card IX or X following its inhibition due to the after-effects of dark shock, corresponds to the after-discharge. And since a stimulus adequate for producing color shock, presented by card VIII (the colors), is continually operative during the inhibition, a damming-up effect also makes itself felt, usually in the form of a significant intensifying of the color shock at card IX and sometimes X, occasionally leading to total rejection. This intensification may also often be seen in the interference phenomenon occurring at card IV, since at card V a clearly visible dark shock sometimes appears with a strength that otherwise is found only in response to cards IV and VI. Thus, if we may conceive of the interference phenomenon as a conflict between two colliding psychologic impulses, the law of urgency can also be brought to bear upon their interpretation, that is, in the interference phenomenon, the reciprocal forces of dark and color shock can be observed. *In the interference phenomenon occurring at card VIII, the dark shock predominates; in the interference phenomenon occurring at IV, color or red shock predominate respectively.* In the double interference phenomenon, the two are in equilibrium. In the light of the physiological relationships in the dark shock, we

[17]Rudolph Brun, Biologische Parallelen zu Freuds Trieblehre, Wien, 1926, p. 16 and: Allgemeine Neurosenlehre, Basel, 1946, p. 256.

[18]Rudolf Brun, Biologische Parallelen, p. 18, and Allgemeine Neurosenlehre, p. 259.

may say that the presence of the interference phenomenon at card VIII is for the most part an accentuation of the constitutional components of the condition in question. This is of great importance for differential diagnosis and prognosis. For example, phobics who do not display the interference phenomenon at VIII are much more accessible to psychotherapy than those who do. Correspondingly, the presence of interference phenomenon at IV points to a stronger participation on the part of the environment. In this case, usually, a still more favourable prognosis must be made than when the interference phenomenon is completely absent.

12. BLUE SHOCK. Similar to red shock, there is also a specific blue shock. For many subjects, the blue details are distinctly repulsive, and they turn from them sharply. "This blue color here irritates me," "I am bothered by having blue here," "I can't see anything in the blue," are examples of these rejection trends. Naturally, blue shock can only appear at cards VIII and X. It is also to be counted as present if the Subject says "green" but means the blue.

Blue shock appears very infrequently. As to its symptom value, much still remains to be said. It appears to have a value which parallels that of dark shock, and is probably nearer to it than to color shock. In any event, it is also accompanied by a sense of discomfort.

Fritz Salomon (by letter) ascertained blue shock in men with strong castration anxiety during the sexual act; in most cases the potency was reduced, or there was ejaculatio praecox. Women with blue shock had an unconscious castration wish against the man and were orgastically impotent.

13. BROWN SHOCK has also been observed in rare cases, mainly in the Bero-test and the Z-test, but occasionally in response to Rorschach's cards IX and X as well. Here, too, there is a particular rejection of the brown spots. According to Fritz Salomon (by letter) the phenomenon occurs in anal erotic fixations with reaction formation, i.e., in compulsive neurotics, latent or overt homosexuals, and bisexuals, and in cases of psychosomatic ailments of the gastrointestinal tract; in the last mentioned case, the brown shock is mostly combined with a strong color and/or red shock.

14. WHITE SHOCK is, in fact, a special case of stupor in response to sexual symbols. Because of its psychological importance and its specific symptom value it is entitled to a position of its own among the special phenomena. The designation "white shock" was chosen on the grounds of propriety in analogy to color, red and dark shock. The somewhat obscene designation "hole shock" would, in fact, be more correct.

White shock consists of a peculiar ambivalent attitude of the Subject to the space details; they have attraction for him, and he occupies himself with them greatly, but he does not succeed in coming up with a response. Sometimes the result will be an embarrassed response, usually "hole." For example, the Subject may say, pointing to a space detail, "This here," hesitate a bit and then go on, "I find this very interesting, it has something attractive about it—it strikes a familiar chord but I don't know what it is—possibly a hole."

White shock is rather rare among men and even more so among women. Concerning its symptom value, which we describe in Rorschachiana I "with greatest caution," we can now say the following with a fair amount of certainty:

Among *men,* white shock is usually an expression of sexual anxiety concerning the female genitals. This leads either to a fear of contact with women and consequently to sexual reticence (fear of marriage in the sense described by Hitschmann), or to an outspoken ambivalence towards women, a neurotic battle-marriage, or finally to a paranoid misogyny. All these varieties, in fact, occur. Behind these symptoms there lies a "hatred between the sexes," a "fear of the sexual partner," the real cause of which is the special difficulty the individual has in repressing the characteristics of the opposite sex in his own mental makeup.[19] The stronger the female identification is in the mind of man, the more rigidly must he repress these feminine tendencies in order to remain "a man." The hatred for the women in his environment is then a projection of the hatred for the woman within himself. Karen Horney[20] prefers the expression "the distrust between the sexes" and points out that it may have many roots, first of all the castration fear in man, which makes him feel threatened and weakened by women and secondly, what is often forgotten, his envy of child bearing. Thus the woman hater is not only hostile to a part of himself, but he also depreciates that which he fears and envies. At the deepest level, naturally, it is the ancient tabu of women that is haunting him, the primitive blood fear of the menstruating woman and her evil eye.[21] As late as the Middle Ages there was a close connection between prostitution and delusions about witches, devils and magic, and in this thought-climate, temptation by a woman was equivalent to temptation by the devil.[22] This connection has by no means died out in the deeper layers of the mind of modern man.

[19]See: Hans von Hattingberg, Psychoanalyse und verwandte Methoden, in "Die psychischen Heilmethoden," Leipzig, 1927, p. 219.

[20]Karen Horney, Das Misstrauen zwischen den Geschlechtern. Die psychoanalytische Bewegung, Vol. 2, 1930, pp. 521-537, especially pp. 531 and 534-535.

[21]See: Magnus Hirschfeld und Berndt Götz, Sexualgeschichte der Menscheit, Berlin, 1929, p. 23 ff.

[22]Magnus Hirschfeld, Geschlechtskunde, 3. Vol. Stuttgart, 1930 p. 333.

The fact is that in the protocols of man with white shock, M Original +
responses which point to feminine identifications, are not infrequently found.
Moreover, the fact that the lower edge of card VI with its teeth and claws
may evoke white shock, is certainly no accident. The not infrequent, although naturally deeply repressed, vagina dentata fantasy of many men
with castration anxiety, may well come into play here.

Among *women* with white shock there are usually clear signs of male
identification with an unconscious rejection of the feminine role and its
biological functions. The attitude of these women is less a rigid repression
of masculinity than a strong wish not to be a woman, a denial of femininity. Thus it is not the contrary of white shock in men. White shock always
means a struggle against the female element in *both* sexes.

15. THE VOID SHOCK. This phenomenon which resembles white shock so
much and yet is different from it, was first observed by M. Orr and called
the "choc au vide." Later it was explored more in detail by Loosli-Usteri.[23]
While Orr wants to limit the void shock strictly to card VII, Loosli-Usteri
understands by this expression "any stuporous reaction to cards VII and
IX," i.e., rejection or initial rejection, prolonged time of reaction, restlessness, unfavorable object or subject criticism, first interpretation upside down,
quantitatively or qualitatively poor associations, in addition, reminiscences
from children's books or toy responses, mirror responses, and anal responses
indicating a "momentary regression," responses with an aggressive content
and, finally, a specifically dysphoric elaboration of the "women" interpretation of card VII. According to Orr, the void shock also manifests itself in
responses pertaining to animals, plants, dead objects, or bones instead of
the female popular response ("degradations" and "devitalizations") and
F− and F±, Ds or DsW responses respectively.

It is obvious that the main difficulty in identifying this phenomena is
in drawing the line between it and color shock (at card IX) and possibly remnants of a dark shock (at card VII). If shock phenomena appear
only at VII and IX, void shock would be indicated, whereas the shock
combination IV and IX would rather indicate dark and color shock with
interference phenomenon at VIII. But color and void shock may also occur
cumulatively at card IX. Only very experienced persons will be able to interpret the individual case correctly in the face of this difficulty.

According to Loosli-Usteri, the void shock always indicates a "disturbed
relation to the maternal element." Orr[24] considers it in its original form
(at card VII only) as "a symptom of an abandonment complex and a

[23]Marguerite Loosli-Usteri, A propos du choc au vide, Rorschachiana IV, Berne,
1954, pp. 21-43.
[24]By letter.

negative mother imago." She thinks that it is the main symptom of the experience of the withdrawal of maternal love and its neurotic consequences (reduced ability to love). This may be considered a valuable suggestion, but it has certain limitations. For card VII is no more "the" mother card (Orr, Fred Brown) than card IV is "the" father card. It is true that card VII, because of its middle space detail (uterus symbol) and the female genital symbol in the middle black detail, as well as through its popular female interpretation, presents many reactions pertaining to women or mother. On the other hand, not all persons who do not respond to these suggestions can be said to be neurotic. Conclusions about father and mother conflicts can only be drawn when the content of the interpretation of cards IV or VII, in either direct or symbolic form, permits it. Beware of "wild" interpretations.

16. KINESTHETIC SHOCK. As Rorschach recognized, not only may the emotional life, the extratensive aspect of the experience balance, be the object of neurotic repression, but also the kinesthetic experience, the introversive side (Rorschach, p. 191). It is customary today to refer to this movement repression in terms of Loosli-Usteri's "kinesthetic shock."[25]

It is indicated when persons usually disposed to M reactions produce no M responses to cards that usually evoke them (I, II, III and IX), and also the general level of their responses to these cards sinks markedly (Dd, Do responses, banal content and the like).

It should be clear, however, that the movement does not produce the shock mechanism directly in the same way that the gay colors or the dark ones do. On the contrary, we are dealing here with a special form of shock mechanism which prevents the M responses from developing. The fact is that M responses are not caused by factors outside of the Subject—a blot has color but not kinesthesia—but are rather projected into the response from *within*. The thing that hinders the kinesthetic reaction, the external disturbance causing kinesthetic shock, might in some cases be the red color of cards II and III, in others the dark of card I, or in still other cases the multi-coloring of card IX. Kinesthetic shock is thus a special case of red, dark, or color shock. It deserves to be separated from them insofar as it constitutes a special case of anxiety defense, consisting of an armor rigidity of the musculature corresponding to the death feint of animals. Thus we find kinesthetic shock chiefly in stiff compulsive neurotics or compulsive characters with general hypertonus.[26]

[25]Marguerite Loosli-Usteri, Le diagnostic individuel chez l'enfant de moyen du Test de Rorschach. Paris, 1938, 2 ed. p. 36.

[26]This hypertonus may be quantitatively determined by means of the so-called safety-margin. See David Katz and Georg Korjus, Muskeltonus der Hand und Sicherheitsmarginal. Acta Paediatrica, 1944, pp. 378-397.

17. SIMULTANEOUS AND SUCCESSIVE COMBINATIONS. The most important facts about the combinatory whole responses have already been stated in chapter 3. D responses, too, may naturally appear in combinations, which is usually the case in the DsD responses.

Among the "special phenomena," it is only useful to mention whether and how many combinations appear, and whether we are dealing with simultaneous or successive combinations or both. The difference between these two is hardly of very great significance. At most it may be said that the simultaneous combinations stand somewhat higher artistically and is a sign of good organizational ability.

18. DESCRIPTIONS. Many side remarks and "non-responses" cannot be formally scored, but are nonetheless of diagnostic value. Among these belong descriptions. Here, too, it is important to mark in parentheses the cards at which the descriptions appear. One might note, for example, "Six descriptions (I, III, IV, 2×IX, X)." From this it may generally be seen at a glance whether a manifestation of dark or color shock is in question. In the colored cards, descriptions are a variation of color shock, and constitute a reaction usually found in people who intellectualize or estheticize their repressed feelings. They register instead of experiencing. As a general thing the descriptions are a sign of inhibited aggression.[27]

The descriptions of light-dark seem to play a special role. In regard to the black cards, descriptions are usually entirely formal: "Here in the middle there is a line and on the sides there are large and small indentations," and the like. When the descriptions pertain to the shading itself, this should therefore be especially noted, e.g., "six descriptions of which two are light-dark." Rorschach listed them mostly as color responses, e.g., card IV, "Two colors, here lighter, there darker," W C color; card VI, "Two colors, here lighter, there darker, both sides equally pretty," W C color; card VII, "black and gray, light black," W C color. These can also sometimes be noted as color naming (as in Rorschach's examples). It depends on how they are formulated. Usually they are not expressed in this way but rather like the following: "Two things one on top of the other—the dark and light"; or "beautiful shadings." In this form they are very similar to Binder's light-dark naming, and are indeed almost identical with it. Actually it is usually a matter of taste whether one calls it light-dark naming or light-dark description, especially since Binder's treatise does not make it clear whether he intends to treat these comments as responses (in which case there would be a minimal difference to light-dark descriptions) or not.

It is possible the light-dark descriptions imply other symptom values,

[27]See Hans Zulliger, Einführung in den Behn-Rorschach-Test pp. 69, 169 and 180.

besides inhibition of aggression, but as yet we are not able to outline these symptom values clearly.

19. KINETIC DESCRIPTIONS. In a relatively few cases one may come upon descriptive phrases which relate to a mechanical movement in the picture without this movement being tied down to any concrete object. The Subject, in response to card VIII, may describe "a sucking movement through the center, as though an air jet is going through it." Or in card X he may find "something rotating with a center." Or, responding to the same figure, "as if gas and air were coming out of a nozzle." Beck's example, "a certain pull towards the center,"[28] belongs in this category.

These remarks have nothing to do with kinesthesia. Therefore they are not "kinesthetic" descriptions. They are by no means identical with the similar m introduced in America by Klopfer (falling objects, and the like), and are to be noted as remarks only, not responses. This is in better practice, since the manner of approach in them usually cannot be established. They are probably quite close to the abstractions, but represent nevertheless a specific category of description. Rorschach, too, included associations like, "On the whole it gives me the impression of something powerful in the center to which everything clings" (card IV) and, "A symmetrical figure with a mid-line axis which is sharply accentuated. Everything is remarkably arranged around the axis," in the category of "responses which cannot be formulated," belonging among "the descriptive responses," (pp. 185-186). However, he regards these descriptions as being parallel with the abstracts (p. 212).

When we consider this close relationship between descriptions and abstractions, it is no accident that kinetic descriptions have been encountered almost exclusively among schizophrenics and schizoid personalities. Similarly, when Klopfer maintains that his m responses are manifestations of inner tensions and conflicts,[29] he also points in the same direction. Although one can never diagnose schizophrenia or schizoid personality on the appearance alone of kinetic descriptions, these observations may still be regarded as a building block for the schizoid syndrome (see below).

20. THE PSEUDO-C are color answers which border on simple descriptions, and which, at any rate, do not have the clear liveliness of "true" color responses. This entire category is not very important, since these reactions may just as well be treated as descriptions without losing anything. In a very few cases, however, they are better scored as genuine responses rather than descriptions. The tone and tempo in which they are uttered

[28]Samuel J. Beck, Rorschach's Test, I. Basic Processes, p. 93.
[29]Klopfer and Kelley, the Rorschach Technique, pp. 279-280.

may be the decisive factor. "Blood stain" is without a doubt a true CF; the response "red blots," or "spilled red ink," or "red figure," are formally also CF, but they are suspiciously close to descriptions. A rare variety is "red copy"; for example, the middle red in card III is "red copy of the bottom black." These responses cannot be grouped with the true CF responses, but are closer to color naming and to the intellectualized light-dark responses. On appearance of these pseudo-C responses (usually CF), it is best to compute the experience balance twice, as with color naming, and for purposes of evaluation, to go only by the narrower, where the pseudo-C has been left out.

The symptom value of the pseudo-C response is similar to that of description.

21. COLOR NAMING. We have already stated as much as is necessary regarding the differentiation of color naming from simple interjected remarks under the heading, "What is a response?" Binder[30] and others correctly distinguish between the symptom values of color naming and of true color responses. In this case too the interpretation takes its point of departure from the small experience balance (with color naming discarded).

Color naming is found in oligophrenics, (usually only in medium and severe cases), epileptics, persons with organic deterioration (and correspondingly after electroshock),[31] schizophrenic deterioration; and among normals in schizoids and more frequently in ixothymics.

22. THE INTELLECTUALIZED LIGHT-DARK RESPONSES of Binder do not appear in the scoring summary. They are therefore to be noted in the listing of the special phenomena.

According to Binder (op. cit. p. 25) they represent the Subject's effort "to say something original; to make an impression by his outstanding knowledge and culture." Like the descriptions to which they are related, they are found among those neurotic wisdom-spouting individuals who employ a pseudo-intellectual façade to conceal their inner uncertainty from themselves and from others.

23. THE INTRAPSYCHIC INHIBITIONS of Binder are sthenic counter factors in the psyche of the Subject, which act in a negative and over-compensating manner against the tendency toward dysphoric mood lability. This denial of feelings stems from the ego and unites "with a strong intellectual

[30]Hans Binder, Die Helldunkeldeutungen etc., p. 24.
[31]Hans Lowenbach and C. J. Stainbrook, Observations on Mental Patients after Electro-Shock (lecture) as cited by Klopfer and Kelley, The Rorschach Technique, p. 332.

drive"; that is, with conscious defense efforts (hence its name). This striving for ego control creates compensatory tendencies, which manifest themselves in the content of the shading and the light-dark responses.[32] In the shading responses, F(C), the content shows either intentional objectivity, like "cooking pot with milk boiling over"; or they are set in a far off place, like "evening sun on a far-off mountain chain on the horizon." In the light-dark responses, the struggle against the mood emerges either in the form of topological distance or a distance of time in relation to the perceived object; e.g., "far off prairie fire," or "lunar landscape"; or in a symbolic manifestation of distance, "figures turning away in an oppressive landscape"; or else it takes the shape of an intentionally sober objectivity, e.g., "the lines of equal heights on the map of an exotic island," or finally, in the sudden appearance of a Ds response or an affected F response. One overcompensation related to this denial of feelings and consisting of a kind of intellectualized light-dark response, manifests itself in the perception of monumental buildings, usually in a somewhat artificial way and generally following a more moodlike ("genuine") light-dark response (see previous discussion of the symptom value of architectural percepts). The same phenomenon is also seen sometimes in the use of religious symbols (e.g., "madonna floating above the clouds"; or "the picture of the cross appears above the smoke-clouds of hell").

Whenever such intrapsychic inhibitions occur, we are always dealing with a sthenic character component which makes the prognosis quite favorable. This is important in making judgments as to indications for psychotherapy.

24. ZULLIGER'S "IMPRESSIONS" (or feeling responses, as he sometimes calls them) are descriptive reactions in which an impressionistic account of the general appearance of a card is given (Bero-Test, pp. 55-56, 71-72, 104, 107). They cannot be scored by any formula, and the best thing to do is to note down "impression." Examples: "airy, delicate colors," "chaotic," "dirty," "spring mood," "summer colors with a gay appearance," "something sad, melancholy; possibly a fir tree wrapped in mist or snow; winter, cold." They are usually a form of color or dark shock, characteristic of individuals with an artistic or esthetic disposition. If they appear frequently, they indicate an exaggerated sentimentality, of the kind found in people who revel in moods at the expense of the issue at hand.

25. EMPHASIS ON SYMMETRY (in Rorschach terminology simply called "symmetry"), is a very common phenomenon. The better educated Subject

---

[32]Hans Binder, Die Helldunkeldeutungen im psychodiagnostischen Experiment von Rorschach. Schweiz. Arch. f. Neurol. u. Psychiat., Vol. 30, 1933, pp. 235, 236, 252-256.

often says directly, "The card is symmetrical" or "A very marked symmetry dominates this." Others perhaps say only "This is the same on both sides." "Both sides are alike." Still other Subjects try to find out whether the card is completely symmetrical or not, and then may decide triumphantly that they see a slight irregularity. The simple announcement that "The figure is *not* quite symmetrical" is also to be recorded as symmetry.

The symptom-value of emphasis on symmetry varies depending on the way it appears. Incidental accent on symmetry is usually only a shock symptom, a form of filling in when no other idea comes to mind, and beyond that has very little meaning. Forced searching for symmetry is, according to Zulliger (Bero-Book p. 71), a sign of inner insecurity, a fear of one's own impulsiveness. It is frequently seen among psychasthenics. Finally, a stereotyped repetition of symmetry description in response to all or nearly all of the cards, possibly using the same words, is mostly an indication of an epileptoid personality (epileptic or ixothymic). The same applies to a fourth type of emphasis on symmetry, the "complaint of lack of symmetry" ("why don't we see it on the other side") which, according to Zulliger (Tafeln-Z-Test, p. 82), occurs not only in epileptics and ixothymics but also occasionally in schizophrenics and schizoids.

In order to evaluate this type of stereotypy, not only should symmetry be noted among the special phenomena, but the card should also be identified in parentheses, e.g., "symmetry (I, II, IV, V, VI twice, IX)."

26. THE "OR" RESPONSES are generally known but, outside of the American literature on the subject, where they are called "precision alternatives" (Beck), little account is taken of them. They are identified as such only when the Subject gives two or three responses at one time using "or" to separate them, e.g., "a bat or a butterfly," "a mountain or rather a large pointed hat." If one response is made and disposed of and after some reconsideration a second response is offered, this is not an "or" reaction. It is desirable to make two scores for "or" responses, also if both are P as in "bat or butterfly." The doubling of the P responses is evidence of the poverty of the ideas in these cases.

The "or" are, according to Zulliger (personal communication), always a sign of a certain insecurity in judgment, or fear of responsibility (fear of taking a definite stand). We have noticed them often among psychasthenics, insecure psychopaths, and anxious neurotics.

27. THE PERSPECTIVE RESPONSES are mainly found in DsD or DsW combinations; or in shading responses (Ds F[C]+). However, they may occasionally be found together with pure form responses. Their symptom value is a more urgent form of that given to the architecture percepts and

building responses in cases with intrapsychic inhibition: an urge to over-
compensate a feeling of inner lack of support (Rorschach, pp. 199-200).
Like the intrapsychic inhibition which takes the form of "pushing away,"
the perspective responses express a "pushing into the background." According to Zulliger, they should therefore be considered indications of a
tendency to repression.[33]

28. PEDANTIC FORMULATION (briefly "pedantry") is an especially verbose,
stiffly stereotyped manner of speech, with all possible details carefully described. Sometimes the stereotyped repetition of a phrase predominates,
sometimes the verbosity, e.g., to card II: "Oh, yes, here we have symmetry
again; a vertical axis . . . the black color is not laid on very evenly." Card
III: "Oh, yes, here we have symmetry again; a vertical axis, the same
colors are laid on . . . the black is somewhat heavier . . . the red too is
unevenly laid on." Card IV: "This is symmetrical again, with a vertical
axis, it is set in the black," and so on.

As is known in clinical psychiatry, this pedantic verbosity is a sign of
genuine or traumatic epilepsy, or an epileptiform character alteration.
Thus it is often found together with a stereotyped emphasis on symmetry
and color naming. (The example is from a case of traumatic-ixophrenic
pseudo-psychopathy.)

29. CONFABULATIONS are found not only in DW– responses, but poor
W, D, and S responses may also contain them. They are Orig– responses,
and are pulled completely out of thin air. Examples: card II, the black,
"squirrel," D F– A Orig–. Card V, "there is some kind of a stag in it,"
DW F– A Orig–. Same card in > position, "one could also get a lion out
of it," D F– A Orig– (traumatic encephalopathy). Card II, white space
detail, "a bird," Ds F– A Orig–. Card IV, "a rat," W F– A Orig–. Card
VII in v position, "a hare," DW F– A Orig– (uncontrolled pseudological-
psychopathy in a fifteen year old girl). Card I, "a camel," DW F– A Orig–.
Card VII, upper third, "two kangaroos," D F– A Orig–; lower third, "two
hares" (laterals of upper contours as the heads, the ears of the usual
"rabbit" in the v position as the "legs"; pseudological-psychopathy in the
twin sister of the former Subject).

Also the confabulated combinations (chapter 3) should be mentioned in
the list of the special phenomena.

30. CONTAMINATIONS are likewise not always W, but also appear in D
responses.

[33]Hans Zulliger, Schwierige Kinder, Berne, 1951, p. 138, moreover: Psychoanalyse
und Formdeut-Versuch, Psyche 1950, Fasc. 11.

The contaminations of old schizophrenics are often at the same time neologisms. These are probably never found in healthy schizothymes and schizoids. Here the contaminations take on reality orientation (e.g., the response to the upper red, card III, "an ape-like animal with bird's wings, a mythical animal," or they take a borderline form as in the not infrequent mixing, crossing or "in-betweenness." In all these cases reality testing is clearly preserved. The Subject himself feels that these mixtures are not consistent with reality.

As is the case with the number and position responses, contaminations occasionally occur in children of pre-school age and indeed especially in five-year olds and particularly in girls (Ames et al.).

Confabulations and contaminations are to be strictly differentiated from one another. They may occur together, but this is in fact a very infrequent occurrence since the elements of the contamination, when taken alone, are usually good forms.

31. THE SECONDARY M RESPONSES should have already been included in the scoring (one may write, for example, M=5 [1–, 2 sec]). But they should be mentioned again in the list of special phenomena, due to their great significance for diagnosis.

Although they are also said to appear among manics, their most important diagnostic value is without doubt in relation to epilepsy. In the rare cases in which they appear among normals, they are almost always an indication of an ixothymic character trait, and usually there are other symptoms pointing in this direction.

The extremely rare *confabulated F-M* should likewise be included among the special data, so that they are not overlooked in judging the general picture. They should probably never appear in the protocols of normals.

32. THE SUPPRESSED M RESPONSES are extremely rare, and the beginner may safely disregard them.

As has already been pointed out in "Rorschachiana I," responses are produced now and then which have unmistakably originated as M responses, but are finally produced in a formulation which robs them of their kinesthetic character. The kinesthetic impulse is banned from consciousness, the experience is rejected, and the liveliness of the response is, as it were, artificially "killed off." The suppressed M responses are thus the opposite of secondary M responses; the kinesthetic experience in the secondary M develops after the response has already been verbalized. In the suppressed M responses, the kinesthetic experience has already been lost by the time the response is formulated, but was present before the response.

Examples: The large lateral detail of card IV, "a shadow of someone who is climbing a mountain" (FLD+); the large lateral extensions of card VI, "stone monument representing a bowed figure" (F+). One would have to be a Pygmalion or a Rodin to identify with a stone, but before the response became stone, the identification was there. Similarly the "soldier standing at attention" (upper part of card VI) becomes a tin soldier (F+).

It is important and often difficult to differentiate the suppressed M response from the repressed M. In the repressed M, in "kinesthetic shock," there has never been any M. Responses like "caricatures of two men with long necks," to card III or "scarecrow" to card IV involve no kinesthesia. In contrast, in suppressed M responses a kinesthetic experience, though present at first, has been turned aside. F associations to card III are usually M repressions. Nevertheless, on one occasion, the "men" of this card were responded to with a suppressed M: "shadow pictures of two men that are lifting a vessel off the ground." The fact that the suppressed M actually contained movement experience at first may be seen from an example in which the whole process, so to speak, is played off in slow motion. This border case is from Beck's textbook[34] and reads: "Looks like two women making faces at each other . . . or the statues of two women making faces at each other . . . or the busts of two women making faces at each other . . . mounted peculiarly on a rock."

In disagreement with Beck, we believe it more correct to score these responses as F (or FLD) reactions. One may then add "suppressed M." In any event, these reactions should be listed among the special phenomena.

Freud discusses "Negation" in a short essay.[35] He believes it to be a compromise between intellectual recognition and affective rejection. In the same way, the suppressed M can be understood as a compromise. The natural experience is venturing forth in the form of a kinesthesia, but this is rejected by a resistance which cannot be entirely broken through. This is a reflection of the conflict between two psychologic tendencies, the admission of an attitude or identification with a person, and the resistance which attempts to keep this attitude or this identification in the unconscious. But the resistance is too weak and eventually there is a break-through by the repressed material. The fact is that these reactions are almost without exception produced by Subjects who are either in psychotherapy or in some life crisis which compels them to abandon a previous neurotic adjustment. Thus a nineteen-year-old girl who was in the process of separating herself from parental authority but had not yet succeeded, and who therefore still acted like a dependent child, interpreted the lower detail in the "chair leg" of card VI as, "a child's figure with a round head and a small body, not a live child." The suppressed M responses are thus the

[34]Samuel J. Beck, Rorschach's Test, I. Basic Processes, New York, 1944, p. 103.
[35]Sigmund Freud, Gesammelte Werke, Vol. 14, pp. 11-15.

sign of a loosening-up process which liberates old inhibitions. They are important complex-determined associations, the content of which often allows us to penetrate to a problem in life or in the therapy with which the Subject is at the moment deeply concerned. One may say that the repressed M responses are the sign of an inhibition. They may be best understood causally as pointing to the past. The suppressed M are the sign of a release, best understood purposively as pointing to the future. The repressed M responses show us only the end result of a neurotic process; the suppressed M responses show us a process of healing or readjustment. Therefore it is not so strange that both forms of response occasionally appear in the same protocol, as where the same Subject who gave the "shadows of mountain climbers" response, had previously responded to card III with "two marionettes" (F, repressed M).

Mention is to be made also of the possibility of *suppressed small M* responses, often made in reaction to the small gray figure in the lower middle of card VII.

33. M RESPONSES WITH DOUBLE MEANING have been described by Zulliger in the textbook accompanying the Bero-Test (p. 61). Zulliger gives the following example of a response to card III: "Two men want to shake hands—or both are drawing back." Another example would be the response to card VII, in the ᵥ position; "Two girls, one is making a welcoming, the other a rejecting gesture" (this response naturally came from a woman). According to Zulliger, we are dealing here with a tendency to screen one's inner feelings and a desire not to see. Thus tendencies toward flight or splitting off are operative here. We find this type of response among neurotics, schizoid characters (both may of course occur together) and, in the case of two opposing moods (laughing and crying), among ambithymics.

34. THE MC RESPONSES WITH BODILY SENSATIONS were likewise mentioned by Zulliger in the Bero-Book (p. 62). He gives as an example the association to card III: "Two poor, freezing, ragged chimney sweeps are warming themselves by a fire."

Associations of this kind are indicative of an ability to experience enthusiasm and ecstasy. By "ecstasy," all creative exaltation, good or bad, is to be understood.

Ecstasy plays an important role in modern social psychology. It is, as Karen Horney[36] appropriately puts it, the extreme manifestation of the "dionysic" (Nietzsche) tendency to absorb and submerge God, the world, nature, or the State (as a substitute for religion), all into one greater unity.

[36]Karen Horney, The Neurotic Personality of Our Time, cited here in the Swedish Edition, pp. 196-197—see also: Erich Fromm, The Fear of Freedom.

This tendency is what is also called "losing oneself." It is related to masochism.

35. PERSEVERATION. By perseveration is understood an inertia of ideational content, i.e., its tendency to obtrude itself in the mind.[37] It is a *sine qua non* for any learning process. In the clinical sense the term is understood only to mean a heightened inertia, and this is the way we shall use it.

In speaking briefly about perseveration in the Rorschach test, we have in mind, in the first line, perseveration of content. Strictly speaking, this may appear in three forms. To these we may add two more formal types of perseveration. We have then five different kinds of perseveration in all.

a) The most severe is the so-called *gross, or organic perseveration.* Here the same content recurs in two or more responses following one another, to the extent that the same one is not infrequently carried over from one test card to the next. In the most severe cases the same response may be given to all ten cards ("monotypical record"). This type, even when only slightly indicated, leads to the suspicion of an organic (exogenous) disturbance, but it may also appear in epilepsy (which in the United States is usually listed among the "organic" mental diseases). It may now and then appear among schizophrenics and the feeble-minded as well. Monotypical records may also occur in these two groups (Beck).

b) While this gross form is generally typical for organics (in the narrow sense of the term), perseveration in genuine epilepsy usually appears in another variation, the so-called *"sticking to a central theme"* (Bovet).[38] The Subject does not continue giving exactly the same response, e.g., "dog's head," but does confine himself to the same general content category with little variation, e.g., "horse's head," "cat's head," "snake's head," "crocodile's head," and so forth, all heads of animals. Should a new theme emerge, say flowers, this also will be closely adhered to for a while (roses, cornflowers, snap dragons, etc.). In between there will generally also be some cases of "true" perseveration.

c) A weakened form of perseveration very frequently found in mild cases of epilepsy and organic damage is that displayed in the *"ruminating type"* (Bohm). In this group the same association reappears with exactly the same content, but with several other responses in between. The saying is brought to mind, "If you can't think of anything new, try something old." This does not refer to a simple piling up of the same P (e.g., "bat" repeated twice for cards I and V, or "animal skin" twice for cards IV and

[37]Basic investigation: Arthur Wreschner, Die Reproduktion und Assoziation von Vorstellungen, 1907-1909.

[38]Th. Bovet, Der Rorschach-Versuch bei verschiedenen Formen von Epilepsie. Schweizer Archiv f. Neur. u. Psychiatrie, vol. 37, 1936, pp. 156-157.

VI). However, if the not quite common responses, "a bridge across a river," "a church steeple," or "a bird's tail," should be given twice, they are to be taken as perseveration, even if several other associations are produced between them. Occasionally, however, this only stems from some complex, and is not organic, or even schizophrenic. We must always give great attention to form and content. Anatomical and sexual responses, in particular, when they are the only perseveration of the ruminating type, are in the main only neurotic.

In children up to the first year of school, perseveration is physiological.

d) A purely formal perseveration, but with specifically epileptic coloring, is the *"perceptional perseveration"* described by Guirdham.[39] It is characterized by the kind of approach taken. The Subject chooses similarly formed details (usually D or Dd) to which, however, he responds differently. One individual sees all the similarly formed peninsulas, another all the rounded bays, and so on. Especially easy to note is the perceptional perseveration at times displayed in the apprehension originals, as when the black detail in the lower middle of card I together with the two lower space details are interpreted as a duck (head downwards) and then the same detail in card II together with the black point (head) and the middle part of the middle red (legs) are seen as a goose. Or the subject may interpret the space detail in the blue of card VIII together with the medial part of the gray as "a grotesque head with a very high forehead, a caricature of King Gustaf of Sweden" and then describe the medial part of the middle gray in card X as "a comical character with a silk hat, the way you might see yourself in a distortion mirror." Another example (although these would not be apprehension originals) would be furnished by the responses, "an eagle turning its head to the right" to the whole of card I in the ∨ position and "a flying man, facing right, with artificial horse's ears" to the whole of card V, where in each case the small asymmetric spot on the head is noticed.

e) *Perseveration of the perceived area* is the weakest kind of perseveration, likewise merely a formal variety. The perseveration here does not occur in the response. It consists of the Subject's fixing on a particular part of the ink blot and giving several responses to it. He cannot tear himself away from the detail. So several little series of two or more responses to the same detail (and of course also to the whole card) make their appearance. This perseveration of the perceived area is found to an especially marked degree preferably in normal ixothymics, i.e., in normal subjects with epileptoid character traits, but it is also found in others.

The various responses to the same detail may differ considerably, since

[39]Arthur Guirdham, The Rorschach Test in Epileptics. The Journal of Mental Science, vol. 81, 1935, p. 890.

this is not a matter of similarity of content. In general they also tend to be good form responses. Only in rare instances does the pressure to give several responses to the same detail result in a loss of sharpness of form, as in the following example, in which a law student of superior intelligence saw the blue of card VIII at first as a "corset," and then added, "or a human chest," and confirmed the fact, when asked, that both times he meant the whole blue figure, and not the white space.

36. THE ANATOMICAL STEREOTYPY. We come now to the various stereotypies. The most general form is naturally a high A per cent. The varieties considered here under the "special phenomena" are only variations. Differentiating a stereotypy from "sticking to a basic theme" may make for difficulty now and then. The epileptiform sticking to a basic theme is due to a difficulty in *shifting*, while in the stereotypies we are dealing with the preference for a *particular* theme. In sticking to a basic theme, *several* topics are thus usually in evidence, each constituting its own separate chain, with jerky transitions between them. Stereotypies are usually identified by the predominance of a *single* content category, and occur for the most part in several responses scattered throughout the entire protocol. Stereotypy as such has nothing to do with true perseveration, i.e., with the recurrence of the same responses to different blots, nevertheless, a stereotypy may sometimes occur in combination with perseveration (see below).

Thus, anatomical stereotypy means a preponderance of anatomical responses in the content column. *It is a quandary in the Rorschach test, for* it may overrun large sections of the protocol or, not infrequently, all of it, and thus well-nigh choke off all other test factors. Should the percentage of anatomical responses in a test be very high (60-100 per cent), that test is in most cases of little value. Intelligence can in this case hardly be estimated, and a diagnosis is practically impossible or at best highly uncertain. For although Rorschach still believed that anatomy stereotypies were limited to persons with an "intelligence complex," and to hypochondriacs, epileptoids, and accident-neurotics, the range of cases in which anatomy stereotypy has appeared has increased considerably. Veit found them in postencephalitic Parkinsonism,[40] Oberholzer in compensation neurosis,[41] Mahler-Schoenberger and Silberpfennig in amputees,[42] Singeisen in people with

[40]Hans Veit, Der Parkinsonismus nach Encephalitis epidemica im Rorschach'schen Formdeutversuch. Zeitschr. f. Neurologie, Vol. 110, 1927, pp. 301-324.
[41]Emil Oberholzer, Zur Differentialdiagnose psychischer Folgezustände nach Schädeltraumen mittels des Rorschach'schen Formdeutversuchs. Zeitschr. Neur., Vol. 136, 1931, p. 620.
[42]M. Mahler-Schoenberger and J. Silberpfennig, Der Rorschach'sche Formdeutversuch als Hilfsmittel zum Verständnis der Psychologie Hirnkranker. Schweizer Archiv. f. Neur. u. Psychiatrie, Vol. 40, 1937, pp. 302-327.

heart and lung ailments,[43] and Zolliker[44] affirms that he has observed anatomical stereotypies "just about completely occupying the entire protocol"
in practically every nosological group, in schizophrenics, epileptics, in the
most diverse organic psychoses, kleptomaniacs, perverts, neurotics, and
others. To these would also be added patients lately treated with electro-
convulsive shock, who often produce up to 100 per cent anatomical responses. All that can be gleaned from this kind of protocol is that it is
"not normal," and that it is "a narcissistic preoccupation with the body
image" (Mahler-Schoenberger and Silberpfennig). But this, in the language
of the streets, is "no great shakes."

When the anatomy per cent is somewhat lower, 50-60 per cent, the rest
of the responses in some cases permit a glimpse into the intelligence of
the Subject, and a diagnosis may be arrived at. When the anatomy per cent
is under 50, this stereotypy with its completely unspecified symptom value
is usually no longer a hindrance.

We are in a somewhat better position when the anatomical stereotypy
is *combined with perseveration,* i.e., when the perseveration attaches to the
anatomical associations (as when "chest cage" recurs five times in a single
protocol). This perseveration is mainly of the ruminating type. In these
cases it is usually only necessary to decide between the ixoid personality
(Rorschach's epileptoid), genuine epilepsy with hysteric character, traumatic epilepsy (Bovet) or a hypochondriac neurosis, frequently an organ
neurosis.

37. BODY-PART STEREOTYPY is a stereotyped preference for human detail
responses which are not faces or heads, but arms, fingers, legs, necks, and
the like. If it is very pronounced and if, in addition, the responses are
largely Do, it should be viewed mostly as indicating feeble-mindedness, in
case of low intelligence factors; otherwise we may suspect serious psychic
infantilism, possibly combined with feeble-mindedness.

38. FACE STEREOTYPY, on the other hand, is generally a symptom of
phobic anxiety. We will return to this point in the discussion of the neuroses.

39. INFANTILE RESPONSES similarly belong for the most part to problems
of content. (For the two exceptions, the one involving inverse responses,
and the other infantile abstractions, see the sections following.) A number
of content categories preferred by normal children may be interpreted as

[43]Fred Singeisen, Rorschach-Befunde bei chronisch Lungentuberkulösen und Herz-
kranken. Schweizer Archiv. f. Neurologie u. Psychiatrie, Vol. 45, 1940, pp. 230-247.
[44]Adolf Zolliker, Schwangerschaftsdepression und Rorschach'scher Formdeutversuch,
in "Psychiatrie und Rorschach'scher Formdeutversuch," Zürich 1944, p. 77.

infantile reactions when grown-ups produce them. According to Löpfe,[45] among these belong finger, letter, numeral, and map responses, reminiscences from children's books, and increased object and nature responses. To this must be added Rorschach's observation (p. 176) that children from six to eight have a predilection for plant responses. In addition, we must mention the pars-pro-toto responses. If genuine, they must be scored as A or H.

The *infantile* M responses constitute a problem by themselves. Since children, as a consequence of their totem-type living, can identify with the less "human" kinds of animals we may find many animal M responses among children which are not classified as such among grown-ups. One might then conclude that such a response, when found in adults, constitutes psychic infantilism. This in itself is undoubtedly true, but in practice offers considerable danger, because inexperienced testers, or those with inadequately developed intuition, may be tempted to interpret animal responses, in which movement is only *described*, simply as M, although these are not instances of identification. A false conclusion of infantilism may then be drawn. Thus the greatest caution should be exercised in this matter and only those animal responses should be recorded as infantile M in which there is an incontrovertible manifestation of the identification experience. For example, in response to card VII, upper third, "A little turkey-chick is drinking: it is stretching its neck and putting its head back, like this," (and the Subject goes through the motions). Since this response is also an oral complex response, its interpretation as an infantile fixation is the more plausible. However, there is *no* M in "a dog climbing among rocks," even though the dog is closer to man phylogenetically than the fowl.

40. THE INVERSE INTERPRETATIONS are an infantile category of a formal kind. As William Stern showed as long ago as 1909,[46] among children from one and one half to four years old, the form of a perceived thing does not change if seen upside down. But adults show an "anisotropy" in such instances. According to F. Oetjen, a student of G. E. Müller's (1915), and according to a later study by R. Mouchly (of the Lewinian school), this "superiority" of children may also be seen among older children (Oetjen, ages 9-13; Mouchly, ages 5-8), but considerably weaker than in the 3 to 4-year olds (Mouchly).[47] It is not strange, therefore, that Weber[48] obtained

[45]Adolf Löpfe, Über Rorschach'sche Formdeutversuche mit 10-13 jährigen Knaben. Zeitschr. f. angew. Psychologie, Vol. 26, 1926, pp. 202-253.

[46]William Stern, Zeitschr. f. angew. Psychologie, Vol. 2, 1909, p. 498 ff.

[47]F. Oetjen, Zeitschr. f. Psychologie, Vol. 71, 1915, p. 332.—More details, also about Mouchly in Wolfgang Köhler, Gestalt Psychology, New York, 1945, p. 215 and Wolfgang Köhler, Dynamics in Psychology, London, 1942, pp. 19, 21, 22.

[48]A. Weber, Der Rorschach'sche Formdeutversuch bei Kindern, in "Psychiatrie und Rorschach'scher Formdeutversuch," Zürich, 1944, p. 59.

inverse interpretations from about ten per cent of the children he studied. For the identifying of this response, see above, chapter 3, Inquiry.

Among grown-ups we have observed inverse interpretations in cases of senile dementia and in persons with pronounced pedagogic powers. It seems that the "positive psychic infantilism" of the pedagogue manifests itself more often in reminiscences about children's books and inverse interpretations, and less in other infantile associations. According to Ulrich Moser inverse interpretations, as well as other infantile responses, also occur in technicians, some of whom have preserved the instinct to play in their occupation with mechanics. Such interpretations may also at times occur as part of the narcissistic syndrome and, finally, they have also appeared in a few cases of traumatic brain disease and epilepsy (Salomon), and seem to occur more frequently in ixothymics.

41. THE INFANTILE ABSTRACTIONS are also a formal peculiarity of the infantile way of perception. According to Zulliger (Tafeln-Z-Test, p. 82) they are global conceptions of the whole with exclusive regard to the exterior outlines (e.g., "vase" to the whole of card III, "flower bulb" to the whole of card VIII). Many of these responses look like figure-background-fusions, but are not always such. This kind of infantile abstraction is "normal" until the age of 8. Later it must be considered an infantilism, a retardation of intellectual development. In particular, reality testing is somewhat imperfectly developed in such persons, as in the case of young children who cannot distinguish between fancy and reality. These responses are also often apprehension originals, which likewise indicate a somewhat incomplete sense of reality.

42. REPETITIONS. By repetition is understood the reiteration of the same response to the same blot. Although the association has been given before, the subject forgets this and believes the second response to be a new one. How this is determined has already been explained above. "True" instances of repetition are almost always a sign of an organic disturbance in recent memory. They may appear occasionally even in mild cases of chronic alcoholism.

43. THE EVALUATING REMARKS are side remarks that contain a value-judgement, e.g., "This card is not as attractive as the one before." "This one should be drawn differently—it is inharmonious," "This one has been done very nicely," etc. Negative value judgements are, naturally, often simply shock symptoms, and positive judgements may be, too ("Beautiful colors," and the like). Otherwise, esthetic as well as moral value judgments of this kind appear especially among epileptics, persons with organic

pathology and the feeble-minded. They may appear occasionally among artistically disposed normals, and those who delight in giving their opinions.

44. SELF-REFERENCE, sometimes called "I-reference," in its crudest form, consists of a projection of one's own person into the percept, for example, to card VIII, "Two pigs, yes, that is what I was," (Rorschach, p. 162); or "That's me" (VI); or "a mask, is it I?" "That's me, in front of a mirror." Or it may appear as an entirely unmotivated side remark like, "I had a terrible toothache today." In a more diluted form, the self-references may only consist in connecting the response with a personal experience: "That reminds me of a sweet little dog that we used to have at home"; "In my childhood I had a doll that looked exactly like that." Zulliger[49] distinguishes between true self-references and personal memories, but I think that we are here facing a difference of degree rather than a difference of kind.

The gross self-references are chiefly found among schizophrenics and epileptics; more rarely among organics and the feeble-minded. The milder forms are not rare among neurotics (egocentricity), but occasionally appear also in healthy persons, particularly schizothymes (and of course also in schizoids).

45. THE NUMBER RESPONSES and 46. THE POSITION RESPONSES are naturally to be included in the summary. It is advisable, however, to include them also in the list of the "special phenomena," so that these important factors are not overlooked in the evaluation. The very fact of their appearance has diagnostic significance, and is almost always indicative of schizophrenia or a schizoid, provided it is not a matter of young children.

In *anatomical position responses,* instead of the perception taking precedence over the assimilation of its significance, the reverse is true; here the content of the response, i.e., the self-referent anatomical representation of the body image, comes first and the matching of the blot against this idea is only secondary (Mahler-Schoenberger and Silberpfennig, op. cit. p. 314). This mechanism appears chiefly among oligophrenics and schizophrenics, in addition to those with bodily injury.

47. BLACK AND WHITE AS COLORS. In a relatively few instances, regular color responses (usually FC, less often CF) are given to the black, gray, or white. For instance, as a black or gray response to card VI, "blue fox"; as gray responses, "elephant," to the detail in card VII (FC−) or "mouse pelt," to card VI (FC+); as a white response, "snow man" (space detail in card IX, FC+). Responses like "black butterfly" to card V (W FC+), and "raven's head" for the outer half of the wing detail in card V (Dd

[49]Hans Zulliger, Der Tafeln Z-Test, Berne, 1954, pp. 76 and 77.

FC+), also belong here. In the computation it is useful to make special note of the black, white, and gray percepts, even though they are true color responses; for example, "FC = 6(+), (including 2 black)."

As Schneider reports,[50] Rorschach observed these responses among epileptics and normals consciously developing depressive moods (affect avoidance). The white responses, "a magnificent white dome of marble," and the like, especially when more than one appears, Binder[51] ascribes to an euphoric mood. Rorschach himself describes the appearance of black and white responses as having color value in epilepsy and occasionally also in very confused schizophrenics (pp. 30 and 39).

Zulliger has pointed out (Tafeln Z-Test, p. 243) that white responses are mainly given by oversensitive and easily offended persons, who try to dissimulate their sensitivity.

Should the black and gray responses approach Binder's "primitive light-dark responses," that is, should they have an *amorphous and indefinite form,* they take on another meaning. These associations (e.g., "piles of coal," "something burned," "molten metal") are, according to Oberholzer[52] found among traumatics and traumatic defectives and constitute a sign of indolence and indifference, occasionally even torpor and apathy. They are found too among people of passively resigned disposition, like the Alorese.[53] This is also connected with their appearance in emotionally unfixated psychopaths.

Thus when black, gray, or white are interpreted as colors and when the responses are fairly concise, one should think of epilepsy, constitutional ixothymia, lesion resulting in ixophrenia, or electro-shock effects. If the responses are amorphous, indolence, lack of emotional fixation or a traumatic effect should be looked for.

48. COLOR DENIAL. This phenomenon has been described by Piotrowski[54] and takes the form of the Subject expressly denying the influence of color on the interpretation, although it is obvious, e.g., "Flowers, but not on account of the color." According to Piotrowski, the symptom value of color denial is a deliberate endeavor to repress feelings, "probably for fear of painful disappointments."

[50]Ernst Schneider, Eine diagnostische Untersuchung Rorschach's auf Grund der Helldunkeldeutungen ergänzt. Zeitschr. f. Neur., Vol. 159, 1937, pp. 5/6.

[51]Hans Binder, die Helldunkeldeutungen etc., p. 59.

[52]Emil Oberholzer, Zur Differentialdiagnose organischpsychischer und psychogen bedingter Störungen nach Schädel und Hirntraumen vermittels des Rorschach'schen Formdeutversuches. Report at the International Neurologic Congress at Berne, 1931.

[53]Oberholzer in Cora Du Bois, the People of Alor, Minneapolis, 1944, p. 597.

[54]Zygmunt A. Piotrowski, A Rorschach Compendium—Revised and Enlarged, The Psychiatric Quarterly, Vol. 24, 1950, p. 578.

49. CHROMATIC RESPONSES TO ACHROMATIC CARDS. Now and again bright colors appear in response to the black cards. Thus a Subject may, on the presentation of card I, say, "blood." Often a whole symphony of color will be imagined into a dark card. Klopfer likewise refers to this phenomenon: ". . . many Subjects see multicolored tropical butterflies reproduced in the blots as in a photograph."[55]

The symptom value of this response is still somewhat unclear. In some cases we appear to be dealing with a special type of confabulation. Thus a woman patient, responding to the middle line and the projection of card VI, says, "Flower-stand in a park"; then, pointing to the main detail, continues, "then this here must be something green." Piotrowski[56] explains this phenomenon, analogous to our "disavowal," as a flight from desperate pessimism to a confabulated cheerfulness that is not "genuine."

50. EQa RESPONSES. Occasionally responses appear which contain some inner attribute, usually three-dimensional, like weight or solidity, e.g., "a heavy lump of lead." Guirdham[57] has proposed that these be designated by the signum EQa (essential quality astereognostic). This designation rests on an error in language. Guirdham as a neurologist borrows the term from "astereognosis," but he takes no regard of the negating force of the alpha privative. It would be more correct to say "essential quality stereognostic." On practical grounds it is preferable to retain the signum as it was intro- duced into the English literature. The most important thing is that we be entirely clear about the meaning. It is advisable to write EQa after the scoring formula in the protocol and to list the finding again among the special phenomena.

According to Guirdham these associations should appear among intelli- gent persons with outstanding abstracting and synthesizing ability.

51. EQe RESPONSES. In the same work,[58] Guirdham describes responses which in addition to an H, Hd, A, or Ad contain some particular emotional expression. These he terms EQe responses (essential quality emotional), e.g., "evil grinning," "friendly smiling," "anxious," "mocking" faces, and others. They are found, according to Guirdham, in intelligent persons with creative artistic powers. In our experience they appear to reflect an especial affinity to a talent for acting.

[55]Klopfer and Kelley, op. cit. p. 141.
[56]Zygmunt A. Piotrowski, A Rorschach Compendium—Revised and Enlarged, The Psychiatric Quarterly, Vol. 24, 1950, pp. 577/578 and 581/582.
[57]Arthur Guirdham, On the Value of the Rorschach Test, The Journal of Mental Science, Vol. 81, 1935, p. 863.
[58]op. cit. 863/864.

52. MF RESPONSES. As is well known, Klopfer and Piotrowski designate animals seen in movement as FM. Loosli-Usteri[59] has suggested that this category be adopted as MF. (The reversal is necessary in order to avoid confusing it with Rorschach's confabulated FM.) According to Loosli-Usteri they are less an expression of infantile affect than one involving "inner attitudes subject to strong taboo" which are projected on to the animals. Active MF are to be evaluated as indicating important "quiet reserves." On the other hand, the passive ones are a sign of "deep-seated lack of psychic energy."

Naturally, movements in non-anthropomorphic animals are simple F responses, to be scored accordingly. But it can be quite useful to add MF in striking instances of movement, those that approach the anthropomorphic (i.e., in borderline cases), and to mention these responses among the special phenomena. Thus anthropomorphic movements in non-anthropomorphic animals would be MF. They often take the form of richly informative complex-determined associations, and in these instances Loosli-Usteri's hypothesis is well borne out. But the movement must definitely *say* something, "attacking bull," "prettily sitting rabbit," etc.); walking leopards, flying ducks, and the like are unimportant.

53. THE m RESPONSES, Loosli-Usteri also utilizes Klopfer's m as m responses (in German, "b") (op. cit. pp. 17-18). In this category belong nature creations and objects seen as if in motion. According to Loosli-Usteri, these reflect "very deeply unconscious" attitudes which have either been strongly repressed or have never appeared in consciousness. It is a question whether "flying carpet" or "falling vase" truly manifest this tendency. Experimentally one may utilize m as a double formula (in the same way as MF). But the primary scoring would naturally be the regular F (or FC, or whatever the case required) in order not to distort the raw data for purposes of the evaluation. Aside from this, we need to guard against any confusion with kinetic descriptions.

54. LACK OF SUBJECTIVE CLEARNESS IN THE MANNER OF APPROACH can be described as the inability of the Subject to localize what he sees. It is found principally in the confabulation of excitable oligophrenics (Pfister).[60]

55. EMPHASIS ON THE MIDDLE OR SIDES means that the medial or lateral details are heavily drawn upon in the selection of perceptions. Forced emphasis on the sides is in fact hardly ever found, since practical persons

[59]Marguerite Loosli-Usteri, Persönlichkeitsdiagnostik, Rorschachiana II, p. 17.
[60]Oskar Pfister, Ergebnisse des Rorschach'schen Versuches bei Oligophrenen. Allgem. Zeitschr. f. Psychiatrie, Vol. 82, 1925, pp. 198-223.

who at first focus on the sides usually respond also to some middle details. In contrast, an anxious preoccupation with the middle sections with few or no lateral responses is not at all rare. According to Zulliger, as we have already noted, it points to an inner uncertainty, a fear of losing oneself (Zulliger, Bero-Test p. 106).

56. ACOUSTIC ASSOCIATIONS are an exceptionally rare phenomenon. It may happen that the Subject, while under the influence of the ink blot to which he is reacting, *hears* something and describes what he has heard. Usually these are musical reminiscences, a theme from a particular passage in a symphony or the like. But these associations are not necessarily always musical ones. Thus, reacting to the blue of card VIII, one Subject declared, "That is a piece of cloth that some one is tearing, you can hear it go 'zip.' "

Acoustic associations are found almost exclusively among active, or at least passive, musically minded persons. Kuhn also has reported them (barking dog, chirping crickets, and ringing bells) in a woman musician.[61] To what extent this phenomenon is related to a tendency to synesthesia has not yet been explored.

57. INITIAL TEST INHIBITION. An isolated dark shock in response to card I is not likely to appear. If this figure should give trouble because of its darkness, this will usually also be the case in response to card IV, providing there is no interference phenomenon at IV, and in the other dark cards as well. Difficulty in responding to card I *alone* must consequently be looked on as a phenomenon *sui generis*. We have called it initial test inhibition (Rorschachiana I). It may manifest itself in a number of ways, for example, where almost all responses to card I show poor form perceptions, while in the other cards few or no F– appear; or where the only Do responses in the entire protocol are found in this card; or where there are DW here which do not reappear. It is a presumption for initial test inhibition that (1) no dark shock in response to any other dark card is discernible (in that case we would consider also the disturbance at card I a dark shock) and (2) the level of response to the first card is considerably below the average of the whole protocol. The most frequent and mildest form of this disturbance is perhaps an anatomical F– as the only anatomy percept for the entire test. When the whole protocol shows lowered F+ per cent, initial test inhibition may sometimes be a factor, but it is best not to note it as such, for it cannot be ascertained with any finality.

[61]Roland Kuhn, Über Rorschach's Psychologie und die psychologischen Grundlagen des Formdeutversuches, in "Psychiatrie und Rorschach'scher Formdeutversuch," Zürich, 1944, p. 44.

The beginning of any activity requires a stronger volitional impulse; once it is well embarked upon, it flows of its own accord.[62] And so a certain initial inhibition is the usual behavior in the Rorschach. Morgenthaler has explicitly shown this in his comparison of the first half with the second half of the test.[63] A certain initial test inhibition is, therefore, always present, brought on by the effort of starting the task, but it is usually so trifling that it is not conspicuous. Only when it stands out do we speak of initial test inhibition in the technical sense.

The symptom value of this phenomenon is not entirely clear yet. Without doubt Oberholzer's "anxiety at the unknown" (see above, under dark shock) plays a certain role. The types of Subjects described by Morgenthaler (op. cit. p. 47) as tending to have negative choice reactions to card I, provide some points of reference: insecure persons, depressives, anxious persons and anxiety neurotics, some esthetes, and certain neurotics with tendencies toward overcompensation (masculine protest). Unfortunately, in some of these groups the initial test inhibition, in our sense of the term, cannot be observed, owing to dark shock. (Dark shock does not rule out initial test inhibition, it only screens it.) In general, we have found this phenomenon among insecure persons, and occasionally in ixothymics, who not only have difficulty in shifting, but naturally also find it difficult to get started.

We readily accept as frequently correct Weber's interpretation that initial test inhibition indicates a conflict with the father's authority, as well as Loosli-Usteri's hypothesis that "initial shock," when it occurs with female figure responses to card I, points to a conflict with the mother.[64] Very likely, however, we are dealing in both these cases with the effect of a dark shock, which neither author has distinguished from the initial test inhibition as such. Just because both do occur together so frequently, and because the symptom value of the dark shock is already known, it is undoubtedly preferable, for purposes of research, not to assume test inhibition in such cases when dark shock is present but rather to reserve this for the rare cases in which there is no sign of dark shock. The factor to be examined must be isolated.

58. THE ILLUSION OF SIMILARITY is the erroneous fancy on the part of the Subject that two or more cards resemble one another. It manifests itself in spontaneous side remarks, such as, "Didn't I see this one already?" "Isn't this almost the same card as the one before (as the first, the second, etc.)?" "It is the same thing all the time"; "All the cards are almost alike."

[62]See Ludwig Klages, Handschrift und Charakter, Leipzig, 1923, p. 9.
[63]W. Morgenthaler, Über Modifikationen beim Rorschach. Rorschachiana II, p. 42.
[64]Loosli-Usteri, Persönlichkeitsdiagnostik, Rorschachiana II, p. 20.

These are obviously signs of embarrassment. It is the momentary lack of association which causes an unpleasant feeling, but this inner condition is projected onto the object of perception, the ink blot. The illusion of similarity is, therefore, a rationalization through projection. It must never be confused with perseveration with subjective criticism ("How awful that I always see the same thing"), because in the latter case nothing is being projected, no illusion is present. Still, a "true" illusion of similarity may be sometimes combined with perseveration. One sees this occasionally in epileptics and schizophrenics.

Concerning the symptom value of this phenomenon, the last word has not been spoken yet, but the following may be said provisionally:

A *single* illusion of similarity is apt to be an expression of color shock or dark shock; that is, a *horror vacui*. This is especially so among psychasthenics, also, if combined with epileptoid features, among epileptics, and epileptoid paranoid psychopaths (Buchholz-paranoia).

*Recurrent* (often four or five times or even more) illusions of similarity are found among asocial characters of the "smoothy" type who try to project their own difficulties onto the world about them, and to shift the blame away from themselves wherever possible (avoidance of responsibility). The recurrent illusions are likewise found among persons with paranoid sensitivity, especially in the presenile psychoses of paranoid coloring (involutional paranoia). Occasionally, however, the illusion of similarity occurs singly (once or twice) also among paranoids.

59. DISAVOWAL is a very strange phenomenon that usually (perhaps even exclusively) seems to occur with dark shock. The Subject shows clear signs of dark shock (reduction in the number of responses, Dd, Do, disturbance in sequence, inaccurate forms, etc.) but expresses especial pleasure in the dark cards. He says, for example, in reaction to card IV, "How light and airy, it dances," or greets card VI with the exclamation, "Oh, but these are merry pictures"; and then does not know what to do. This condition is analogous to assimilated color shock, but where in the latter case we are dealing only with a variant of affect-repression; disavowed dark shock involves an obvious discomfort (anxiety), which is being denied both in regard to the ego and the environment.

This rare phenomenon seems to appear almost exclusively in chronic hypomanics, or at any rate in persons with a clearly cyclic temperament. From psychoanalysis we know about the quasi-defence mechanism, the "denial in fantasy," and the "denial in word and deed."[65] And Helene Deutsch and Bertram D. Lewin have, in fact, found the disavowal

[65]See Anna Freud, Das Ich und die Abwehrmechanismen, Wien 1936, pp. 81 ff. and pp. 97 ff.

mechanism operative in chronic and transitory hypomanic states (see Anna Freud, op. cit. p. 96, footnote). This appears to be one of the psychogenic "trigger mechanisms" which hasten the probably endogenously caused swing from the depressive to the hypomanic phase.

60. DENIAL AND RESPONSES IN QUESTION FORM. Very often responses are given in the negative, "It's not a bat"; "A leaf; but no, it can't be," or as a question, "Would that be a four-footed animal?" To regard these negative associations merely as additions, as Klopfer has suggested,[66] in our opinion does not quite correspond with their character. It is best to look on them formally as positive reactions, and to evaluate their negative aspect as a special phenomenon. The same holds also for the responses in question form. This procedure has also been followed by Kuhn.[67] According-ing to Fränkel and Benjamin (op. cit.), both reactions, the negative responses and those in question form, stem from a combination of subjective and objective criticism.

Their practical symptom value is principally concentrated in three areas:

(a) Like objective criticism and to a more serious degree, subjective criticism, and like the indefinite F– responses arising from a tendency to hold back, both denial and question responses are symptoms of unsureness. Beck remarks very pertinently; "Self-confident individuals do not ask, they tell you."[68] Thus both kinds of responses are usually found in the same protocol, characteristically among psychasthenics (sub-valid), insecure psychopaths, and anxious neurotics. Isolated negative responses and those in question form may appear in any person in whom insecurity is a charac-ter trait, including incipient schizophrenics as well as virtual "normals."

(b) Inasmuch as they reflect criticism of the percept, both these cate-gories have important value for differential diagnosis in pointing to organic dementia as against mental deficiency.

(c) In certain cases, especially when the response is F– or is otherwise formally peculiar, we may be dealing with complex-determined material in which the repression is half emerging. (Again we refer to Freud's work on "Denial," see section above concerning suppressed M.) In Nietzsche's famous and beautiful words describing the phenomenon of repression, "I did it, says my memory, I couldn't have done it says my pride, and remains inexorable. Finally the memory concedes." (Herbart introduced the concept of repression into psychology in 1816.) If the repressing agent, that which

[66]Bruno Klopfer and Douglas McGlashan Kelley, The Rorschach Technique, New York, 1942, p. 71.

[67]Roland Kuhn, Der Rorschach'sche Formdeutversuch in der Psychiatrie, Basel, 1940, p. 15.

[68]Samuel J. Beck, Rorschach Test, I, Basic Processes, New York, 1944, p. 50.

Nietzsche terms pride, should weaken, the memory comes to the fore; however, the residue of pride makes another attempt. But the repression no longer succeeds, and only achieves a denial. This would be the explanation of the rather rare occurrence of complex-determined responses, with denial.

61. FUSION OF FIGURE AND BACKGROUND is perhaps the most psychologically interesting phenomenon to be found in the Rorschach test. Without exception, it occurs in shading percepts composed of a space and an adjoining black or colored detail; the score Ds (C)+ or DsD F(C)+ is usually given to these, or in some instances Ds FC+.

Nevertheless, the Ds F(C) responses are not by any means all *eo ipso* figure-background fusion. In regard to their perception, three groups must here be differentiated:

(a) the *usual* Ds F(C) which is seen neither as three-dimensional nor as figure-background fusion. For example, the response to card VII, "a crater-lake, with lava peaks above it," is seen quite naturally. The white and gray details are two figures by themselves, and the lake is seen as background to the mountains, or conversely, the mountains as background to the lake. The same holds for percepts like, "land (green) with reeds (the lighter part) and water (space details)," in response to card IX, and "two mountain ridges with a lake between them" in response to the arms and legs of the men and the space detail in card III. In these cases nothing is fused.

(b) The *perspective* Ds F(C), as, for example, the well-known "avenue with trees, in the background a pagoda with stairs," to the black and white of card II. These perspective responses are the opposite of figure-background fusion.

(c) The Ds F(C) responses *with figure-background fusion*. Before we adduce examples here, we must refer to the relationships between figure and ground which have been explored by Edgar Rubin.[69] He mentions seven ways in which figure and ground are differentiated, and which we call figure qualities. One of them (number 4) is Rubin's so-called "subjective difference in localization," namely, the figure shows a tendency to become localized in front of the ground. This tendency is altered in the phenomenon we are describing, since the Subject makes a new "super figure" out of a figure and a part of what is otherwise experienced as ground. In this new percept, figure and ground lie in one and the same plane, and the new figure lies in front of a *new* ground. In it, figure and ground no longer lie one in front of the other, but are fused to form an entirely new percept. And something else has happened. Rubin describes the "tendency to

[69]Edgar Rubin, Visuell wahrgenommene Figuren, Copenhagen, 1921, p. 83.

perceive a unified single-colored field either entirely as figure or entirely as ground" and this is what our Subjects do *not* do. Since it is the fore-aft relationship of the parts in the percept that is mainly altered by the new fusion, and since instead of the usual figure-ground relationship, another unusual one enters, we have deliberately designated this phenomenon figure-*back*ground fusion. Rubin, on the other hand, with equally good reasons for the *universal* applicability of his research, speaks only of *ground*, although, to be sure, it is in most cases also background. Only in instances in which the Subject is able to disregard this subjective difference in localization (and naturally, too, to break up the single-colored field), is this new concept possible. Nearly all of these figure-background fusion responses are thus *eo ipso* apprehension originals.

Some examples: the space detail of card II in the ᐯ position will sometimes, combined with the gray stripes in the middle of the point, be seen as "a ballerina" or as "a pair of bellows." In the latter percept, the black in the red may possibly be the handles. Or the same figure in the ᐱ position is seen as "a bottle with stopper." Another example is the middle gray of card III with the space between seen as "water with reflections." The simplest example is the "gull's head" response to the upper lateral details of card IV in the > or < positions, with the white "filling" as a white spot on the head of the bird. Card X presents a great number of possibilities. The most frequent is probably the "goat's head," seen in the ᐯ position and composed of the yellow eyes (center), brown nostrils, gray beard and green horns with the entire white inter-space forming the connection.

The Bero series presents in fact the best examples. Here the large space detail between the two dogs in card II becomes the upper half of a flagon with a stopper (the gray middle detail and the tip) and with red ornaments. Or the large space detail in card VII is a church, but the black column on the "bridge" is the portal *within* the church front, not a column in front of it, as is customarily seen. Finally, the brown details in card VIII in the ᐯ position may be perceived as a "calf's head," with the inverted white dinner bell (the space) as a star on the face of the animal.

This last response demonstrates that these percepts may also be scored Ds FC+, i.e., not only as shading but also as form-color responses. To this category also belong the following two responses (Rorschach again) : to the interspace plus the red of card IX in the ᐯ position, "red glass bowl" (Ds FC+) ; and to the lateral space figures plus the blue plus the red middle of card VIII in the ᐯ position, "two men are sitting at a table (blue) under a lamp (red)."

One may indicate figure-background fusion in the protocol by any sign, for example, a little red star or cross. K. W. Bash has proposed that the sign Ve (Verschmelzungsantwort, i.e., fusion response) be used for this type of response. It would then be best to write it in only as a sub-formula, in order not to lose any of the color value in the experience balance. In every instance, the appearance of figure-background fusion is to be noted among the special phenomena.

Turning now to the symptom value of the phenomenon, it must be kept in mind that these responses are, in most cases, also apprehension originals and as such indicate a high grade of structural lability. That is, they point to mental flexibility, and as a matter of fact the figure-background fusions are found together with a low A per cent. The reverse of the medal is, indeed, a somewhat reduced sense of reality. (See chapter 3 under "Symptom Value of the Apprehension Originals.") Experience has taught us that this phenomenon appears principally in five kinds of Subjects: artists, pseudologic psychopaths, some neurotics, schizophrenics, and epileptics.

(a) *Artists* usually give several Ve responses, if any. This applies not only to practicing artists, but also to those who are merely gifted in a passive sense, those who have the artist's eye but not his manual skill. In this we see the flexibility of artistic thinking *as well* as its remoteness from practical everyday-life.

(b) In *psychopaths with pseudologia,* figure-background fusion may well be principally the expression of an undeveloped sense of reality.

(c) In *neurotics* the central complex-determined associations (frequently not very deep) often take this form. Rorschach himself has already noted (p. 199) that wish fulfillments are often hidden in DS F(C) responses. However, this holds for *all* three groups of the responses mentioned above, of which the Ve responses are of course only one variety. Naturally, disturbances of the sense of reality also play a part here. Occasionally homosexuals or subjects with masturbation conflicts see the men (or women) of card III wearing "a white apron" or "a bathing suit" (the wish to cover something). Not infrequently such a complex-determined association is the last in the entire test.

(d) In *schizophrenics,* structural lability often develops into structural distintegration. Their Ve associations are original in the highest degree, but reality testing is entirely lacking and the form perception usually poor. Examples: card II, the two red details with the white, "a human face with eyebrows (upper red) and a beard (lower red without the black)"; or card III, "a human face with hair (the lateral red) on the temples" (DsW Orig–).

(e) It is most difficult to explain the appearance of *epileptics* in this group. Epileptics are neither specially gifted artistically, nor are they structurally labile. On the contrary, they perseverate and are excessively stable in their thought structure. It is, therefore, the more surprising that a *low* A per cent appears side by side with their perseverations (Rorschach, p. 44) and, in addition, these Ve responses. Theoretical considerations as well as experimental evidence on the so-called Köhler phenomenon of reversible figures[70] makes it probable that we are here dealing with a consequence of Lennox's dysrhythmia. Thus it seems that either structural lability or cerebral dysrhythmia may result in the figure-background fusion.

The entire question relating to figure-background fusion responses and the psychologic problems they entail has by no means been cleared up yet. The question posed by Elmgren[71] as to the possibility of a differential Gestalt psychology, might possibly find an affirmative answer should this problem be pursued experimentally.

62. CENSORSHIP, INITIAL OR FINAL. Ego censorship comes into play in the Rorschach test just as it does in dreams. This may best be observed when several complex determined responses with analogous content are found in the same protocol, one following the other or, more frequently, scattered at various points here and there throughout the test. The first complex response is often symbolically veiled or distorted, while the later ones become more clear. Conversely, the first complex response may be expressed in clear, unequivocal language, while those that follow are censored. The first variety we are calling initial censorship, the second, final censorship. Censored fantasies are quite frequent. What we are concerned with here is an alteration in the vigor of the censorship (or conversely, the force with which the instinctual wish becomes embodied in the fantasy in question). A shift of the psychic energies in the course of the test is thus indicated. This manifests itself either in a breaking through or in a by-passing of the censorship (Freud, in the "Interpretations of Dreams" speaks of "dimming"[72]), either at the beginning (final censorship) or at the repetition of the fantasy (initial censorship).

Censorship provides an excellent indication of the relationship between the strength of the ego and the force of the drive. When a repressed complex makes itself felt, the ego is constrained to prevent the breaking through of the repressed material by reinforcing the repressing mechanism. Should this succeed, the corresponding complex responses will be the more strongly masked (final censorship). Thus final censorship is evidence of a *strong ego*. In doubtful cases it suggests a *neurosis*. Should the continued effort at repression not succeed, a break-through of the repressed material eventually develops (initial censorship). Initial censorship is hence a sign of a

[70]See Wolfgang Köhler, Dynamics in Psychology, London, 1942, pp. 58/59.
[71]See David Katz, Gestaltpsychologie, here quoted from the Swedish version, 1942, p. 146.
[72]Sigmund Freud, Die Traumdeutung, 8 ed. Wien, p. 421.

*weak ego.* In terms of differential diagnosis, this indicates either a psychogenic or another type of *psychosis,* or at least a tendency in this direction. We may also be dealing with *perversion,* which likewise presupposes a certain ego weakness, and usually also a psychotic taint in the family.

The following is an example of *final censorship.* A young woman, who is afraid of the perils of the big city, sees a human being at the edge of an abyss three times (all three responses M Orig+); the first time it is a "woman," the second and third times only a "person." In addition, the "abyss" was changed to a weaker, less equivocal "slope" in the second and third responses. The identification becomes less clear.

Example of *initial censorship* in a hysterical psychotic: in the upper extension of card VI is seen, "a face with a beard," then follows a W response, and then the same detail is seen once again as an "idol." As the first response to card VIII appears the complex-determined association with figure-background fusion, "An idol, or the face of my father," all in one breath. The ambivalent feelings of the patient towards the father, whom she feared and at the same time idolized and loved as an idol, are here beautifully demonstrated; she would talk to the nurses about this father for hours at a time.

Following is an example of initial censorship in a pervert (exhibitionism) : as the second response to card V, the space detail between the two lateral details, "a large caterpillar, which is crawling on a twig" (note the raised head). In the third response the space between the legs is "a carrot, which is turned upside-down, and sticking out of the ground." Fourth interpretation, the white contour at the lower edge of the wing, "a slope on which a weasel is sticking his head out of a hole." Finally, as the eighth percept, a small white indentation at the upper edge of the wing is seen as a "relaxed penis, hanging down." Comments would be superfluous.

63. SEXUAL SYMBOL STUPOR. As is well known, Rorschach's cards contain a number of details that more or less suggest the male and female genitals. The most definite is perhaps the upper middle of card VI. Many Subjects are embarrassed by these details, though the embarrassment may be of varying degree. In most cases, however, a response is produced, and even if this is not manifestly a sexual response, the sex thinking, consciously or unconsciously, usually betrays itself. For example, the projection in card VI may be perceived symbolically two or three times in succession ("a stake," "little man" and the like), and at the same time the sequence is reversed. With adequate inspection this complex-determined disturbance may be very clearly differentiated from dark shock. Often the mere fixating

on such a detail is enough to disclose the true nature of the difficulty.[73]

At times, however, this embarrassment in regard to such a detail, grows into an associative stupor. The subject attends carefully to the detail, often points expressly to it, but declares himself to be unable to respond. He says, for example, "I just don't know what that is," "I can't make a thing out of the top," "I don't get anything at all out of that," "It's too hard to say what it is," "Here's something, too" or "What could that be?" and then pause (with or without subsequent response).

Following is a list of the most important places in Rorschach's ten cards at which this stupor usually sets in. In the parentheses are given some abbreviated identification notes, and we have added whether the symbol is male or female.

1. Light spot in the middle of card I (hole in the middle of I, female).
2. Pointed detail of card II (point II, male).
3. The middle part of the red, bottom of card II (red middle II, female).
4. Pegs on legs of the men of card III (peg III, male).
5. Ivy leaf in top part of card IV (point IV, female).
6. Middle of upper projection of card VI (point VI, male).
7. Lower notch in card VI (notch VI, female).
8. Small humps (eggs) in the bottom notch of card VI (eggs VI, male).
9. Black in the lower middle of card VII (middle VII, female).
10. Top projections of card VII (projections VII, male).
11. Slits in the space detail of card IX (slits IX, female).

Thus, in recording the phenomena, we would write: "sexual symbol stupor (point II, eggs VI, projections VII)" etc.

The symptom value of this stupor, of course, depends on the sex of the Subject and the kind of symbol, whether male or female. In *men,* stupor at male symbols generally warrants assuming the presence of a castration anxiety; stupor at female figures has the same significance as white shock (see above) which, as we have said, is only a special case of sexual symbol stupor. In *women,* stupor at the male symbol is generally a symptom of hysteric genital-anxiety, the stupor at female symbols betrays either a rejection of femininity (see above, white shock) or, if manifest female sexual responses appear in the same protocol, a rejection of sexuality entirely, as something sinful (consciously or, as is more usual, unconsciously).

In general, then, sexual symbol stupor represents a form of sexual anxiety and is basically not too different from its opposite, the forced, too frequent sexual responses. In stupor we probably see a more primitive form of neurosis, one that is likely to be more accessible to therapy than the more complicated character neuroses with their many sexual responses, by which the Subject tries to display his "liberal ideas."

[73]See Marguerite Loosli-Usteri, Persönlichkeitsdiagnostik, Rorschachiana II, p. 20.

64. THE MASK RESPONSES. Roland Kuhn has devoted a special study to the not at all infrequent mask responses.[74] He distinguishes among three groups: Group I, whole answers of the Ws type, show a mask of approximately natural size from the front. Group II consists of D or Dd responses of a mask in profile, and Group III of whole dressed-up figures (including clowns) in motion. The mask responses of Group I are usually poor forms and are characteristically found in youths up to their twenties. They betray a strong concern with one's own facial expression and are associated with a defective differentiation between the ego and the outside world (undifferentiated ego-consciousness and a labile conception of oneself, in Jasper's sense). They stand in close relation to magical identification thinking. The responses of Group II indicates little concern with one's own face. They are found in persons with differentiated ego-consciousness and stand in close relation to objective, logical, theoretical, abstract thinking. These Subjects show for the most part a fear of something threatening (and so, phobic anxiety). Finally, subjects with Group III responses usually show psychasthenic traits of weakness and irresponsibility. Should the M responses be stiff (death, etc.), we have a suggestion of depersonalization experiences. Kuhn has never ascertained interpretations belonging to all three groups in the same protocol.

In recording the mask responses in the summary, the group to which they belong should be noted in parentheses, e.g., "two mask responses (Group II)."

The mask responses generally stem from a stiff and lifeless view of the world and point to a deficiency in affective contact. Zulliger found mask responses in people who feel themselves observed, and interprets them as a tendency to secrecy and self-concealment. (A caution concerning Group III is in order, to watch out for Subjects who are from areas in which southern carnivals are still celebrated.) Subjects giving those responses usually show psychasthenic traits with a tendency toward depersonalization. According to Kuhn, mask responses are found not only in psychasthenics; but also among hysterics, phobics, and compulsives; and also in normals with a tendency to such reactions. They are often found together with face content stereotypy.

65. AMNESTIC WORD FINDING DIFFICULTIES are one of the clinical symptoms which appear in connection with the Rorschach test. The Subject has in mind a well-defined idea, and would like to use it, but cannot find the appropriate words. As a rule the Subject goes into a state of obvious embarrassment, hems and haws, and not infrequently asks the Examiner if he does not know what he means. Occasionally, however, these Subjects

[74]Roland Kuhn, Über Maskendeutungen im Rorschach'schen Versuch, Basel, 1944.

manage to conceal their embarrassment quite cleverly. The disturbance is then only to be noticed in more or less striking circumlocutions, such as, "one of those birds that fly around at night," (bat); or "a kind of thing that lies on the floor," (animal skin), and the like. This difficulty in finding words is usually but not always an organic symptom. Caution is in order in respect to bilingual persons.

66. AGGRAVATION AND OTHER CLINICAL OBSERVATIONS. Aggravation is another clinical symptom that may develop in the test situation. Many Subjects complain continually about headaches, feelings of dizziness, flickering in front of their eyes; they may, however, by mild diversion and encouragement, quite easily be induced to associate. One sometimes hears remarks like "My eyes hurt so, I don't know if I can go on with it," or "Must I really dream about all these pictures tonight?" Naturally, this kind of conduct may now and then raise the question whether the test can be completed. Nevertheless, with the proper attitude on the part of the examiner, the protocol may in most cases still be gotten through. It is recommended that such complaints not be discussed. When it is a question of a surface exaggeration, it may be waved aside with a little joke, but if the contact is not very good, the effect may very easily be the opposite, intensifying the aggravation. Usually a quiet, non-interested attitude, "a gentle sternness," is in order. If this manner is adopted, the test can usually be completed. In some circumstances, this may require a certain amount of self-discipline. Such might be the case if the Subject should get up in the middle of the test, vomit in the nearby sink, and without any further request sit down and begin associating again. Another case in our experience was that of a woman in a psychogenic psychosis, who carried on in wildest fortissimo with the most frightful complaints and accusations; "they" had burnt out her intestines, her insides were one large eaten-out cavity, and so forth. But on the mild, friendly, but firm entreaty of the examiner, she produced quite normal and commonplace responses in a most indifferent tone of voice. These fluctuations occurred several times until the entire test was completed.

Other clinical symptoms which one has occasion to observe in administering a Rorschach test must naturally always be noted. Most important among these are the speech disturbances that appear spontaneously, such as stumbling over syllables, hesitations, stuttering and others. Extraordinary expressions of the eye also belong here, distrustful, penetrating, empty ways of looking; and likewise peculiar facial expressions, such as grimaces, tics and so forth; and stereotyped movements, tremor (of the finger, the eyelid, etc.). There is no rule prohibiting Rorschach examiners from keeping their eyes open.

67. THE COMPLEX-DETERMINED responses are so important in the diagnosis of neurosis that we shall postpone full discussion of them until we
reach that point.

The interpretation of any particular protocol is facilitated if the more
important complex-determined responses are emphasized not only in the
protocol itself (for example, by underlining the respective scoring formula
in red), but also if they are listed together in a summary at the end of the
special phenomena. It is advisable, at the end of such a list, also to mention
whether and how often "eyes" has been interpreted. This survey constitutes
the summary of all the raw material that has been gathered. It consists,
then, of the exact computations and also the special phenomena. Among
these the complex-determined associations are arranged according to
their types.

# PART THREE
# EVALUATION

## CHAPTER VI

# General Principles. The Psychogram

## BASIC PRINCIPLES OF EVALUATION

In CHAPTER 3, we pointed out that the Rorschach protocol with its types of succession and modes of approach may be understood as a "Gestalt," and the experienced interpreter does just that. American psychologists have once expressed this (in respect to the projective methods in general) as follows: "It seems that the competent clinician evaluates the test protocol not on the basis of isolated signs, but in terms of a configuration of complex indications—the total pattern plus past experience."[1]

The Rorschach test follows the same *basic rule* of evaluation as the older science of graphology and the more recent Szondi test. It is: *intuitive perception of the whole along with scientific control of the components* or, as Ludwig Klages has expressed it ("Grundlagen der Charakterkunde," p. 11), "One must see the totality before one can successfully begin to explore the parts." This is not at all "unscientific." Oriental philology, for example, presents exactly the same situation. In order to read and understand a Japanese sentence one must know each ideogrammatic Chinese character. However, nearly all of these have more than one meaning, and it is only the context which shows how they are to be read and understood. So one must survey the entire sentence in order to understand each individual character.

This is also the case in the interpretation of a Rorschach test protocol. Although specific factors do at times furnish rather important diagnostic clues, especially if they are quite rare, nevertheless *it is only the total picture that is decisive.* It is only in relation to the total picture that the details, which may have a variety of meanings, can be interpreted in terms of their diagnostic significance. This requires a highly complex Gestalt-like thinking, and is what makes the test so difficult to evaluate properly. (This fact probably accounts for most attempts at "improvement.") But it is this very feature that gives the instrument its superiority over many other diagnostic tools which can be applied in a more mechanical manner. One factor

[1]Henry P. David, Martin Orne and William Rabinowitz, Qualitative and quantitative Szondi diagnosis, Journ. of Proj. Tech., *17*: p. 77, 1953.

is related to and checks another, and in many cases it is possible to arrive at the same result by two or three different routes. Only when "all roads lead to Rome" can one feel relatively secure.

On closer scrutiny, the complex Rorschach test procedure breaks down into three phases:

1. An intuitive total impression derived from the raw protocol.
2. Scientific examination of the components.
3. The intuitive and at the same time critical synthesis of the whole.

Says Goethe: "One look into the book and two looks into life must give form to the spirit." It is by this process that the correct form of the Rorschach psychogram emerges: first we look at the living protocol, then we look into the "book" of statistics, empirical data and theory, and lastly we look at the living whole. It is essential always to combine the *static approach* of computation and examination of syndromes with a *dynamic* mode of thinking. The latter consists of combining all the conspicuous findings of the protocol and its content, with due regard to the sequence.

*First Phase.* The term "intuition," referring to the intuitive total impression given by the raw protocol, is used in August Forel's sense. It is a subliminal process of drawing conclusions, an "automatized and crystallized intelligence,"[2] thus a short-cut thinking made possible by the reservoir of previous experience.

*Second Phase.* The scientific scrutiny of the components involves a fully conscious, disciplined type of thinking. This is the only part of the interpretation that can be learned. The most important rule here is: *Always begin with the formal aspects, and only then turn to content!* This makes very good sense psychologically. In solving problems, the thought process remodels structures which derive from tensions, which in turn arise from an unsolved situation and result from the general striving toward the good Gestalt.[3] The smoothness of this process depends on the firmness of the structures. If one faces too great a profusion of unsolved structures, the tension may become so strong that the material is experienced as chaotic. We must then relate the raw data to a schematic framework in order to simplify the problem artificially. Only from this simplified scheme is it possible to proceed, and to achieve the "good Gestalt" of the final result.

As Morgenthaler's introduction to Rorschach's "Psychodiagnostics" (p. 232) very clearly shows, we can best integrate the two aspects of form and content if, after completing the computation and attending to the other raw data, we again go over the entire protocol "response by response and card

[2] August Forel, Der Hypnotismus oder die Suggestion und die Psychotherapie, Stuttgart, 1919, p. 29.
[3] See Richard Meili, Psychologische Diagnostik, Berne, 1951, pp. 52 ff.

by card." We inspect these in the light of the computation and the findings obtained so far, until finally all findings are seen in mutual relation.

It is advisable to proceed methodically at first. Even the best mind is not always immediately alerted to the task, and in the tight mesh of a reasonably productive protocol it is easy to overlook something which may modify the total evaluation of the case.

Finally, one must not forget to take into consideration the behavior of the Subject. Turning the plates around, for example, also has a diagnostic significance. Bochner and Halpern[4] give an excellent summary of the possible relevant behavior here. While the normal Subject will occasionally turn the plate in the course of his free associating, the dependent individual who lacks initiative does not turn the plate at all (and this, it is to be noted, *in spite* of being instructed that he is allowed to). The tense and restless individual turns it continuously and aimlessly, as does the hypomanic individual (due to inability to concentrate), and also the intellectually limited person (due to a dearth of ideas). Sudden and conspicuous rotating and turning usually stems from color or dark shock. The compulsive perfectionist turns every plate systematically. The so-called "edging" phenomenon, Beck[5] has observed only in schizophrenics.

*Third Phase.* The intuitive and critical synthesis of the whole into a psychogram again involves short-cut thinking. It aims at a characterological classification and a psychiatric diagnosis in which the peculiarities and finer features of the individual are to be worked out as clearly as possible. In cases in which sufficient material (the complex-determined responses) is available, a depth analysis may be arrived at, and this at times offers insight into the genesis of the person's present state. But notwithstanding the need for intuition and the importance of taking the peculiarities of the individual into account, the psychogram must follow a systematic plan.

## THE PSYCHOGRAM

1. *Two Varieties.* Basically, a Rorschach psychogram can be constructed in two ways. One may either use a *systematic* design, or one may start from "a certain angle," that is, from a particularly conspicuous and *central problem.* The latter technique requires greater experience, but even so, the approach should only be used if the case is particularly suitable for this kind of presentation. The systematic approach is especially advisable in cases where the material is to be used in statistical research. It lends itself much more readily to comparative study. On the other hand, because of

[4]Ruth Bochner and Florence Halpern, The Clinical Application of the Rorschach Test, New York, 1942, p. 78.
[5]Samuel J. Beck, Rorschach's Test, II, New York, 1949, p. 60.

its more "artistic" form and its more specific posing of the problem, the other method may be preferable for case work publication, and for purposes of more detailed discussion.

2. *Procedure in the systematic psychogram.* There is no universal rule which can be followed in making a systematic presentation. However, the very nature of the Rorschach test sets certain limits. A schedule for developing the Rorschach test psychogram, one that has in general proved very useful, will be presented as a *model.* How far this or any other plan is to be followed is, of course, a matter of taste.

The procedure is to start from intellectual functioning to affectivity and mood, then to proceed to any pathologic aspect (neurosis, psychosis). Finally, an attempt may be made to extract the constitutional matrix. In detail such a psychogram looks about like this:

*Schedule for Psychogram*

a) *Quantitative* evaluation of intelligence (*level* of the endowment); possible determination of oligophrenia (intellectual *deficiency*) or dementia (intellectual *impairment*); possibly intellectual *inhibition* due to affective forces (neurotic, depressive).

b) *Qualitative* evaluation of intelligence (*type* of intelligence), i.e., description of typical approach to intellectual tasks, and possibly special aptitudes (abstract, technical, artistic). The *phantasy* and its characteristics (creativity, originality, eccentricity, remoteness from practical everyday-life, dependability, trends to pseudologia, etc.).

c) *Affectivity,* i.e., structure and regulation (braking and inhibiting) of the affective life. *Social contact* is a closely related topic.

d) *General Attitudes,* such as ambition (quantitative or qualitative), need for self-assertion, inferiority feelings, aggressiveness, obstinacy, inhibition of aggression (bashfulness), and the like. These traits may also be treated under the headings: type of intelligence, affectivity, or a possible neurosis.

e) *Mood* (neutral, elated, depressed, anxiety, and so forth). Mood, too, can in some instances be better discussed in connection with intelligence or the affect.

f) *Neurotic Traits,* type, structure, and details.

g) *Possible Psychiatric Diagnosis* (oligophrenia, psychosis, organic defect or consequences, neurosis, psychopathy).

h) Possible *constitutional peculiarities* of the Subject, as far as they can be established.

i) Report of possible *complementary examinations,* e.g., other tests.

j) Possible *background material* concerning the *family, personal habits, conflicts,* etc., to aid the physician.

k) Possible remarks as to *prognosis* of the case and *indication* of certain psychotherapeutic techniques (analysis, suggestion, hypnosis, persuasion), to aid the physician.

l) *Suggestions for additional examinations* along certain lines (lumbar puncture, pneumo- or electroencephalogram, hyperventilation, and the like). It is preferable, of course, to discuss these matters verbally with the consulting, or the institutional, physician.

Perhaps it is not superfluous to note that any diagnosis, prognosis, or therapeutic indication derived from the Rorschach test must be understood as representing only the Rorschach test approach, regardless of whether the examiner is a psychologist or a physician. The results should therefore be communicated only to the physician who treats the case, and not to the patient. The final diagnosis is, of course, the responsibility of the physician.

Such a scheme as ours cannot, of course, be standardized in too much detail. The individual factors of a psychological state are so intimately related to one another in so many ways that they cannot always be separated from one another. When translated into concrete patterns, many variations of the above outline may emerge. It can therefore be considered only a very crude and tentative directive scheme.

It is important never to omit a detailed documentation of one's conclusions. This is best done by enumerating in parentheses the test factors on which the conclusions are based, quantitative as well as other data are included. With reference to the main diagnosis or diagnoses, the entire Rorschach syndrome is to be cited in parentheses. Current abbreviations are naturally to be used here. It implies lack of respect to a great number of our colleagues who are acquainted with the Rorschach test (physicians, psychologists) and who may see the psychogram, to treat them like untrained laymen. The entire protocol need not necessarily be produced for purposes of the hospital chart or the practicing neurologist or psychiatrist. However, the results of the computation, other raw data (the "special phenomena"), as well as the complex-determined responses arranged in groups, must always precede the psychogram because we refer to those data in the documentation.

Oberholzer also recommends the practice of putting the reasoning in parentheses immediately after the conclusions. He writes[6] "I put in parentheses references to the test findings from which a statement was drawn. The flow of characterization is inevitably disturbed by this procedure, but it is the only one by which such references can be made briefly."

3. *Multidimensional Diagnostics.* The question of so-called multidimensional diagnostics for psychiatric purposes is an issue which is pertinent here. We must, therefore, go into it to some extent. The impulse in this direction as well as the term derive from Kretschmer who as early as 1919[7] urged that we enlarge the pathologic picture into a "picture of the life and family" of the individual. Only by means of personality research could this plan be psychologically realized. "We exchange one key, 'brain and soul,' for

---

[6]Emil Oberholzer in Cora Du Bois, The People of Alor, Minneapolis, 1944, p. 609.
[7]Ernst Kretschmer, Gedanken über die Fortentwicklung der psychiatrischen Systematik, Zeitschr. f. d. ges. Neur. und Psychiatrie, Vol. 48, 1919, pp. 370-377.

the other of 'character and experience.' " Because of the peculiarity of the psychologic approach, "the *science of character* arises as a second and independent discipline alongside of the science of constitutional factors." The endogenic and the psychogenic pictures of pathology "are not situated side by side but are superimposed on each other. The characterological pattern lies above the constitutional, but their limits are not identical. . . . What we are striving for here is *not a mixed diagnosis but a diagnosis at various levels.*"

Kretschmer explains what he has in mind by the following example: "We would diagnose: litigation mania (not 'pseudo' litigation mania) as existing in a constitutionally hypomanic matrix; hysterical reaction in a catatonic matrix (not 'hysteria with misleading catatonic- like symptoms') ; or conversely schizophrenia with features of sensitivity; constitutional depression with compulsive tendencies, and so on. We are looking for just that which previous diagnostic procedures have as a matter of principle avoided: the coincidence of different pathogenic mechanisms in a pathological picture" (op. cit. p. 375).

According to Kretschmer, differential diagnosis should "only be made between disease types at the same level," for instance, between circular and schizophrenic psychosis but not "between constitutional and characterological forms of disorder, e.g., not basically between schizophrenia and hysteria, between depression and sensitive delusion of reference." However, it is obvious that even constitutions can be of mixed types.

The multidimensional diagnosis has now long been accepted and is the customary one in most modern clinics today, only the diagnostic schemes are not everywhere the same. There are differences, too, in the concepts of levels and dimensions. It is probably best to proceed "from the surface down." We may begin by describing the illness *symptomatically* (e.g., psychosis, schizophrenia, neurosis anxiosa, insufficientia depressiva, etc.). The second step would be to classify it as far as possible from an *etiological* point of view (endogenous, psychogenic, post-infectious, traumatic and others). Finally we may try to develop the *constitutional type* (possibly mixed type), out of which the condition has developed. The etiological classification can usually be omitted where we are dealing with one of the major endogenic psychoses and with the neuroses, insofar as these latter are primarily conceived of as psychogenic, though of course based on constitutional factors. In other pathological states, etiology may not be omitted. The developing of the constitutional type depends naturally on the type system we are using (Kretschmer, Ewald, Sjöbring, Sheldon), and whether one of the usual classificatory systems of psychopathy (Kraepelin, Ewald, Kretschmer, Kahn, Kurt Schneider) is used, which might imply an additional constitutional type. We shall generally follow Kretschmer's system as supplemented by Strömgren (ixothymy). Thus we shall say, for example, manic depressive psychosis in a schizoid personality, neurosis hysteroides in a cyclothymic personality, organic affective insufficiency (incontinence) in an ixothymic-schizothymic mixed constitution, insufficientia (or pseudo-psychopathy) ixophrenica traumatica, depressio mentis (or insufficientia depressiva) psychogenica in post-traumatic defect with subvalid personality, etc.

More than any other psychological instrument, the Rorschach test serves in the construction of multidimensional diagnoses. To use it, it is therefore necessary to know all the clinical facts and symptoms pertaining to the patient's case as well as to his entire life situation. Only against the background of these facts can the findings of the Rorschach test be seen in their true light and in proper relief.

For this purpose, it is best to proceed stage by stage from the surface down, just as is done in arriving at a clinical diagnosis. After a purely descriptive presentation of the most important *character traits* (including displacement of mood, anxiety, etc., as above indicated) the first of the situational factors to be elaborated are the *psychogenic* mechanisms (i.e., the reactive ones). Insofar as neurotic mechanisms are concerned, the type of neurosis and its structure (possibly mixed type) should be delineated. Particular trends in the development of the neurosis are to be elaborated insofar as the test indicates them (e.g., identification with an unduly harsh mother). If *external somatic* factors are present (intoxication, infections, traumata, possibly with organic mental deficiency), it is well to make them the point of departure, especially if they dominate the picture, that is, if they are of a pathogenic nature. If, however, they are only contributory (pathoplastic), they had best be discussed after the psychogenic factors. In any case, the mutual interaction of both external factors must be discussed. Thus one might say: traumatic encephalopathy with strong neurotic trends; or, traumatic sequelae with particular neurotic traits of this or that kind; or hysteroid neurosis with pronounced lability of affect due to additional affective incontinence on organic basis (commotio antea), and so forth.

The possible *endogenous* factors are next to be reported (schizophrenic, circular and epileptic), insofar as there is suspicion of a regular psychosis (everything else is to be discussed with reference to constitution).

Finally, the constitutional basis is to be elaborated as far as possible; this in turn may also be a mixture of different components (schizoid, cycloid, ixoid components).

Lastly comes the interaction of the various levels. Here the intensification of a certain symptom or character trait or, conversely, the intensification of a conflict, is to be high-lighted. This kind of intensification of traits would, for example, be illustrated by a psychogenic depression developing in a cycloid temperament; or a neurotically hypochondriacal conflict over masturbation appearing in a schizoid personality, in which case an increased readiness to hypochondriacal reactions is constitutionally present. Examples of conflict intensifications are: economic difficulties in an ixothymic father with several children, who in consequence of his ixothymic good nature and his strong family ties, thinks first of his wife and children, and so is always himself personally neglected. Similarly, a moral conflict (e.g., infidelity) will be much more intensely experienced by an ixothymic personality because of the stronger affective clinging to the "legal" sexual partner. A disturbance in his sexual potency can only be understood on the basis of the joint operation of psychogenic and constitutional factors.

All this can, of course, be developed only if the test offers the requisite raw data, which is by no means always the case. However, it is always necessary to utilize *all* the raw data. *Nothing may remain unused.* Therein lies the surest guarantee against faulty diagnoses. The entire puzzle must be resolved.

Let us emphasize once more that the construction of such multidimensional diagnosis requires considerable knowledge of the neuroses, of constitutional and hereditary processes in relation to the psychiatric point of view, and of clinical psychiatry. This can never be expected as a matter of course from a clerk or even a kindergarten teacher, however highly trained.

# CHAPTER VII

# Intelligence

## QUANTITATIVE EVALUATION

### WHAT IS INTELLIGENCE

THE QUESTION OF what is "intelligence" has for decades been a matter of dispute among psychologists, and still is. As Kuhn[1] has noted, not without an undertone of humor, Bleuler headed one of the chapters of his text book " 'The' Intelligence," obviously to accent the fact that there are varieties of intelligence. Rorschach, however, writes "The 'Intelligence,' " setting the word itself in quotation marks, as though to question the meaningfulness of the entire concept. This, however, did not prevent him from entering into a thorough discussion of the diagnosis of intelligence. From a practical standpoint we will adopt Terman's position that it is not important to know what intelligence is, so long as we can determine and measure it. And that is possible. As a matter of fact we use electric lights even though theoretical physicists continue to argue about the nature of electricity.

But just as it would have been impossible to invent the electric bulb without first thinking about what electricity is, so students of applied psychology cannot completely avoid dealing with theoretical problems of intelligence. Thus a few remarks about the problem of intelligence will be in order for purposes of orientation, the more so as the Rorschach test occupies a special position in the measurement of intelligence.

1. GENERAL CONSIDERATIONS. According to William Stern's concept, which still has many followers today, intelligence may be regarded as the general ability to adjust and solve new demands and life situations by means of thought processes. Porteus'[2] definition would be a variation of this concept: in his view, intelligence is the ability to react to a sequence of relevant stimuli. This means a stimulus "to which it is biologically advantageous for the animal to respond." This holds good for man, too. It is clear that Porteus' definition leaves much more room for a number of different kinds of intelligence. Another variation of this concept of intelligence as a general ability, one deriving from philosophical Positivism, places the emphasis

[1] Roland Kuhn, Über Rorschach's Psychologie und die psychologischen Grundlagen des Formdeutversuches, in "Psychiatrie under Rorschach'scher Formdeutversuch," Zürich 1944, p. 39.
[2] Stanley D. Porteus, The Maze Test and Mental Differences, New Jersey, 1933, pp. 11 and 15.

on the anticipation of experience by means of an "experiment in thought" (using Baudouin's phrase). Thus Beck defines the "degree of intelligence" as the "degree of ability to predict experience."[3] This would correspond to the well-known phrase of Auguste Compte: "Savoir pour prévoir, prévoir pour prévenir."

C. Spearman has attempted to master the pecularities and complications involved in the problem of intelligence in a different way.[4] In his Two-Factor theory he isolates from a number of specific factors (s-factors), a general factor (factor g). By means of factor analysis, this general intelligence factor can be derived from a number of special tasks and their solution. Spearman later extended his theory so as to split this general factor into several components, from which he distinguished the factors p (perseveration), o (oscillation), and w (will). (These can easily be analyzed out in the Rorschach test: p through A per cent, Orig per cent and perseveration; o through A per cent, Orig per cent, and the distribution of M and of color responses; and w through G and sequence.)

Thorndike[5] started out with a theory which, in striking contrast to Stern and Spearman, completely rejected a common factor. He did not allow for any common elements in the various intellectual functions, and emphasized their relative independence. His division into abstract, concrete and social intelligence arose out of this multifactor theory. We shall deal with this later on. In later years he eventually approached Spearman's point of view. With the remark that intelligence is naturally dependent on nature and nurture, he agreed in effect that Spearman had got closer to the nature factor (Anastasi, op. cit. p. 303). In his main work, "The Measurement of Intelligence" (1926), he finally reached a point of view which more closely resembles that of Spearman. According to this quantity hypothesis of his, Thorndike sees the essence of higher intelligence as "a larger number of connections of the same sort" (meaning "physiological connections"). The total possible number of such physiological connections within an individual as determined by his native capacity, is called C. This is a reappearance of the factor g.

Eugen Bleuler also uses this quantity hypothesis in his textbook[6] when he

[3]Samuel J. Beck, Rorschach's Test, II. A Variety of Personality Pictures, New York, 1945, p. 2.

[4]C. Spearman, "General Intelligence," Objectively Determined and Measured, American Journal of Psychology, Vol. 15, 1904, pp. 201-293, as cited by Anne Anastasi, Differential Psychology, New York, 1937 pp. 299 ff.

[5]E. L. Thorndike, W. Lay and P. R. Dean, The Relation of Accuracy in Sensory Discrimination to General Intelligence, American Journal of Psychology, vol. 20, 1909, pp. 364-369. (As cited by Anastasi.)

[6]Eugen Bleuler, Lehrbuch der Psychiatrie, Berlin 1937, p. 10.

conjectures that intellectual achievements are "primarily a function of the number of possible associations."

The holistic concepts of modern experimental psychology, especially the Gestalt theory, have by no means simplified the problem. Richard Meili,[7] on the basis of the researches of Wolfgang Köhler, Max Wertheimer, and Kurt Lewin, conceives of acts of intelligence as changes in the formation of structures. These structures result from tensions produced by unsolved situations as a consequence of the general tendency to strive toward the "good Gestalt." In this sense "structure" means an "integration of several parts in which the meaning of each part is co-determined by each other part as well as by the whole" (Meili, p. 52).

2. THE FORMAL FACTORS OF INTELLIGENCE. From a purely practical point of view, however, it is necessary to extract the various aspects of intelligence on a theoretical basis. Thorndike differentiates four: level, range, area, and speed.

Meili[8] differentiates the following formal factors of intelligence: 1. Intellectual sensibility or capacity to make fine distinctions, the ability to perceive subtleties; 2. Complexity, the simplicity or complexity of structure, which depends primarily on maturity, and which is measured by the Binet-Simon test; 3. Unity, the tendency to think in terms of an over-all view or in terms of details; 4. Firmness of structures, to which intellectual mobility and originality are inversely related. 5. Intensity of inner stresses and, consequently, speed of thinking. This last factor is practically identical with attention. Meili[9] later reduced the number of intellectual factors to four. He now distinguishes between: 1. The factor of *complexity;* 2. The factor of *plasticity* (a greater or lesser capacity for restructuring); 3. The factor of *wholeness* (the integration of hitherto separate parts), and 4. The factor of *fluidity* (the term is derived from Lewin and Cattell), i.e., "the easy transition from one idea to another."

3. CAPACITY AND ACHIEVEMENT. As we understand it in every day life, intelligence is the available intellectual achievement potential. This, of course, depends primarily on the native endowment, but is not identical with it. Achievement potential is a product of endowment plus its utilization or exercise (education). Porteus (op. cit. p. 8) compares intelligence with the volume of a cylinder, with the height corresponding to native endowment and the diameter to acquired knowledge. The totality of in-

[7]Richard Meili, Psychologische Diagnostik, 2 ed. Berne, 1951, pp. 51-60.
[8]Op. cit. pp. 41-43 and 67 (1 ed. Schaffhausen, 1937).
[9]Richard Meili, Grundlegende Eigenschaften der Intelligenz, Schweizerische Zeitschrift für Psychologie, Vol. 2, 1944, pp. 166-175 and 265-271.

tellectual endowment is usually called *capacity*. Thus capacity is not identical with intelligence. Two people with identical capacity may show considerable difference in intelligence, depending on the education each enjoyed, especially during childhood. Intelligence, however, can also function at a lower level than capacity, namely, whenever the achievement potential has been reduced through an organic (dementia) or neurotic process (affective inhibition of thought).

Strictly speaking, a distinction must even be made between achievement potential and achievement. Even with his achievement potential intact, a person may not always produce the same level of achievement in all situations. The actual intellectual achievement depends on a number of easily modifiable factors (sleep, nutrition, climate, interests, mood, etc.), while the achievement potential does not change from day to day. For the sake of simplicity, however, these minor fluctuations will be disregarded in the following pages. Thus, whenever achievement is mentioned, we shall usually be referring to achievement potential.

*Capacity and achievement do not usually coincide.* Most people perform below their capacity because their achievement potential has been reduced due to neurotic causes (frequently also because of depression). From the point of view of native endowment, the intellectual level of a population should distribute itself in accordance with the Gaussian curve, that is, there should be about as many who are above the average as below. It was therefore very surprising when intelligence examinations of 1,700,000 American soldiers in the First World War by means of the "army tests" uncovered a marked skewing of the curve to the left: 10 per cent had a mental age of 10 years or below, 15 per cent a M.A. of 10 to 11 years, 20 per cent a M.A. of 11 to 12 years, and the average 25 per cent was 13 to 14 years. But only 16.5 per cent had a mental age of 15 to 16 years, and only 9 per cent a M.A. of 16 to 17 years, and only 4.5 per cent a M.A. of 18 to 19 years. Porteus justly remarks (op. cit. p. 45) that the 12 year limit for mental deficiency according to Binet-Simon, as well as the entire intelligence quotient definition of mental deficiency, has been reduced to absurdity as a result of this examination of recruits. It was then that the first signs of anxiety arose over the future of democracy—and rightly so. One cannot rely on the "sound common sense" of the masses.[10] According to more recent experiences, this shift of the Gaussian curve to the left is due much less to the ability of man, nor is it exclusively (although partly) a result of the one-sidedness of the tests used (overemphasis on theoretical intelligence), but is caused primarily by the enormously widespread affective in-

[10]See also Eden and Cedar Paul, Creative Revolution, and later, Erich Fromm, The Fear of Freedom.

hibition of thinking. The late Austrian pediatrician Joseph K. Friedjung liked to formulate the problem in his lectures with a quotation from Alexandre Dumas: "One meets so many bright children, but so many stupid adults." How come?

The most important reason for this widespread affective thinking inhibition is of course the colossal amount of seriously faulty education. Siegfried Bernfeld characterized parents, unfortunately quite correctly, as follows: "To be sure, they have a vocation, but not to bring up children."[11] One of the major faults of adults is the inconsistency in their handling of the child's effort to form judgments. They are pleased by independent thinking in the child and encourage it "as long as that thinking does not lead him to question sexual and religious matters, or the authority of the adults."[12] The result is the development in a great many children of a general thinking inhibition, or as Ferenczi says, "a kind of affective mental deficiency." Then, too, the need for punishment, itself a fruit of faulty education, may produce intellectual inhibitions.[13]

THE SPECIFIC CONTRIBUTION OF THE RORSCHACH TEST TO THE PROBLEM OF THE MEASUREMENT OF INTELLIGENCE.

The Rorschach is *not* a "test of intelligence." For quantitative determination of intelligence, especially for comparative purposes, the following tests are recommended: for children and adolescents, Terman's adaptation (Stanford Revision) of the Binet-Simon test, possibly in combination with the Porteus Maze test, or (especially for group testing) Meili's analytical intelligence test; for adults the Wechsler-Bellevue Scale is preferable.

The Rorschach test does not yield an intelligence quotient. It permits an appraisal only. In spite of this it is, in certain respects, superior to most intelligence tests. Rorschach claims (and rightly so) that his test presents "an intelligence test almost completely independent of previous knowledge, memory, practise and degree of education" (p. 180). In addition, the Rorschach test has the positive advantage that it is almost entirely independent of verbal understanding, and that at the same time it offers a qualitative picture of the intelligence. Ernst Schneider in a comparative research project[14] actually demonstrated that the Rorschach test as an intelligence examination is equal to the other techniques investigated (Bobertag-Hylla, Döring, Binet-Simon, and ratings given by school teachers). Further-

[11]Siegfried Bernfeld, Sisyphos oder die Grenzen der Erziehung, Wien, 1925, p. 17.
[12]S. Ferenczi, Populäre Vorträge über Psychoanalyse, Wien, 1922, pp. 181/182.
[13]Hans Zulliger, Schwierige Kinder, Berne, 1935, p. 74.
[14]Ernst Schneider, Die Bedeutung des Rorschach'schen Formdeutversuches zur Ermittlung intellektuell gehemmter Schüler, Zeitschr. f. angew. Psychologie, Vol. 32, 1929, p. 160.

more, it was able "to take into consideration phenomena of inhibition" and to furnish certain qualitative information (type and direction of endowment).

Beck[15] emphasizes the following three advantages offered by the Rorschach test as an instrument for the measurement of intelligence: 1. The results are "free from influence of schooling"; 2. The test material is objective and simple in its presentation; 3. The same material can be applied to all levels of intelligence.

Another advantage, which at first glance looks like a disadvantage, is the fact that all Rorschach factors simultaneously depend on intelligence and affectivity, even though to different degrees. But this is just what happens in reality.[16] This apparent disadvantage becomes, in actual practice, the most important advantage of the Rorschach test for measuring intelligence. The reason is as follows:

If, as we have seen, capacity and achievement so greatly deviate from each other in practice, it is important to determine capacity directly. The ideal examination of capacity has so far not been achieved. Even the Rorschach test does not achieve this, but it approaches it very closely. It cannot measure capacity in and of itself, but it can demonstrate that there is a difference between capacity and efficiency, and thus it shows the presence of a so-called inhibition of intelligence, an affective restriction of thinking and achievement.[17] (For the time being we are not concerned with the relatively rare cases of dementia.) The amount of the discrepancy can, to be sure, only be approximated, and even that cannot always be done. (There is usually a tendency to underestimate the difference.)

In *this* respect, therefore, the Rorschach test occupies a special position among intelligence measuring tools. That it also gives us a qualitative diagnosis of intelligence is a feature which it has in common with a few other specific intelligence test instruments which only investigate efficiency (Meili's analytic intelligence test, Wechsler's Bellevue scale). More precisely, with the Rorschach it is possible to determine whether reduced efficiency is due to *lack* of intelligence (genuine oligophrenia), an intelligence *defect* (dementia), or *inhibition* of intelligence (pseudo-deficiency).

Classical psychiatry, so far, has on the whole neglected this area. (However, there are numerous papers on the topic in psychoanalytic literature, those, for instance by Sigmund Freud, Paul Federn, Hans Zulliger, K.

[15]Samuel J. Beck, The Rorschach Test and Personality Diagnosis I. Feeble-minded, American Journal of Psychiatry X, 1930, p. 48.

[16]Manfred Bleuler, Der Rorschach-Versuch als Unterscheidungsmittel von Konstitution under Prozess; Zeitsch. f. d. ges. Neurologie und Psychiatrie, Vol. 151, 1934, pp. 572-573.

[17]See also Klopfer and Kelley, The Rorschach Technique, New York, 1942, p. 266.

Landauer, Alfhild Tamm.) The Norwegian psychiatrist Nic Hoel[18] has referred to these matters in an excellent paper (published in Norwegian). She writes, "I do not deny at all that hereditary oligophrenia exists, but I believe that more extended cooperation with psychologists, experimental physiologists and psychotherapists will increase the number of cases of pseudo-oligophrenia." Nic Hoel herself has worked with a psychologist, Åse Gruda Skard. She summarizes the experience gained from this collaboration and states at the end of her paper: "A valuable diagnosis can only be achieved by comparing Binet-Simon results with those in the Rorschach, with anamnesis, with family history, and with what we know about the structure of the neuroses and the dynamic effects of education and of the milieu."

THE TECHNIQUE OF QUANTITATIVE EVALUATION OF INTELLIGENCE BY MEANS OF THE RORSCHACH TEST

1. NORMAL INTELLIGENCE (refer to the summary in "Psychodiagnostics," p. 256):

The intelligence picture of normal and above normal individuals contains the following Rorschach factors: a high F+ per cent; orderly sequence; a large number of W; approach type W, W-D, or W-D-Dd (so-called "rich" approach); low A per cent; medium P per cent; medium Orig per cent; and a few M.

a. *F+ per cent* should optimally be 80 to 95. The maximum occurs only in pedants, depressives or melancholics. This factor presupposes sharp engrams, thus good observational capacity, good recall capacity, as well as ability to concentrate, good attention and persistence. In terms of Meili's factors, it represents partly sensibility (fineness of differentiation) and partly intensity of inner stress.

b. *Sequence* should be "optimally rigid," i.e., orderly. Rigid sequence again is symptomatic of pedants and compulsives. Very loose and confused sequence is symptomatic of manic and schizophrenic individuals. This factor depends on the stabilizing of the attention and on the habitually logical disciplining and precision of the thought processes. Sequence (due to capacity for attention) is also related to Meili's intensity factor.

Both these factors, F+ per cent and sequence, are acquired and conscious functions which can be modified and increased to a certain degree. The other intelligence factors (with exception of the Approach) are less susceptible to training and practice.

c. *W* should be plentiful, at least 7 to 10, or more. They are of positive

18Nic Hoel, Pseudodebilitet, Svenska Läkartidningen, Vol. 35, 1938, pp. 1521-1531.

value only if they are at the same time F+ or M+ (W+). They, too, presuppose clear engrams and good recall capacity besides the ability to take the whole view (perception of wholes). In addition, W is also related to a factor of will. It is an index to the affective charge and the dispositional drive for achievement found in individuals ambitious for high quality performance as well as in expansive and hypomanic persons. In depressives and pedants, W is usually limited. Here Meili's intensity factor is clearly perceptible, but of even more importance is his conception of "unity," his "wholeness." However, the factor of complexity is also involved.

d. The *approach type* of the intelligent individual should be "rich," i.e., have a certain number of W. To what extent D and Dd play a role, in addition to W, is more a question of the quality of intelligence (more about this later). Meili's "sensibility" requires a few Dd, his "detail thinking" requires numerous D. Here, too, attention plays a part. A well distributed approach type, according to Rorschach, is an indication of "sound common sense."

e. The *A per cent* should be low, that is, not over 50 per cent in younger subjects. However, it is to be borne in mind that the A per cent increases with age. Individuals over 40 years of age seldom produce less than 50 per cent, and subjects over 50 years of age seldom less than 60 per cent. The size of the A per cent is a direct function of Meili's "firmness of structure," i.e., it bears an *inverse* relationship to the plasticity of the associations (fluidity), the modifiability of established attitudes or sets, and the variability of the thinking. Thus manics show a minimum, depressives a maximum of this quality.

f. In intelligent individuals we find a medium *P per cent* (20-25 per cent, children 10-15 per cent), or even lower than medium. This, too, is an expression of "common sense," an intellectual adjustment to the community and the environment. P per cent is also directly proportional to structural firmness.

g. *Orig per cent* is, so to speak, the counterpart of A per cent. With intelligent individuals it should be medium, since too high an Orig per cent smacks of shop talk or remoteness from practical everyday-life. The optimal limits are around 50 per cent. The variety of content is also important. Orig per cent is an indication of a certain number of highly individualized engrams, the capacity for original associations. It corresponds to Meili's structural lability (originality), the factor of plasticity.

h. *The M factor* is finally the spice of the whole matter. Non-neurotic or non-depressive intelligent individuals always produce some M. This factor is directly proportional to W and to Orig per cent and is inversely proportional to A per cent. M specifically represents creative capacity, artistic inspiration or religious experience. Thus it is found highest in individuals of inventive imagination and lowest in dry, matter-of-fact persons, and in some depressives. Among Meili's factors, "complexity" comes closest to it. (However this is more specifically expressed in the combinatory W.) Individuals with an essentially reproductive type of intelligence yield fewer M than those with the productive kind.

In cases in which there is no neurotic M reduction, Beck's and Klopfer's rules[19] gives the approximate picture: 0-1 M in low intelligence (barely average to average) ; 2-5 M in medium intelligence (good average to somewhat above average) ; 5 and more M in high and very high intelligence.

i. In addition to these main factors, a number of others are of importance. The *reaction time,* taken together with number of responses, F+ per cent and W+, yields the "speed factor" (Meili's intensity). *Type of W* is also significant, whether it is popular or original, simple or constructed from various parts. The relation of H and Hd should be H > Hd. In limited intelligence or depression this is reversed. Finally, the *variety of content* (and of the originals) is significant even for the quantitative evaluation of intelligence, although primarily on the qualitative side. Klopfer's observation[20] is no doubt correct that in reasonably high intelligence with its broad interests at least 25 per cent of the responses are usually not H, Hd, A or Ad. In individuals of lower endowment, on the other hand, these four categories usually comprise more than 75 per cent of all responses. But it should be noted that in neurotic inhibition of intelligence (especially in neurotic depression), A per cent as well as Hd may be substantially increased! The reverse of the symptom is thus no proof of low intelligence.

In general, one had best be rather careful in diagnosing the intelligence of strongly religious personalities quantitatively. The protocols of such subjects usually contain a relatively high number of M responses, the religious content of which may serve both as a guidepost and a warning. The total impression in such cases may sometimes be more favorable regarding formal .intelligence than is the actual fact. The other factors (F+ per cent, W+, A per cent) must be given more weight in such instances (Orig per cent may also be unreliable here). This is one of the rare situations in which one tends to overrate the intellectual level.

2. SUBNORMAL INTELLIGENCE LEVEL. If the Subject's intelligence level is below average, three possibilities are to be considered: inhibition of intelligence, lack of intelligence, or defective intelligence.

[19]Klopfer and Kelley, op. cit. p. 268.
[20]Klopfer and Kelley, op. cit. p. 272.

a. *Inhibition of intelligence* is affective inhibition of the thought processes. This is as good a proof as one could wish of the close tie-up between the affective life and intelligence. *Neurotic* and *depressive* inhibition of intelligence are to be differentiated. The depressive inhibition of the thinking process is an inhibition in the more literal clinical sense, a slowing down and impoverishment resulting from the general inhibitory effects of the depression (this also refers to the motor functions). Unless the depression is chronic, these inhibitions may be very transitory and may disappear from one day to the next. Neurotic intellectual inhibitions, on the other hand, are more lasting and are generally not modified without psychotherapeutic treatment. They very often tie in with milder depressive inhibitions since many neuroses comprise chronic depressive moods.

It is to be noted that intellectual inhibitions do not necessarily result in below average achievement potentials. Most intellectual inhibitions are found even in individuals of normal or high intelligence whose capacity could classify them as intellectually above average or even higher. Whereas the individual of high average or superior intelligence still attains normal achievements, an inhibition in the barely average person makes for a condition of pseudo-deficiency.

The principle on which the Rorschach diagnosis of intellectual inhibitions is based is simple. It is derived from a striking *incongruence in the intelligence factors of the test.* In cases of clear pseudo-deficiency, one is reminded of the words of the poet Uhland: "*One* tall column still bears witness to past magnificence." For example, there may be particularly good originals, not found in cases of genuine deficiency, or a relatively large number of W+ or M+.

(i) *Neurotic intellectual inhibitions* can be recognized from clear neurotic symptoms which are present (color and dark shock, unstable color values, Do and other indicators of anxiety, blocking at sexual symbols, etc.), in addition to definite reduction in some intelligence indicators together with a high level of quality in other such factors. A very frequent type of neurotic intelligence inhibition is a large number of poor anatomy responses, as well as a number of Do responses (hypochondriacal anxiety). Here F+ per cent may be reduced considerably. If, in addition to this, W is reduced and A per cent is increased owing to a psychogenic depression, then the original intellectual endowment can be recognized only in the M and Orig responses. Similarly, M and Orig may be lost, while a relatively large number of W+ remain in addition to a possibly not too high A per cent. Almost all combinations and variations occur, and it may be fascinating to derive the structure of the neurosis and its impact on the Subject's intellectual functioning from the particular discrepancies between these factors.

The level of the original capacity however, can in many cases be appraised only with great difficulty.

(ii) *Depressive intellectual inhibition* produces a corresponding picture. In it, however, the depression will be more prominent than the neurosis. But the depressive syndrome (in the numerous psychogenic depressions) is usually incomplete in these cases. The specific condition of the individual may be determined from the unique pattern of reduction of certain intelligence indicators along with the presence of certain depressive symptoms (while other factors remain intact).

In depressive reduction of achievement, indefinite F– are frequently found. Where they are not present we usually find a specific inhibition in productivity, indicated by a reduction of M and W responses, high A per cent, with high F+ per cent. This then is less a qualitative than a quantitative inhibition of efficiency, a *working* inhibition, often misunderstood as "laziness." But the depressive inhibition of productivity is in a certain sense a qualitative change, too, in that such patients seem dry, monotonous and sterile. However, the quantitative inhibition of productivity, the disinclination to work, is the central feature of the disturbance.

It is usually easy to determine when an intellectual inhibition is a depressive one. However, greatest care must be exercised in the quantitative assessment of intelligence, if there are indications of depression. Since W and Orig, and sometimes M, too, are seriously reduced, one may in most of these cases (i.e., by means of F+ per cent) determine that the Subject originally possessed normal intelligence, but it is usually very difficult to estimate his real capacity correctly. The situation is thus quite similar to what it is in neurotic inhibitions of intelligence. Even with specific intelligence tests, correct results cannot be obtained from depressed individuals. In psychiatric clinics and hospitals one frequently finds case histories of patients whose intelligence quotients have risen substantially. It can be then determined that the initial low results were misleading because they were results of examinations given while the patient was depressed.

b. *Lack of intelligence (Oligophrenia).*

(i) *Concerning the psychology of mental deficiency.* The difference between the mental defective and the normal individual is primarily a lack of surveying, anticipating and planning. The defective individual can only understand that which is immediately at hand, the concrete here and now. Anything that requires looking ahead or complex ideation can be carried out only under supervision.

As a result, the defective is suggestible in his social attitudes; he is impulsive, inconsistent and undependable. Socially he thus depends on the guidance of others. On the other hand, the notion of hypersensitivity and of excessive capacity for feeling on the part of defectives is a myth. These are psychopathic traits which are found in a small number of defective individuals, in the same way that difficulty in social conformity and adjustment is found in others. "Pure" mental deficiency does not imply emotional, social or moral difficulties of adjustment.[21]

(ii) *Rorschach test diagnosis of mental deficiency*. All these traits and sub-groups of mental deficiency are also found in Rorschach test research on the subject. Rorschach himself only included 12 morons and imbeciles in his study. Our present knowledge of Rorschach test patterns in the mentally deficient is based mainly on the work of Pfister,[22] Zulliger,[23] and Beck.[24] On the whole they show good agreement. The following can be deduced from their work.

Interpretation awareness is usually reduced or completely lacking in the mentally deficient. The number of responses does not show any definite tendency. It may vary from above to below the average. Response time is usually considerably increased. Pfister found 60-70 minutes for 15-25 responses. F+ per cent, of course, is low, 0-60. Morons range between 45-60, imbeciles between 0-45 (Beck). A per cent is high 70-100 according to Rorschach, 60-100 according to Beck, around 60 according to Pfister. P per cent is usually reduced, but varies with social conformity. In individuals who are very well adjusted socially it approaches the average level; with poorly adjusted and anti-social individuals it is especially low (Beck). Orig per cent (poor Orig) is fairly high, 30-40 per cent in morons, 40-70 in imbeciles, according to Beck. The mentally deficient usually produce very few W+, and these are of the lazy and most common types (inability to synthesize). Pfister and Beck agree in finding 0-3 W+, Beck in exceptional cases up to 5 (with 3 as an average). Anything beyond that is practically always of poor form and frequently DW or even DdW (Zulliger). Dd is correspondingly increased and usually selected from the inner and outer periphery of the blot (Zulliger). The approach is usually D–Dd (Rorschach, Beck). In some cases, many Do responses appear, as observed by Rorschach (in them the F+ per cent usually yields too favorable a picture!), how-

[21]See also: Stanley D. Porteus, The Maze Test and Mental Differences, New Jersey, 1933, pp. 33-37.
[22]Oskar Pfister, Ergebnisse des Rorschach'schen Versuches bei Oligophrenia. Allgem. Zeitschr. f. Psychiatrie, Vol. 82, 1925, pp. 198-223.
[23]Hans Zulliger, Jugendliche Diebe im Rorschach-Formdeutversuch, Bern, 1938, p. 136.
[24]Samuel J. Beck, The Rorschach Test and Personality Diagnosis, I. The Feeble-Minded. American Journal of Psychiatry, X, 1930, pp. 19-52 and: The Rorschach Test as Applied to a Feeble-Minded Group. Arch. Psychol., Vol. 136, 1932, p. 84.

ever, this is not the rule (Pfister, Zulliger). Beck found this in only 29 per cent of his cases. Sequence is usually orderly, but sometimes loose.

It is very important to note that the mentally deficient as a rule have no or only very few M, generally no more than one. On this point there is a close agreement between Rorschach and all later investigators. Where morons do respond with M, it is usually the popular M of card III, in some few instances the popular M of card II. Thus, wherever there is a good M response, for instance to card IV, and it is the only M, we may seriously doubt whether the deficiency is genuine.

Color responses differ according to temperament. Torpid defectives (and they are the majority) do not produce many color responses according to Pfister; the excitable ones, on the other hand, tend to have more. Beck found a general average of 3.7. Thus, as a result of the lack of M, the experience balance is extratensive, often egocentrically extratensive. Color naming (due to associational poverty) is not unusual. According to Pfister, 70-80 per cent of all pure C in the mentally deficient is color naming. This is found chiefly in imbeciles and in idiots, but occasionally also in morons. It should be noted that the symptomatic meaning of the various categories of color is unreliable in the mentally deficient (Pfister).

Color shock is probably not found in *simple* mental deficiency. At any rate, Rorschach, Zulliger and Pfister deny it. However, cases may appear in which a slightly moronic person is also neurotic, and in these color shock is not so rare. On the other hand, color attraction is rather frequent. In that case the responses to card VIII and following ones will definitely be more frequent and the reaction time shorter.

Anatomical positional responses ("head" because it is at the top, etc.), appear quite frequently in the mentally deficient. Moreover, these persons usually produce more Hd than H responses (fingers, hands, feet, nose, eyes). When A per cent is not very high, other stereotyped responses like stones, branches, etc. are usually found.[25] Real perseverations may also occur.

Other peculiarities characterizing the mentally deficient are self-assuredness in regard to interpreting as well as lack of subjective clearness in regard to the manner of approach, i.e., an inability to point to the parts of the blot selected (Pfister, Zulliger). Confabulations occur occasionally, but they usually are not very pronounced.

With a mentally deficient individual, it is not enough to recognize that he is deficient and to what degree. For treatment purposes, an understanding of his character traits is equally important. This, too, can be achieved through the Rorschach test. Adjustment and conformity, as well as tem-

[25]Manfred Bleuler, Der Rorschach'sche Formdeutversuch bei Geschwistern. Zeitschr. f. Neurologie, Vol. 118, 1929, p. 390.

perament, are of particular practical significance. As has been shown above, sociability can generally be derived from P responses (absolute number and per cent); temperament can be deduced from color responses. Porteus' thesis that heightened affective excitability does not go with mental deficiency as such was fully vindicated by Pfister's researches.

c. *Intelligence Defect* (*Dementia*)

Partial loss in original capacity and achievement potential is a frequent by-product of schizophrenic and various organic processes. We speak then of schizophrenic or organic dementia. Both kinds of impairment occur in varying degrees, from very slight losses, hardly noticeable in daily life, up to most severe defects. Schizophrenic disturbances are qualitatively different from the organic. Both these types of dementia will be discussed further in the chapter on the psychoses. It suffices to say at this point that in the case of dementia, in addition to the negative aspect (the mere reduction of intelligence) there is also something positive, which is not usually the case in neurotics or depressive intellectual inhibitions or in mental deficiency (the presence of absurd or far fetched Orig–, disturbances of the recent memory, insecurity, criticism, confabulations and the like).

3. THE HIGHLY INTELLIGENT. The performance of persons of superior intelligence is, of course, in every respect opposite to that of the mentally deficient. A rich approach, high originality and a dilated, ambiequal experience balance are its main characteristics. In addition, such persons produce W+ responses of especially high quality with combinations, MC, and similar rarities. The entire level of the content with its rich variations and its picturesque and original ideas is usually at once obvious. (Further details are given under qualitative assessment of intelligence.)

TERMINOLOGY

A *table of terms* for the quantitative evaluation of intelligence is given in the following paragraph. Its purpose is mainly to make the terminology more uniform. There is no point in replacing these terms by an intelligence quotient since the Rorschach test usually produces more and different kinds of facts than a mere intelligence quotient. In addition, the intelligence quotient is usually misleading since, especially in superior individuals, there is a great difference between different types of intelligence at the same intelligence quotient level (cf next section). The total impression given by the entire protocol is the significant thing.

The mid-line of the following schedule is conceived of as the statistical average, the mathematical mean of a population. It is recommended therefore to designate the different quantitative levels of intelligence as follows:

*Intelligence*

Genius
Very superior
Superior
Above average
High average

---

Barely average
Dull
Retarded
Moron
Imbecile
Idiot

The "normal" range comprises the categories "dull" up to "high average" (IQ of about 80 to 105). "Above average" designates a *somewhat* better endowment. A capable professional man should have at least superior intelligence. "Retarded" designates an intermediate level between normal intelligence and genuine mental deficiency, with an IQ of about 70-80. An IQ of about 140 and above is designated as genius.

## QUALITATIVE EVALUATION

### CLASSIFICATION BY TYPES

#### 1. THE THEORY OF INTELLIGENCE TYPES

Basing his theory on the consideration that we live in a world of books, things and people, all of which make their demands on us, Thorndike[26] identifies three types of intelligence: Abstract or verbal, concrete or mechanical, and social intelligence. Most intelligence tests are biased in favor of abstract intelligence and, according to Rudolph Pinter[27] tests like the Stanford-Binet or Army Alpha are valid only for abstract intelligence; concrete intelligence is somewhat neglected in them, and social intelligence entirely disregarded.

Meili, on the other hand, besides the formal factors we have mentioned, makes material distinction between theoretical-abstract (logical) and practical-artistic (intuitive-concrete) thinking. He also gives an opinion regarding practical intelligence.[28] By means of experiments with a lever test, he has shown it very likely that practical intelligence is related to the manipulation of things. In the Bühler-Hetzer infant tests, too, this manipulative

---

[26]E. L. Thorndike, Intelligence and its Uses, Harper's Magazine, Vol. 140, 1920. pp. 227-235, (as cited by Anne Anastasi, Differential Psychology, New York, 1937, p. 303).

[27]According to Stanley D. Porteus, op. cit., p. 25.

[28]Richard Meili, Bemerkungen zum Problem der praktischen Intelligenz, according to the Autoreferat in Schweiz. Zeitschr. f. Psychologie, Vol. 7, pp. 310-311.

ability is considered a component of the maturation process, which is independent both of mental productivity and of social contact.

Both classifications have their merits. Since they possess two coinciding groups (theoretical and practical intelligence), we now have four types of intelligence in all: theoretical, practical, social, and artistic. In spite of the fact that in theory and practice it is possible to distinguish between intellectual and affective contact with people, it must be realized that social intelligence, the ability to deal with others, depends on and is related to affective factors to such a degree that from a purely practical point of view it is preferable to deal with the problem of social interaction in connection with affectivity (see next chapter).

Thus there are *three types of intelligence or endowment*.

a. *Abstract-theoretical* intelligence is based on a special perceptual sharpness of the distant receptors (observational capacity). It consists of an ability for mental manipulation of abstract associations, i.e., for conceptual-theoretical and speculative thinking, so-called verbal or mathematico-causal thinking. Typical of this type of endowment is systematic-thinking productivity.

b. The *concretely-based practical* intelligence rests much more on tactile and kinesthetic (motor) experience. Insofar as this includes a capacity for material and motor manipulation, it is related to practical thinking, calculative and purposive thinking. (There is a relation between the practical man and the materialistic-purposive thought process, which has not as yet been closely investigated.) Practical intelligence is characterized by an active and practical productivity and by constructive work, insofar as it deals with palpable material. (There the boundary between this and artistic thinking is quite fluid.)

c. *Intuitive-artistic* endowment is based on a special plasticity of the imagination. It promotes the ability for picturesque, imaginative thinking, for so-called "creative ideation." It takes the special form of poetic, inventive and artistic (formative and musical) productivity. We purposely include "inventive" in this category because invention of an entirely new technical idea is much nearer to artistic-creative thinking than to mechanical construction, to "manual dexterity."

It is to be observed that these three types of endowment, which may clearly be differentiated in the Rorschach test, coincide closely with the old grouping into intellectual (conceptually oriented), material (factually oriented), and spiritual (imaginatively oriented) abilities.

## 2. RORSCHACH SYNDROMES IN THE ENDOWMENT TYPES

The qualitative evaluation of intelligence by means of the Rorschach test presupposes a certain quantitative level of intelligence. The type of endowment can generally be differentiated only if the level of the Subject's intelligence is at least "high average" or better still "above average" or more. The protocols of less intelligent persons are usually so "poor in material" that finer differentiations are hardly possible except in very unusual cases.

As for all psychological types or pathological pictures, the types of endowment are derived from Rorschach *syndromes,* that is, from typical clusters of certain Rorschach findings, which, however, need not *all* be present in each individual case. It should be remembered that these intelligence types are abstractions, which are not always "pure" in real life. The same is true for the Rorschach pictures.

a. *Abstract-theoretical* endowment demands primarily a good ability to synthesize into larger unities, a sense for systematizing and seeing theoretical connections. This means a fairly large number of W+, particularly the so-called "abstract" W, not the built up combinatory W. In persons of "reproductive" intelligence, the M need not be particularly high (they are higher in productive-creative scientists). However, Orig per cent is usually pretty high. Experience balance is not as dilated as in artists, but is usually ambiequal. F+ per cent must of course be high, and A per cent low, as in all well-endowed individuals. This results in the following syndrome:[29]

Many abstract W+ ("exclusively theoretical" persons: at the same time an increase in Dd)
High F+ per cent (85-95 per cent)
Rather rigid sequence (in those who start with and build on detail, sequence is reversed)
Some M+ (fewer in reproductive persons, more in creative ones)
Fairly high Orig per cent (20-30) (in creative individuals: elaboration originals)
Relatively low P per cent (15 per cent, 3-5 P)
Low A per cent (35-45 per cent)
Experience balance somewhat coarcted, usually ambiequal
Possibly EQa responses

b. *Practical* endowment in the first place, denotes a purely practical intelligence, the ability to manipulate things, to be able to take hold quickly.

(i) *Practical intelligence* is revealed primarily in an emphasis on D, but still includes some W as well. (Thus there is no pure D type, otherwise the Subject would lack the ability to anticipate, something which is required of the practical man also.) Experience balance is usually extratensive ("adroitness"). Originals are found mainly in the D and Dd responses. Just as the proportion H:Hd is related to theoretical intelligence, the proportion A:Ad has, peculiarly enough, a similar correlation to practical intelligence (Zulliger, Bero-Book, p. 72). If to the above we add the already mentioned ten-

[29]Arranged according to Hans Zulliger, Einführung in den Behn-Rorschach test, p. 103.

dency on the part of the practical person to perceive lateral details (Zulliger, op. cit. p. 105), we arrive at the following syndrome of practical intelligence:

Experience balance: extratensive
Approach W—D—(Dd)
A > Ad;
Orig D (and Dd)
Tendency toward perceiving more lateral details

(ii) *Technical endowment* is a specific variation of practical intelligence. In a way it is more, for the following must be added: constructive ability, a certain logical stringency (sequence usually pretty rigid), and in regard to invention and drawing, certain artistic trends are needed. The most important aspects of the Rorschach picture in the technical person are constructive-combinatory W, precision Dd and the sharply perceived F(C), often in perspective (in the broader sense of Rorschach, but usually also in the narrower sense of Binder). Typically, too, the creative capacities of the technical person tend more toward the practical. Thus he is likely to perceive his M preponderantly as D. The syndrome of the technical person looks therefore somewhat as follows:[30]

Many W+ (abstract and constructive-combinatory)
High F+ per cent
Rather rigid sequence
Usually a few precisely and originally perceived F(C) (architectonic-perspective)
Some M+ (more DM than WM)
Frequent presence of "symmetry"
Relatively high Orig per cent (more original motifs than elaborations; original constructive W+)
Low A per cent (30-40)
More A than Ad
Experience balance ambiequal, mostly capable of coarctation
Few, but precise Dd

(iii) The *"reality sense,"* i.e., a dependably functioning ability to test reality, is related to practical intelligence in a certain way. This is readily seen in the fact that those who emphasize reality less, dreamers and people living in a fantasy world, are usually designated as "impractical." We know that persons remote from practical everyday life have a very high Orig per cent and a low P per cent. But this is not all. Normal reality testing requires a certain minimum of accurate form percepts, especially in W responses (possibly also DW). W—, and especially DW—, are clear indicators of reduced sense of reality (dreamers, confabulators and, in certain cases, thieves). Naturally, poor originals (especially apprehension-originals) also indicate disturbed reality testing.

---

[30]Arranged according to Zulliger, op. cit. p. 193.

Thus with regard to the so-called reality sense we may suggest the following contrasting syndromes:

| *Sharp, reliable reality testing* | *Poor, unreliable reality testing* |
|---|---|
| ("reality sense") | (dreamers, fantasts, confabulators) |
| Good F+ per cent | Poor F+ per cent |
| W is mostly W+ | W is mostly W— |
| Little or no DW, mostly DW+ | Many DW, mostly DW— (in dreamers in connection with introversive experience balance) |
| Orig per cent not over 50 | Orig per cent over 50 |
| Normal or slightly reduced P per cent | Severely reduced P per cent |
| | No P in figure V |
| Mostly, if possible exclusively, Orig+ | Several, perhaps mostly, Orig— |
| Not too many apprehension originals | Poor or far too many good apprehension originals |
| | Infantile abstractions |
| No confabulations | Confabulations and confabulatory combinations |
| Not too many small M | Remarkably many small M |
| | M— |
| | Confabulatory FM |

c. *Artistic endowment* is first of all marked by its richness in M. Number of W is usually rather high also. But it is above all Orig per cent which achieves its highest levels here and thus A per cent is correspondingly low. Intuitive-artistic thinking is particularly fluid. Experience balance is mostly ambiequal and often rather dilated. A number of peculiarities are found almost exclusively in artistic thinking. Those are MC, MLDF, small M, combinations, scenes and EQe responses. In artistic individuals, entire sequences are frequently seen as fusions of figure and background. Thus we can set up the following syndrome for artistic fantasy endowment (according to Rorschach and Zulliger):

Many M+ (W, D and Dd)
Often many W+
High F+ per cent
Very high Orig per cent (motif, plus elaboration, plus apprehension)
Relatively low P per cent
Low A per cent
Sequence loose (at times reversed)
Experience balance rather ambiequal (mostly M > C)
Often small M
At times MC
At times MLDF
Scenic, fairy tale and mythologic motifs in content
Good combinatory W and other combinations
At times EQe responses
At times impressions
Often figure-background fusion (usually several of these)
Enjoyment of the act of interpreting the blots

It seems that certain special artistic endowments can be differentiated. In addition to the other factors, formative artistic talent (as in painters, sculptors) displays MC, MLDF, and small M, scenes and (in case of compositional talent) combinations, whereas in the case of talent for acting, these specific categories are less pronounced, and may be entirely absent. Instead there may then be (aside from the principal factors) many apprehension originals, EQe responses (careful consideration of facial expression) and figure-background fusion. (Acting ability is somewhat further removed from reality than formative talent which works in concrete materials.) Literary endowment is recognized mainly by the richly elaborated originals and witty formulations, as also in the greater number of small M and the larger number of H, usually accompanied by an introversive experience balance. Musical endowment has been little investigated. It is probably also associated with a more introversive experience balance. However, one must distinguish between creative and performing musicians. The latter, in Rorschach's opinion, tend to be more extratensive.

THE INDIVIDUAL QUALITATIVE INTELLECTUAL DIAGNOSIS

In contrast to the above discussion of types, individual diagnosis of the kind of intelligence is based on the inter-relationships of the various intelligence factors in the protocol, as is the case with the diagnosis of inhibition of intelligence. However, here the deficiency phenomena are of less importance than the individual's "assets." In each case, the factors of greatest weight indicate the main feature of specific endowment. We turn now to a number of minor, special problems raised here.

1. In intelligent persons $F+$ *per cent* should always be high. An exceptionally high total, up to 100 per cent, is by no means an advantage; except in depressions, it may well be a sign of a certain sterility. If it drops below the minimum of 70-80 per cent, it is usually an indication of poor observational ability, of poor capacity to concentrate, or poor reality testing.

2. Rigidity of *sequence* is a function of abstract logic. In artistic endowment it is correspondingly loosened. In scientists, a loosened sequence stems either from "artistic features" or from neurotic traits.

3. *W*, if good, suggests the ability to survey and to organize (in the more extratensive experience balance) as well as a sense of theoretical relationships and scientific systems. At the same time, one must never lose sight of its affective and volitional components.

This is especially important in evaluating ambition. Rorschach identifies quantity and quality ambition. *Quantity ambition* strives to do as much as possible, it attempts to demonstrate the Subject's diligence. The number of responses here is high. But since W cannot be increased so readily, many Dd responses are the result, and, furthermore, anatomy and geography responses are frequently found (a wish to display school knowledge). *Quality ambition,* on the other hand, is the attempt to produce as high a quality in everything as possible. Quantity does not matter. The response total is low and at times near ten. If at all possible, all of them must be W+. Some Subjects may succeed in this, and some of these good W may even be M+ and even Orig+ responses.

But not everybody with a decided quality ambition is gifted with the natural endowment permitting him to achieve in actuality what he wishes to achieve. These people may perhaps themselves be satisfied with their achievement (though in neurotic quality ambition this is rarely the case), but in fact the achievement falls below the good intention. Such Subjects also react with many W responses, but they are partly poor forms (W±), or even mainly poor forms (W∓). The will to achieve is there, and the theoretical interest is also present, but the endowment is lacking. Such people often have an unfortunate passion for science; in extreme cases one may even speak of "relative mental deficiency" ("Verhältnisblödsinn") (Eugen Bleuler).

When DW is found in connection with an introversive experience type, we are usually dealing with a dreamer. Only when form is very good (DW+), and even then not always, does it occasionally occur in constructive thinkers. DW− is, of course, always a liability (see "confabulations").

A positive correlation normally exists between W, M and Orig. Wherever there is a departure from it, we have hints of qualitative (and quantitative) peculiarities of intelligence and character. Ambition transcending the individual's power was one example. For these W± individuals naturally have few M+ and Orig+ responses. Orig− responses are a little more likely. But the reverse may also be found, namely, protocols with relatively many M± and many good Orig, but only few W. We find this in certain forms of technical endowment (precision mechanics, watch makers) which usually still produce some constructive W; and also in a kind of psychogenic depressions which do not affect the M and Orig factors, but produce a reduction in W. Other shifts in these correlations are also conceivable.

4. Where we are not dealing with a depression, the *approach type* usually tells at a glance the broad outlines of the Subject's approach to his work. The pure W+ type occurs only in very abstract thinkers or in cases of intensely imaginative endowment. The type *W − D − (Dd)* appears in those individuals who are more theoretically oriented, and the type *W − D − (Dd)* in the more practically oriented. People whose work is concerned with details (precision mechanics, dental technicians, watchmakers, optical workers, jewelry technicians, book-keepers and persons in similar occupations) usually have an approach of *W − D − Dd.* Those individuals can be recognized physiognomically by their habit of looking short, in contrast to

mariners, foresters and aviators who have a distant eye focus. We occasionally also find the approach $W - D - Dd$, in which D is relatively neglected. It occurs usually in impractical people who at one moment cling to some minute detail and at another construct daring syntheses, at the same time neglecting the obvious (D). They are usually somewhat peculiar and tend to nag and find fault. Finally, we have the approach type $W - D - Ds$, typical of the problem seekers, for whom "the problem is of greater importance than their fellow men." They may at times "walk all over people."[30]

5. The *A per cent*, where it is not increased by advanced age, by depression or by organic disturbance, can be separated into two large groups. The first includes artists and individuals endowed with a great deal of imagination, whose world is rather removed from ordinary everyday life. They rate a particularly low A per cent, about 20-35 per cent. Secondly, there are the "common mortals" involved in practical occupations and displaying a practical orientation to life, with medium A per cent, about 35-50.

Correspondingly, with low A per cent we usually find a high Orig per cent, and vice versa. A very low A per cent and a low Orig per cent are only rarely found in the same protocol. However, it does show up now and then, as in the cases of a young professional man with A per cent 29; Orig per cent 6; $M = 5$; and an almost 60 year old head nurse with A per cent 44; Orig per cent 6; $M = 1$. In such cases we have a heightened mental fluidity with relatively low originality, a kind of receptive fluidity. In other words, we are dealing with an individual who is not so creative but is well educated and who keeps his mind flexible by maintaining cultural interests and so prevents stereotyping.

6. *P per cent*, too, sometimes discloses a "personal peculiarity." Because of the upper limit of the number of P, both P per cent and absolute number of P are to be considered. The average of the latter is 5-7; 9-12 or more is considered high; 3-4 is low (Zulliger, Bero-Test, p. 223). If P is totally lacking, we most likely have schizophrenic autism or some other severe disturbance of contact. Impractical people and those remote from practical life produce a low number of P. A high number of P responses is found in two very different groups of people. A combination of many P with high A per cent and low Orig per cent simply indicates banality. Those are the bores. Many P (frequently 40 per cent and more) with low A per cent and high Orig per cent (or, in the case of accompanying depression, sometimes high A per cent, but high Orig per cent), is frequently found in people who play an important role in public life, politicians, high officials, journalists, feminists, people who like to join clubs. Such people,

[30]Hans Zulliger, *Der Tafeln-Z-Test*, Berne, 1954, p. 70.

in order to be able to attain and maintain these positions, must not only produce ideas of their own but above all be able to understand and appreciate the interests and point of view of the "common man." This gift of identifying oneself with the "people" in spite of one's own ideational world, constitutes the "political talent."

7. *Original responses* are a rich source of interpretation and evaluation. Complex responses we shall not yet discuss at this point. However, the mere distribution of the originals among the different modes of approach yields various clues. Orig+ in the form of abstract W, are found in creative theoreticians and scientists; Orig+ in the form of built-up W, comes with mathematical and technical endowment (civil engineers and architects); Orig+ in the form of D, occurs in inventive people of a practical nature; Orig+ in the form of Dd, in detail and precision workers with original ideas. If Ds is at the same time Orig+, it is either in individuals who can be original in their criticism of others and in polemical controversies (experience balance extratensive); or original in self-criticism (introversive experience balance) (Zulliger, Bero-Book, pp. 75 and 108/109).

Good W original responses are usually pretty rare. For this reason a few examples may here be cited.[31] Card I (v position), "sugar bowl of old silver." Card II v position), "a bisected brick chimney from which smoke and fire emanate." Card IV, "piano player." Card V, "donkey pulling an Italian cart, loaded with southern fruit, as seen from the rear." Card V (v position), "a girl swimming on the high seas on a life belt" (projections on the side are "arms and legs"; hump on wing is "breasts"), or "two sleeping goblins in a hammock." Card VI, "sparrow leaving a puddle in which he has just taken a bath, and leaving a wake behind him." Card VII (v position), "rococo easy chair with curved arm rest," or "the bridge of a contrabass." Card VIII, "showboat with awning and advertising flags hanging down from the sides." Card IX (v position), "a pompous matron entering the ballroom in festive array" (in fact, the response was a quotation from the Swedish poet Gustav Fröding). Card X, "top of a tower illuminated with Bengalese lights on account of a festival (red and gray), surrounded by the exploding rockets of the fireworks." Such responses always suggest exceptional theoretical or artistic endowment, but one cannot tell from them alone what these people are doing with their gifts. Thus these examples come from a female psychology student who has since advanced very far and has contributed to the field; from the very

[31]The example from card IV is quoted from Roland Kuhn, Über Maskendeutungen im Rorschach'schen Versuch, Basel, 1944, page 117, all other examples from own material.

gifted daughter of a famous sculptor who herself did not dare to do anything with her talents; from the highly gifted but impractically idealistic
daughter of a minister (cabinet member); from a musician; from a university professor who is interested in art; and from a police official in a
subordinate position who comes from an artistically gifted family but who
has developed into a day dreamer due to a depressive inhibition of his
productivity.

The content in the original responses gives some indication as to the
direction of the Subject's interests. Variability of content runs parallel with
many-sided interests. A great number of occupational originals indicate
an inclination to shop talk. Too high an Orig per cent (regardless of
whether occupational or other originals) points to remoteness from practical everyday life.

8. In M the same two groups emerge as in A per cent, although this
time in reverse. Few M are found in the practical realists and in persons
with a reproductive intelligence, whereas many M characterize creative
theoreticians and artists, the productive minds.

Of course, the question of with which experience balance the many or
few M coincide is not unimportant. Thus many M in a strongly introversive person indicate an inner potential which does not always result
in action, and which may remain socially futile. On the other hand, the
M of an ambiequal or even extratensive individual may well be translated into social activity.

Finally, the meaning of the M responses is determined by the total
syndrome in which they appear. The M responses of a theoretician or
scientist are an index to his richness of ideas and his scientific productivity. The M responses of a technical worker are an index to his inven-
tiveness, and those of the artist signify his creative originality. The more
M an artist produces, the less will he be influenced by other styles and by
current fashions of expression. He will tend to go his own way and start
his own school.

# CHAPTER VIII

# *Affectivity*

## KINDS OF AFFECTIVITY

1. COLOR. Affectivity is primarily judged on the basis of the color responses. As has been noted, FC represents adjustive affectivity, while the other two categories, CF and the pure C (both are often called "labile color values"), represent egocentric affectivity.

(a) Thus FC responses are expressions of feelings which presuppose an object cathexis. As Rorschach puts it, they are representative of an affective capacity for rapport, a friendly, positive rapprochement which forms the basis of affective contact. FC thus represents an affectivity which is not only directed toward the outer world, as any affectivity is, but which is also considerate of the outer world.[1] Such adjustive achievement is partly the result of an *object cathexis* in the libidinal energies, but partly also of a *conscious intellectual control*. It is in this way that FC obtains the twofold symptomatic significance (assimilation and intellectual control) described above (chapter 3).

If an attempt is made toward intellectual control (in the course of successful object cathexis), but if it is not effective (due to inadequate or inhibited intelligence), we have FC–. Rorschach employs the following comparison: the individual of labile emotions, when he wishes to make a gift, gives us what pleases *him;* the affectively adjusted person gives us something which pleases *us.* One could extend this comparison and imagine a girl, intellectually not too gifted, who gets the idea of giving her fiancé a necktie of a color she likes but which he does not. She may do so *not because* she likes the color, but because she thinks that if *she* likes this color her fiancé must like it also. She simply does not know that tastes differ and, in order to surprise him, she does not want to ask him. Affectively she is adjusted, she would like to give him something which he enjoys, only she does not know how to go about it. This would be FC–.

Due to the object cathexis quality, FC has yet a third symptomatic value (by way of the identification contained in it): it signifies the *capacity for empathy*. Significant empathic capacity requires a preponderance of FC over the other color categories (color left type). In addition, M must be present. It is also required that there not be too wide a dis-

[1]The FC, like most CF, are experienced as surface colors, i.e., as object-qualities. Only, in the case of the CF, the intellectual control is insufficient, the affective striving stronger. Both categories are directed toward objects, but the adjustment to the object is in fact achieved only with the FC.

171

crepancy between the experience type of the empathizing individual and his object. In addition to FC, the F(C) as described by Binder, and the "impressions" are indications of empathic capacity.

It is, finally, of a certain importance to note the colors at which FC responses occur. People who predominantly interpret the "warm" colors (red, orange, yellow) as FC, may be expected to show greater affective rapprochement and openness. On the other hand, reserved and somewhat cold individuals who insist on civilized forms and distance, will usually interpret the "cool" colors (gray, blue, green).

(b) CF indicates an affectivity which desires and strives for adjustment and assimilation, but which actually does not succeed at it. It is a *labile* affectivity, one that is subject to restless fluctuations, and which overshoots the mark without being adequately engrossed in the situation, and which reacts one way today and another tomorrow. This capriciousness and instinct-ridden restlessness, (as mentioned in chapter 3) is due to the fact that the affective energies which are expressed in these responses are "searching for stimuli" (Brun). In other words, we are dealing here with an affectivity which either is as yet objectless (primary stimulus search) or has again become objectless (secondary stimulus search).

It is not without significance, however, that this kind of affectivity is constantly *searching* for an object. This unending search not only causes the restlessness and lability, but it also makes the individual more accessible to the emotional impact of other people, i.e., it makes him receptive to suggestions. For this reason, CF is at the same time a measure of *suggestibility*. The well-known suggestibility of the hysteric is based, among other things, on the very fact that he has not succeeded in attaining a stable object cathexis. The more difficult the potential for a genuine affective object cathexis, the stronger is the readiness for substitute cathexes of all kinds, and thus also the capacity to absorb suggestive influences.

Suggestibility may vary in strength, intensity, and direction. In strong suggestibility there are many CF, in weak suggestibility, few. In an intensive suggestibility, one that is hard to reach, but lasting, there are, beside the CF, many M. With extensive suggestibility, one that is easily reached but which does not last, there are few or no M with the CF. Positive suggestibility appears in CF without Ds; the more the number of Ds approaches that of CF or even exceeds it, the greater the negative suggestibility.

(c) Pure C, finally, expresses an *impulsive* affectivity, the discharge of which is a goal in itself. The Subject no longer strives for an affective cathexis and adjustment to the environment; he just wants to "let off steam."

Impulsiveness may appear in two forms. If there are few or no M it may take the shape of frequent, almost continuous, but weak, discharges which may be compared to the crackling of a machine gun. If many M are present, the impulsiveness will emerge in infrequent but more massive and powerful discharges comparable to the explosion of a bomb. Individuals with several pure C and many M are therefore potentially dangerous. They "accumulate" explosive energy, and when the other inhibitions lapse, the entire stock of affective energy may quite suddenly and unexpectedly explode. This danger is all the greater if in addition to C and M there are also Ds (especially in extratensive types).

(d) The inner relations of color values to one another—K. W. Bash calls this the color type—yields an insight into *affective structure,* i.e., the affectivity which is *in* the individual in contrast to its expression. This is especially important in cases in which affective expression is neurotically inhibited and where the patient is about to undergo psychotherapy. We know then what to expect in the course of treatment once the facade has been broken through. Affect structure is of course nothing definitive. It can be modified under the influence of treatment (as well as in life generally).

If FC exceeds CF plus C, i.e., in left color type, affectivity is stabilized and equalized. In the middle type, where FC are less prominent and CF become more frequent, and a few C may even show up occasionally, we have a lively but still predominantly adjusted affectivity. With a somewhat stronger shift to the right, affectivity is labile, and we have the irritable-sensitive and insufficiently adjusted person. Finally, in a right type it is labile, impulsive and no longer adjusted.

It should be noted that a minor shift to the right of the color type, i.e., a somewhat stronger appearance of CF than FC, must be considered "normal" for the female sex.[2]

2. *Shading interpretations* are auxiliaries to color, at least those which are "genuine" F(C), in Binder's sense. (Light-dark interpretations indicate inhibition.)

When shading responses occur *without* color responses (in which case form-light-dark and possibly light-dark-form responses usually also occur) they are an indication of *"substitute contacts."* This is typical of the individual who tries to replace his lack of immediate adjustment by a somewhat coldly intellectualized, carefully reserved, indirect adjustment, by learned attitudes.

It is a different matter if, *beside* genuine FC+, there are F(C)+. This points to *especially good empathic capacity,* one capable of the finer nuances. F(C)+ are then, so to speak, the icing for the cake of FC+,

[2]Hans Zulliger, Der Tafeln-Z-Test, Berne, 1954, pp. 42 and 43.

and such people may be characterized as sensitive. If the number of F(C)+ is unduly large and the number of FC+ small, affectivity approaches a mimosa-like sensitivity and if at the same time there are several "impressions," hypersensitivity is possibly indicated. The experience balance is here always to be taken into consideration. In the introversive types such over-sensitivity will be more pronounced.

F(C)+ have quite a different meaning if they occur with CF and C but without FC. Rorschach himself, not having yet systematized this entire area of light-dark, shading and black-white interpretations, in such cases surmised a "conscious struggle against one's own affectivity," i.e., a splitting phenomenon. If we take the sensitive shading responses by themselves and view them beside the labile and impulsive color responses, but without FC, we have the typical *schizoid sensitivity*, often concealed behind the contactless facade of the schizoid individual. (See chapter 11 under schizoid personality.)

## STABILIZING THE AFFECTIVITY

The total effect of the affective factors we have just described, the inner affectivity, is modified by a number of other test factors, that is, it is more or less stabilized in its outward expression. The net result is the total *affective expression* of the particular person. Outward stabilization may develop in two ways: by (physiological) braking; and by (pathological) inhibitory mechanisms.

1. *The braking of the affectivity* is the way it is normally controlled. In every-day language (even in scientific text books) also this form of affect stabilizing is often designated as inhibition. (We tend to talk here about "normal inhibition.") Psychoanalysis, too, understands by inhibition only a delimitation of function, which need by no means be a pathological symptom. We prefer to use the word "braking" instead of "normal inhibition" since the ambiguity of the term inhibition has in recent discussion, especially with reference to pedagogic and mental hygiene problems, produced much confusion. Originally it means a purely neutral restraint on dynamic forces.

Braking of affectivity is shown in three Rorschach test factors, M, F+ per cent, and W+. We may say that the braking process is insufficient if there are many color responses but only a few M, if the F+ per cent is rather unsatisfying, (perhaps between 60 and 70), and if some of the W are poor. As soon, however, as there is "full coverage" for the color responses in M (i.e., when we have an ambiequal or even introversive experience type) and when a reasonably good F+ per cent is present, we may assume adequate braking, regardless of the number of W (which in such cases usually are predominantly W+).

The braking function which M exerts on the color responses is an intra-psychic counter-effect against the extratensive tendencies to affective expression. The reflective, inwardly differentiated person does not burst out on any provocation, since his affective life is at a deeper level. His affective expression is not neutralized thereby, but tonicized, it is expressed in a more controlled manner.

Such tonicized stabilizing exerted by the braking factors only applies to the *expression* of affect. Whatever is behind it is not touched. Rorschach himself says (p. 33) that M responses tonicize the affectivity of the Subject "whether he is normal, neurotic or psychotic." In others words, labile affectivity remains labile, impulsive affectivity remains impulsive, even though it may be hidden from the outside world by the inwardness (M), intellect (F+ per cent), and over-all grasp of the situation (W+).

2. *Inhibition of affectivity* as such is a pathological phenomenon. While the braking of a neurotic-labile affectivity may be a normal process (which socializes and humanizes the inner demon) and prepares the individual to move smoothly in society, an inhibition, on the other hand, is essentially a mechanism of anxiety avoidance. Karen Horney defines it as follows: "An inhibition consists in an inability to do, feel, or think certain things, and its function is to avoid the anxiety which would arise if the person attempted to do, feel or think these things."[3] Inhibitions are likewise revealed in three factors, which, however, differ widely from one another: light-dark interpretations, Ds, and shock phenomena.

*Light-dark responses* function as dampers on affective expression. As Guirdham so well recognized,[4] they are more the expression of neurotic *anxiety* than of psychotic depression. And anxiety is a very effective inhibition of excessively affective outbreaks (concerning anxiety symptoms see chapter 10).

The inhibiting function of Ds is more difficult to understand. We know that the concomitance of Ds and color responses even are an expression of neurotic obstinacy, of open opposition against the outside world. Yet Ds are also counterforces against the color responses. This is true not only in regard to suggestibility (CF), as shown above, but it applies to all color responses. The latter are an expression of libidinal affects, in the last analysis a striving "toward the world." This is true even where this striving does not succeed in achieving adjustment and object cathexis. On the other hand, Ds represent "the constantly negating and denying spirit," the negativistic principle of destruction, *aggressivity*. Both the libidinal and the aggressive drives are directed towards the outside, but the contrast between them reflects the struggle between love and hatred, the "struggle

[3]Karen Horney, The Neurotic Personality of Our Time, London, 1951, p. 53.
[4]Arthur Guirdham, The Diagnosis of Depression by the Rorschach test. The British Journal of Medical Psychology, Vol. 16, 1937, p. 143.

of the giants," which, as Freud expresses it, "our children's nurses try to mollify it by 'pie in the sky!' "[5] Thus Ds responses by no means operate to tone down affective outbreaks: they rather color and connect them up with aggressivity. They inhibit the positive aspects of affectivity which could be constructive, and transform them into sadistic aggression, denial, negativism, and rejection of the outer world. This is not done by withdrawal (as in the case of M) but by strife. Where CF and C occur without DS—which is relatively rare—they are, according to Rorschach, an index to opportunistic drifting, a kind of uncontrolled abandonment to the world, to one's own impulses and notions, in other words, an unbridled capriciousness.[6] If Ds are present they deprive the affects of their yielding quality, their passivity and formlessness, and give them a certain firmness, but the negative firmness of a combative nature. "The aggressivity, for example, increases the firmness, timidity decreases it," says Tramer.[7] Ds thus constitutes a counter factor to lack of firmness, a stiffening into obstinacy. It is an inhibition not of affective expression as such, but of passive defenselessness against external impressions. The prognosis for pathological states responding with many labile color values and many Ds is still more favorable than it is for a condition characterized by lack of firmness, because Ds reveal a vitality which, with adequate canalization into positive aggression (socializing of aggression), may produce useful results.

Color and dark shock work quite differently. *Color shock* is a neurotic inhibition of affect due to *repression*. The affects as such no longer come into consciousness or (in color shock combined with CF), they fluctuate ambivalently between love and rejection. Color shock may either suppress the affects (see following section), or it may combine them into a hate-love blend. In the latter case, color shock has an effect like that of the Ds responses, in connection with which it frequently appears. Very often, however, the inhibition is also here evident in lengthened time and in high F+ per cent, if combined with an extratensive experience balance, and increased Ds and light-dark-form.[8]

*Dark shock,* on the other hand, has an effect similar to that of the light-dark responses. That, too, is an *anxiety* symptom, and as such has a dampening effect on affective expression.

Finally, it is to be noted that neurotic inhibition may result in complete or partial suppression of M and C impulses. Such M and C repression or M and C reduction can be recognized by the fact that in spite of other

[5]Sigmund Freud, Das Unbehagen in der Kultur, Wien, 1930, p. 98.

[6]According to a communication of Ernst Schneider, in the Zeitschr. f. Neur. Vol. 159, 1937, p. 7.

[7]M. Tramer, Lehrbuch der allgemeinen Kinderpsychiatrie, 2 Ed. Basle, 1945, p. 252.

[8]Arthur Guirdham, On the Value of the Rorschach-Test. The Journal of Mental Science, Vol. 81, 1935, pp. 856-857.

evidence for kinesthetic endowment, M responses are lacking at certain points (see above, under kinesthetic shock). Or there are few or no color responses (e.g., refusal of the color cards), in the absence of any depressive indicators. M reduction is the expression of a neurotic armor, a kind of muscular stiffening through defense against anxiety. C reduction is an index to an especially intense affect repression. Both mechanisms are frequent in compulsive neuroses, and especially in sterile, compulsive characters.

## PROTOCOLS WITHOUT COLOR RESPONSES

In the absence of other indicators, this is not in itself a sign of neurotic affective inhibition. Absence of color may be due to various causes.

1. It may be a psychotic kind of affective aridity, a schizophrenic dulling in which the affects just do not function any more. In that case the status of the patient approaches the vegetative level.

2. It may be the dullness of the torpid mental defective whose affective life *may* be just as weak and superficial as his intellect. (The contrary also occurs, the excitable and emotionally labile mental defective.)

3. However, in the great majority of cases, complete absence of color responses is an indication of affective inhibition. This may be either: (a) a depressive inhibition in case of simultaneous indication of depression, or (b) a neurotic inhibition. Related to the latter are the already mentioned character neuroses with coarctative or completely coarcted experience balance.

## SOCIAL CONTACT

A discussion of social contact is appropriate in a chapter on affectivity. A person's ability to establish and maintain such contacts is primarily a function of his affectivity, and it is influenced only to a minor degree by other factors. Thorndike's so-called "social intelligence" is probably only partly a real intelligence type. It is no doubt the result of an affective attitude supported by such intellectual factors as sense of reality and intellectual contact.

Six factors characterize social contact: P and P per cent, FC, D, H and HD, experience type, and the kind of M responses.

1. P and P per cent are the indicators of intellectual adjustment. As Beck[9] has so aptly put it, these may be traced in all types of intelligence. In instances of high intelligence they measure the level of intellectual rapport with the world; in mental deficiency they measure sociability; in de-

[9]Samuel J. Beck, Introduction to the Rorschach Method; a manual of personality study, cited by R. Hertz, The "Popular" Response Factor in the Rorschach Scoring. The Journal of Psychology, Vol, 6, 1938, pp. 27/28.

pressions the severity of the depression (inversely proportional); in manic excitement the egocentricity of intellectual judgment (inversely proportional); in schizophrenia the scope of intellectual rapport with the outside world; in the neuroses the severity of the illness (inversely proportional); and in problem children the degree to which they can be guided.

2. We know FC as the representative of affective contact.

3. As the representative of the sense of reality, D is related to social contact insofar as the latter presupposes a certain minimum of interest in, and sense of, reality. A social worker who is on bad terms with reality is not very useful.

4. H and Hd responses show the degree of relationship to the human factor of surroundings. If they are absent, human contact is either neurotically disturbed (as in the case of children who in the world test of Margaret Lowenfeld do not touch the human figures in the toy kit at all), or it may even be an instance of narcissism. Many H and Hd in the case of left color type indicate human compassion and ability to identify; with preponderant CF, on the other hand, they indicate a strong (conscious or unconscious) tie to the mother (Zulliger, Tafeln-Z-Test, pp. 66 and 179).

5. Experience type, too, is important in this connection, since extratensive individuals usually make better contact than introversive persons, provided that the affectivity is not too labile.

6. The distribution of M between flexor and extensor movements is the last but not the least interesting factor here. In accord with their general symptomatic value "toward the world," extensor movements are a positive finding, while flexor movements, tending "away from the world," are seen as a negative quality. Because of this relationship to social contacts, the extensor and flexor movements are also of prognostic significance for psychotherapy. Extensor movements are favorable, flexor movements are unfavorable for the possibilities of success in psychotherapy (Rorschach, p. 118).

The negative counterpart of the entire contact syndrome would be the autism of the schizophrenic. This we shall treat more completely in the chapter on schizophrenia.

Here, finally, should be mentioned a relatively rare combination of test factors, to which Beck[10] has drawn attention, viz., a relatively high number of responses to cards VIII-X with few color responses. According to Beck this is a matter of persons with *latent* affective contact, with affective contact reserves, which allow a favorable prognosis of a possible psychotherapy, e.g., in cases of psychogenic depression or anxiety.

[10]Samuel J. Beck, Rorschach's Test, III, Advances in interpretation, p. 46, New York, 1952.

# CHAPTER IX

# Constitutional Types and Their Psychologic Correlates in the Rorschach Test

## THE PYKNIC-SYNTONIC TYPE AND THE SCHIZAFFINIC TYPES

IT WAS EARLY RECOGNIZED that, as with so many other psychological experiments, Kretschmer's constitutional types could also be characteristically differentiated in the Rorschach test. As early as 1924, Emil Munz[1] directly correlated the results of the Rorschach experiment with the body types of healthy individuals (pyknics on the one hand, compared with leptosomes and athletic builds as "schizaffinic" on the other). He concluded that pyknic individuals produce more color responses and thus tend more toward the extratensive experience type; schizaffinics, on the other hand, present more M and so tend to be more of the introversive experience type. Differences were also revealed in content. While the percepts of the pyknics were frequently related to current interests, favorite activities, pleasant experiences, manifest wishes and motherhood (becoming and being a mother), this was far less frequently the case with schizaffinic persons. The pyknics preferred warm, soft, woolly objects, and this was found to be more rare in schizaffinics. Pyknics tend to perceive more objects and landscapes than schizaffinics, and sexual responses appeared *only* in the pyknics. (However in schizophrenic patients in contrast to the healthy schizaffinics these are quite frequent as we shall see later.) Pyknics generally showed a tendency towards scenic combinations and completions, whereas schizaffinics usually gave a mere enumeration of details. The pyknics' enjoyment of the interpretative task and their basic readiness to oblige offered a contrast to the affective indifference and, occasionally, even the rejection of the experiment by the schizaffinics.

Willi Enke[2] later corroborated the clear parallel between pyknics and extratensives on the one hand and the predominance of introversion in all non-pyknics on the other (leptosomes, athletics, mixed forms of these, and dysplastics). If the figures of Munz and Enke are compared with those of healthy subjects alone (Enke's material also includes some patients), and if the intellectuals are eliminated, the following data obtains. (Munz's figures, all in per cents, precede Enke's.) Extratensive, in pyknics

---

[1]Emil Munz, Die Reaktion des Pyknikers im Roschach'schen psychodiagnostischen Versuch, Zeitschr. f. d. ges. Neur. und Psychiatrie, Vol. 91, 1924, pp. 26-92.

[2]Willi Enke, Die Konstitutionstypen im Rorschach'schen Experiment, Zeitschr. f. d. ges. Neurolgie und Psychiatrie, Vol. 108, 1927, pp. 645-674.

62.5 and 74.2, in non-pyknics 26.1 and 21.6. Introversive, in non-pyknics 52.2 and 52.1; in pyknics 15.0 and 6.5. With the intellectuals included the proportion is still similar, and if Enke's patients are also included, the shift is quite insignificant. Munz's ambiequals constitute 22.5 per cent of the pyknics and 21.7 of the schizaffinics, while the corresponding figures from Enke (healthy and sick) are 21.0 and 26.2. So far as experience type is concerned, athletics occupy an intermediate position between pyknics and leptosomes. This is not surprising since it has later been found that the athletics are much closer to the ixothymics than to the schizothymics.

Levy and Beck[3] in a later paper found a relationship between manic tendencies and extraversion and between depressive tendencies and introversion. This apparent contradiction may be explained by the fact that the syntonic constitution cannot be based on the same gene as that of manic-depressive psychosis. For the frequency of syntonic-pyknics and schizoid-leptosome types is of approximately the same order. But the frequency of the schizophrenic gene is about 20 times as great as the frequency of the gene for the manic-depressive psychosis in the population at large.[4]

## THE ATHLETIC AND IXOTHYMIC TYPE

1. *Krestchmer.* The third main group in Kretschmer's system of constitutional types comprises the athletics with their "viscous" temperament. In their study "The Personality of the Athletics,"[5] Kretschmer and Enke describe the movements of the athletics as slow, cautious and grave, their gait broad, their speech laconic, dry and simple. Athletics prefer vigorous types of work, using the entire hand rather than the fingers; their talent for precise motor activity is slight. In the Rorschach test they give predominantly M responses; many of them are coarcted; the number of Orig is low, A per cent is high, verbal expression is very short, telegraph style. The great tenacity of attention among the athletics is noteworthy, as is their tendency toward perseveration. Their mode of thinking is analytic, quiet, and solid, usually somewhat dry. Their strong and steady working habits, their thoroughness and their tendency to pedantry are striking. Affectively they are stable, at times torpid. Opportunism and instability

[3]D. M. Levy and Samuel J. Beck, The Rorschach Test in Manic-Depressive Psychosis. American Journal of Orthopsychiatry, vol. 4, 1934, pp. 31-42, cited by Mary Ford, The Application of the Rorschach Test to Young Children, Minneapolis, 1946, p. 11.

[4]Erik Strömgren, Episodiske Psykoser, Copenhagen, 1940, pp. 62-63.

[5]Kretschmer and Enke: Die Persönlichkeit der Athletiker, Leipzig 1936, cited by Ernst Kretschmer, Körperbau und Charakter, Berlin, 1944, pp. 207-215. For the following see also Ernst Kretschmer, Medizinische Psychologie, Leipzig, 1939, pp. 156-158.

is foreign to them; they are faithful friends and good spouses. Their "viscous" temperament ranges from the phlegmatic-indolent to the quiet-energetic kind. It also appears in the following variations: cosy good-nature (with a cycloid admixture); sullen-paranoid coloring (with schizoid admixtures); phlegmatic dullness (in poorly endowed persons); and a critical solidity (in intelligent individuals). The viscous individuals have a primary tendency to explosive reactions, the frequency and intensity of which, however, is socially conditioned. According to Kretschmer, explosiveness is at the opposite pole of viscosity. He emphasizes that in a healthy individual such explosiveness usually only appears in specific situations and only to a moderate degree.

It is noteworthy that temperamental viscosity has been found also physiologically through pharmacodynamic experiments (Hertz, according to Kretschmer, Körperbau, pp. 210-211).

Kretschmer leaves open the question of the extent to which the special epileptoid types share the same biologic roots as the viscous temperaments (Medizinische Psychologie, p. 164). At any rate Mauz[6] found the athletics predominating among 21 epileptoid psychopaths with explosive irritability; but among 81 genuine epileptics he found a predominance of dysplastics. These were less explosive, but "unfree, dry, remote, impersonal, narrow, dependent, rigid, pedantic, circumstantial, heavy . . . ," and they showed hypersocial coloring.

At any rate, athletic temperaments have no clear relation to epileptiform heredity, though according to Kretschmer they have an epileptoid and schizoid side (Körperbau und Charakter, p. 215).

2. *Strömgren.* It is preferable therefore for Rorschach investigators not to begin with body build, like Kretschmer and Enke, but rather with character type. In order to find the Rorschach test syndrome for the third psychologic constitutional type we thought it more expedient to correlate our observations with a type which is based directly on psychological observations. This is the ixothymic psyche of the Danish psychiatrist Erik Strömgren.[7]

a. *The ixothymic type* is then a character type. It is the epileptiform character as it may be found in normals. Persons with more pronounced degrees of these characteristics and with a trace of pathology are designated

[6]Mauz, Zur Frage des epileptischen Charakters, 49. Jahresversammlung der süddeutschen Psychiater, 1926.—Stauder (op. cit., pp. 144-146) in epileptics with heavy personality change ("Wesensänderung") found preponderantly athletics, whereas among epileptics with a process poor in symptoms (only great motoric attacks) only rarely.

[7]Erik Strömgren Om den ixothyme Psyke, Hospitalstidende, 1936, pp. 637-648.

as *ixoid* individuals. If the deviation from normal is based on an organic lesion the term *ixophrenia* is used. Strömgren did not utilize Hoffmann's term "epithymic" (analogous to Kretschmer's terminology), because he wished to avoid confusion; for Braun in Bumke's Hand-Book in 1928 used this to characterize certain patients with tendencious neuroses. The terms "ixothymic" and "ixothymia" were from the Greek word: ιζώδγs (ixódēs) which means "tough, sticky like bird lime."

The principal characteristic of ixothymic characters is, namely, their intellectual and affective "stickiness." Strömgren quotes Bleuler's statement: schizoid persons split off too much, syntonics split off adequately, epileptoids split off too little. While the syntonic is soft and elastic, the schizoid is hard and brittle, and the epileptoid is tough and sticky. Ixothymics show considerable endurance, are persevering workers, but have difficulty in shifting. They are found at all degrees of endowment. They are periodically "bound"[8] and make a peculiarly narrow, pedantic and often egocentric impression. Reactive mood disturbances may occur in them from time to time; these may be of long duration and may sometimes be discharged in sudden explosions. Their good-nature and readiness to help others are striking, as are their conscientiousness and strict adherence to duty. These traits were described by Mauz and Kretschmer as typifying their "hyper-social syndrome." Such persons are men of habit and of family, and because of their self-righteousness they may become excessively dependent on and attentive to the family. Their pedantic accuracy and their need for orderliness often cause them to regret their actions after they have executed them. In connection with their excess sociability, they often develop a peculiar sense of justice. Often they become indignant and explode if injustice is done to someone in their environment. The picture is filled in by an "almost obligatory tendency toward hypochondriasis" and a relative intolerance for alcoholic beverages (danger of explosion).

The following is important, also for the Rorschach student, in connection with differential diagnosis. There are *three forms of pedantry:* 1. The "active" pedantry of the compulsive neurotic or the compulsive character. This functions in the form of a magic ritual mechanism and represents an unconscious defense; 2. the "passive" habitual pedantry of the asthenic (the "subvalids") instinctively concerned with energy preservation; 3. the pedantry of the ixothymic resulting from love of the small, insignificant detail and enjoyment of repetition (iteration). These three forms may

---

[8]The expression "bound" (in German: "gebunden") stems from Hans Delbrück, who uses it to signify the peculiar remoteness of the epileptoids, the "slowing-down" of their processes of thought and sticking to the theme.

be designated as magic pedantry, energy preservation or habit pedantry, and iterative pedantry. Clinically, it is easiest to determine which of the three forms we are dealing with if we prevent the individual from executing the pedantic act. In compulsive neurotics, anxiety or at least depression, arises. The psychasthenic becomes absent minded, somewhat confused and irritated, but develops a new habit as soon as possible if it appears more expedient. The ixothymic simply interrupts the pedantic act and obligingly does that which is required of him so that he can then continue where he left off.

In Strömgren's opinion, the ixothymics and ixoids comprise about 5-10 per cent of the average population.[9]

b. *The Rorschach syndrome in ixothymia.* How, then, do the ixothymics perform on the Rorschach test? Number of responses is usually above average. Once they get going, they keep on producing out of conscientiousness and habit. Surprisingly enough, their reaction time is frequently shortened. Most intelligent ixothymics work reliably but fast. In doubtful cases this finding may even serve as a differential diagnostic sign as against real epileptics who usualy have a markedly lengthened reaction time. (Other differential diagnostic signs are the absence of confabulations and Orig– and the usually good F+ per cent in the ixothymics, except where an increase in anatomy content lowers the F+ per cent.) A clearly increased Anat per cent is frequent (hypochondriasis!). In most, though not all, cases the core symptom seems to be the peculiar perseveration of the perceived area. Some details are interpreted two or three times, sometimes with systematic turning of the card. In addition to this special kind of perseveration, real perseverations are also found, usually of the ruminating type, and in rather rare cases also a "sticking to the theme," as in epilepsy.

Emphasis on symmetry is the next symptom. Zulliger had already considered "the search for symmetry and stability" to be "an equivalent for the much feared impulsivity" (Bero-Test, p. 71). Perhaps the emphasis on symmetry of the ixothymics is a reaction formation against their urge towards explosiveness, just as Szondi generally conceives the hypersociability of the epileptoids to be a reaction to their tendency to violence (Cain and Abel theory).[10] In the ixothymic, emphasis on symmetry is usually found in the stereotyped repeated form, sometimes pedantically formulated ("Now then, we again have, first of all, symmetry," etc.). Often, too, there is a peculiar occurrence of perseveration of the perceived area with emphasis on symmetry expressed in the words, "and correspondingly on the other

[9]Erik Strömgren, Episodiske Psykoser, Copenhagen, 1940, p. 61.
[10]L. Szondi, Schicksalsanalyse, Basel, 2. edit. 1948, p. 280.

side." Some ixothymics also complain of the occurrence of non-symmetrical portions ("complaint of lack of symmetry," Zulliger).

DW and DdW appear frequently, and in some cases black and white as colors ("blue fox," to card VI and the like). Secondary M are very rare, but they show up now and then (though by no means as frequently as in epileptics). The same is true of M-. We have occasionally found color naming and self-reference in ixothymics. Color naming is obviously an expression of their dry pedantry, and self-reference a result of their strong self-righteousness and their occasionally narrow horizon. Object criticism is of course very frequent in these individuals with their extreme concern about accuracy, and so also is the general pedantry of formulation. Occasionally an initial test inhibition is found, corresponding to the difficulty these persons have in shifting. Evaluating remarks are found now and then (a tendency towards moralizing).

Color values differ. In non-traumatized individuals, remarkably many FC often occur, signifying affective stickiness, sometimes even in spite of the additional presence of clear signs of neurosis. The ixothymic constitution may be so intensely dominant that even the physiological correlates (capillary reaction) of the shock phenomena are completely hidden although psychologically speaking the shock itself is still clearly detectable. But, as we were able to establish in an investigation with Steen Warthoe, not only does the temperature curve of the skin show a clear hyperstability, but adrenalin reaction also does. This peculiarity of the ixothymic constitution makes it probable that it is essentially identical with Kretschmer's category of "viscous" individuals. As mentioned above, Herz has been able to determine the same pharmacodynamic "viscosity" of their reactions.

More severe affect lability, with CF and C, is found only in a minority, and that mostly in cases suspected of organic etiology (ixophrenia). Stauder[11] also says of the epileptics that "the explosive syndrome does not go with the typical epileptic personality change," but has an organic basis.

A per cent is usually normal, and presents nothing specific within the ixothymic Rorschach syndrome. In rare cases a high A per cent may stem from a "sticking to the theme" in contrast to the low A per cent of the epileptics. This is likely to be the case especially if no other depressive symptoms are present and intelligence is normal. A positive hint of this sticking to the "animal" topic is the occasionally observed agglutination of Ad, something usually not found with increased A per cent.

The diagnosis of ixothymia or ixoid syndrome can often be supple-

[11]Karl Heinz Stauder, Konstitution und Wesensänderung der Epileptiker, Leipzig, 1938, p. 181.

mented and strengthened by an occupational history of the family à la Szondi. Quite often a striking number of vocations connected with fire or transport, or occupations of social import (clergy, teachers, social workers, and the like), may be found in such families.

Together with definite ixothymia, *paranoid schizoid* signs often appear. This is due to an especially strong attraction between these two hereditary strains, a fact which has been observed by Stefan Benedek. They therefore often intermix in the same families.[12]

Like all Rorschach syndromes, this one, too, is usually incomplete in the individual case. In fact, the form of the syndrome may even change in the same individual. In one of our cases, in a first experiment, the individual combined a stereotyped emphasis on symmetry with anatomic stereotype. In a second experiment, eight years later, the Subject still showed strong anatomic stereotypy, with perseveration, but without the emphasis on symmetry.

Unfortunately we do not have an EEG for this Subject. For now and then it occurs that the EEG of a healthy ixothymic deviates from the normal. In particular, these cases show episodes with low alpha frequency, even though not always to the same degree as in epilepsy.[13] This is not surprising if we keep in mind that cerebral dysrhythmia (as Lennox, Gibbs and Gibbs, and Loewenbach have already stated) is a hereditary phenomenon, which also occurs in the non-epileptic relatives of epileptics.[14]

[12]L. Szondi, Schicksalsanalyse, p. 320.
[13]Torsten S:son Frey, Electroencephalographic Study of Neuropsychiatric Disorders, Stockholm. 1946, pp. 141-143, and: Über psychische Insuffizienzzustände und Elektroencephalogramm. Archiv für Psychiatrie und Zeitschrift für Neurologie, Vol. 183, 1940, p. 69.
[14]Fritz Buchthal and Edmund Kaiser, Electroencephalofrafiens Anvendelse i Klinikken med Beskrivelse af en ny Elektroencephalograph, Bibliotek for Laeger, 1943, p. 156.

# CHAPTER X

# *The Neuroses*

## A SHORT SURVEY OF THE MOST IMPORTANT CATEGORIES OF THE THEORY OF NEUROSIS

THIS SECTION REQUIRES a brief defense, since its subject matter does not strictly belong in a textbook on Rorschach test diagnostics. This book is concerned mainly with the problems of recognizing different characters and psychopathological states, whereas knowledge of character, of psychopathology and of psychiatry proper may generally be taken for granted. But in the matter of the neuroses it is essential to take special considerations into account.

In order to understand what follows, an approximate and general knowledge will not suffice, but a clear and precise grasp of the psychoanalytic theory of neurosis is required. In disagreement with Klopfer,[1] we do not believe that a Rorschach test can be exhaustively interpreted without knowledge of psychoanalytic theory. Neurotic traits are also found in most "normal" tests, and the nature and structure of the neuroses can hardly be understood except on the basis of psychoanalytic principles.

But this alone would not be sufficient reason for a special discussion of the theory of neurosis at this point, for knowledge of general psychopathology and clinical psychology are presumed in other sections of this book. On the basis of other considerations I have decided to make an exception with reference to the neuroses. The facts and modern theories of the neuroses are to a high degree contained in sources not everywhere available, or they are scattered about in journals. As a result, the study of this material, which is just as difficult as it is important, is greatly impeded. Still, a few good summaries are available. I shall only mention the excellent textbook of Rudolf Brun, "Allgemeine Neurosenlehre" (Benno Schwabe, Basel, 2nd edition, 1948). The schematic surveys below are based on this book with the kind permission of the author (on instinctual vicissitudes, anxiety, symptomatology, structure of the neuroses and character neuroses). Reference is also made in this connection to the older book by Hermann Nunberg ("Allgemeine Neurosenlehre," Huber, Berne, 1932).

The Rorschach student, however, is most in need of a schematic survey of the numerous concepts, categories and principles of organization relative to the theory of neurosis, all of which are interwoven with one another; that is, a concise skeletal presentation of this involved science. For

[1]Klopfer-Kelley, The Rorschach Technique, p. 6.

186

he must follow the data of this science step by step in the construction of his evaluations. This short-cut to the theory of neurosis cannot serve the beginner as a substitute for a thorough study of depth psychology. On the contrary, it should stimulate him to make such a study himself. For the advanced reader it may serve as a sort of survey, but we must confine ourselves to that which is necessary for the practical purposes of Rorschach test diagnosis. With regard to details, we must refer to the technical literature and above all to the writings of Sigmund Freud.

GENERAL CONSIDERATIONS

The question: What is a neurosis? partly coincides with the difficult problem of the difference between "health" and "illness." Conclusions will differ, depending on whether anthropological, pathological, hygienic, statistical or social criteria are used. This difficulty is not confined to medicine or to the theory of neurosis; in any science the basic problems are the most controversial (problems such as truth, science, soul, man and animal, law, state, economy, etc.).

Rudolf Brun's definition (op. cit. pp. 7 and 13) reads: "Neuroses are primary functional disturbances of the instinctual, drive-influenced and affective life." This does not mean that they do not affect the intellect. As a result of the rich interdependence of intellect and affectivity, this is just what happens, and to a high degree, as we have seen.

According to Karen Horney, all neuroses have in common: first, a certain lack of flexibility to cope with environmental situations; the neurotic reacts in a stereotyped fashion similar to the animal with its instinct; and second, a discrepancy between endowment and achievement.[2]

The central factor in the neurosis is *anxiety*. Anxiety and anxiety defense are present in all neuroses. Even healthy people suffer anxiety. But that of the neurotic transcends, quantitatively as well as qualitatively, the anxiety common to all individuals of his cultural pattern, and he suffers more than the average person, even though not always consciously.[3]

There are causal and purposive concepts of the neuroses. The causal approach looks for the causes and origins of neurosis; the purposive looks for its life goals. Freud's psychoanalysis is more causally oriented, Adler's individual psychology is more purposively oriented. But the purposive orientation also has its place in psychoanalysis, as in the theory of secondary gains.

In general one may say that neuroses are *infantilisms*. The clinical diag-

[2]Karen Horney, The Neurotic Personality of Our Time, here quoted from the Swedish Edition, pp. 16-17.
[3]Karen Horney, op. cit. p. 19.

nosis "psycho-infantilism" is therefore to a certain degree an undifferentiated and superficial one. In the busy practice of the clinic, it is however, often impossible to go more deeply into the structure of the individual case. The neurosis is then a disturbance of mental development. Certain phases of mental life have remained on a childish level (*fixation*). Or they are a return to an infantile or childish level as a result of conflicts and difficulties (*regression*). Any regression to a certain point of development presupposes a disposition for fixation at this point, which is constitutional or has been acquired early in childhood.

Neurosis as developmental disturbance comprises still something else. As Freud puts it, the individual develops from the pleasure principle toward the reality principle. The young child knows only the immediate satisfaction of needs, without delay. He cannot wait or make any compromises. In Wilhelm Wundt's terms, one speaks here of the "all or none principle," which is generally valid with regard to physiological drives. Only in the course of his development and by means of education does the child learn to adjust to the realities of this world, to postpone a satisfaction, to give it up completely, or to accept partial or substitute satisfactions. At that point he has arrived at the reality principle, and this constitutes his adjustment. Thus the neurotic disturbance is at the same time a partial lack of adjustment, a "maladjustment." If in his book "Psychotherapy in Medical Practice" Maurice Levine says that psychopaths all have in common the habit of acting shortsightedly and for immediate drive satisfaction, this only suggests that the inner structure of neuroses and psychopathy can hardly be differentiated.

However, it is not only difficult to distinguish neurotics from psychopaths, but in some cases from normals. The "normal person" does not exist, except in the minds of certain philosophers. The reader is urged to re-read Rorschach on this point ("Psychodiagnostics," p. 36/37).

## THE FORMS OF THE NEUROSES

*Actual neuroses* are to be differentiated from *psychoneuroses* (or *transference neuroses*). The actual neuroses are "functional-organic (toxic) hormopathies,"[4] i.e., direct disturbance in the vegetative brain centers. They arise under pressure of an original danger, and the anxiety in them is caused biologically. The psychoneuroses (or conversion neuroses) are "primary affect disturbances, based on an unconscious instinctual conflict."[5] Their anxiety is caused psychologically, and is the reaction to a conditioned of derived danger. The actual neuroses include neurasthenia

[4]Rudolf Brun, op. cit. p. 19.
[5]Rudolf Brun, op. cit. p. 17.

(Beard), anxiety neurosis (Freud), and hypochondriacal states (according to Federn's concept, depersonalization as well). The psychoneuroses include hysteria, phobia (anxiety hysteria), and compulsive neurosis. Any actual neurosis may become chronic. It then has the tendency to become a certain kind of psychoneurosis (under certain circumstances, a psychosis). The neurasthenia may become a conversion hysteria, an anxiety neurosis may become a phobia or compulsive neurosis, and hypochondriasis may result in a schizophrenic psychosis.[6]

THE DRIVES

Instinct and drive are closely related concepts. By instincts, Brun understands "hereditary mnemic total complexes," latent in every living substance, which automatically effect a goal oriented (purposive) self-regulation. Drives, on the other hand, are the released (ekphorated) hereditary mnemic excitations themselves, seen in their actual relation to the environment.[7] (In "Beyond the Pleasure Principle," Freud defines a drive as "an urge inherent in the living organism toward restoring an earlier stage which this organism had to give up under the influence of external disturbing forces. It is thus a kind of organic elasticity, or, if we prefer, an expression of inertia in organic life.") Brun distinguishes between instincts of self-preservation and of preservation of the species. Instincts for growth and metamorphosis, for obtaining food, protection and defense go under the category of self-preservation; while preserving the species includes the instincts concerned with sex, procreation and spread of the species (bee swarming, migration of birds etc.), and the parental and social instincts.

The psychoanalytic theory of drives which lies at the basis of the theory of neurosis has changed repeatedly in the course of time. In dealing with this area, Freud works with the *libido* concept. By libido he understands the quantitatively conceived energy in the sexual drives. It may be directed outward (*object libido*), or toward the self (*narcissistic libido*). Freud later contrasted the *death drives* with the life drives (libidinal drives). At the end of its development, this thinking, as it crystallized during Freud's own life time, might be portrayed diagrammatically as in Figure 1.[8]

The asymmetry of this diagram is only apparent. Even the aggressive drives can probably be further differentiated. However, these relations are

[6]Hermann Nunberg, Allgemeine Neurosenlehre, Hans Huber, Berne, 1932, p. 171.
[7]Rudolf Brun, op. cit. p. 186. On the concepts of "Mneme" and "Ekphory," see Richard Semon, "Die Mneme," 1908 and "Die mnemischen Empfindungen," 1909.
[8]First published in my article "Strafe als Triebbefriedigung," Zeitschrift für psychoanalytische Pädagogik, V. 1931, p. 323.

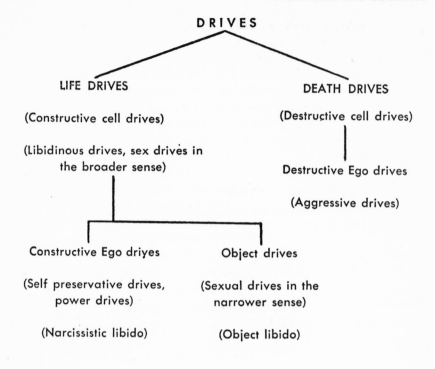

FIGURE 1

hard to demonstrate schematically because of the peculiar combination of the aggressive drives.

LIBIDO AND AGGRESSION

At any rate, the dualistic drive theory of Freud's later years is a distinct advance for psychology. It is immaterial for our purposes whether or not one wishes to derive aggression from Freud's death drive. As a matter of fact, we must reckon with universal aggression in biology and psychology. And aggression is by no means always negative. In both the animal kingdom and in man the two principles exist side by side: "struggle for existence" (Darwin) and "mutual aid" (Krapotkin). In man they seem to be interwoven in a peculiar fashion. Freud speaks of an "alloying" of libido and aggression. An aggressive component is normally part of the ego-libido (self-preservative drive) in the "struggle for existence," and this is also true of object-libido in the "conquest" of the love object and the struggle with the rivals. The sociologists, too, have arrived at this standpoint. Thus Adolf Grabowsky speaks of the aggressive drive "which is rooted in the individual as well as in the social structure, and which cannot always lightly be distinguished from the self-preservation drive."[9]

These components are the socially positive aggressions. However, by way of the frustration-aggression mechanism[10] they may be reinforced and transformed into negative aggression owing to frustration of the libidinous drive components. And if then aggression itself is also inhibited, extremely great accumulations of it may pile up. These may be very dangerous for mental health (if introjected) or for the life of the community (in the event of sudden discharge). Research in aggression is a relatively new approach to the theory of neurosis, and it is of great significance for mental hygiene as for social psychology. Not least of all it has enriched the fields of characterology and of Rorschach research to an exceptional degree.

Depending on the point of the fixation in the individual's development, negative aggression appears in the character either as oral sadism (biting, talking), or as anal sadism (beating, bruising, crushing under foot), or as phallic sadism (stabbing, boring). This brings us to the next section of our survey.

PHASES AND STAGES OF LIBIDO DEVELOPMENT

The fundamentally new point in Freud's concept of libido was its plasticity and changeability. Freud recognized clearly that the energy in the sexual drives did not first arise in puberty, out of nothing, as it were, but that like all other biological phenomena, it underwent a development. To visualize this development clearly, it is well to start with the fact that various aspects can be distinguished in libido (as in any other drive) : the source, the aim, the object, the impetus. When I am hungry, the source of this drive is the empty stomach, the nervous stimulation connected with it and the proprioceptive sensations which are therein localized. The aim of hunger is eating, i.e., drive satisfaction, by means of which the impetus decreases. The strength of this impetus may be measured in terms of the obstacles to be overcome in order to satisfy this drive. The object, finally, is food, the selection of which is subject to definite biological and psychological regulations, but whose connection with hunger itself is only slight. When I am very hungry I do not care whether I get white bread or dark bread. As Freud puts it, the object is only "soldered" to the drive.

[9]Adolf Grabowsky, Die Politik. Ihre Elemente und ihre Probleme. Pan-Verlag, Zürich, 1948, p. 55.

[10]See John Dollard and others, Frustration and Aggression, The Institute of Human Relations, Yale University Press, New Haven, 1945.

In libido development, the impetus alone is of subordinate significance. Its strength changes with the degree of satisfaction, and is thus subject to continuous fluctuation. All other qualities of libido change in the course of its development: the source, the aim and the objects. Libido may obtain stimulation from a large variety of sources. All these regions within the ectodermal system (skin, sense organs, central nervous system) are called *erogenous zones*. The zone which at any one time has precedence over all others is called the *primary zone*. The primary zone is at the same time the source of libido. In the course of the ontogenetic development of the organism a shift of the primary zones takes place within the ectodermal system, and which may be understood and explained in the light of phylogenetic development. The developmental phases of libido have been named according to the sources and shifts of sources: from the mouth (oral phase), via the anus, (anal phase), to the genitals (genital phase), i.e., from the upper to the lower end of the digestive tract, and finally to the skin and mucous membranes of the genitals which originally were connected with the digestive tract. (This differentiation in developmental history can still be clearly observed in ontogenesis. In the female embryo, a substance gradually enters between the exterior genitals and the anus, the perineum, which separates the originally common cloaca into vagina and rectum. In the male fetus, too, the cloaca of the undifferentiated developmental level is divided into the rectal orifice and the urogenital sinus (by development of the perineum.) The genital phase develops in two steps, since (after a short transition period in which the urethra is the libidinal source, the urethral phase), in both sexes the male part of the genitals is at first "charged" with libido; i.e., in girls the clitoris. Then for about seven years development is at a standstill designated as the "latency period" by W. Fliess, and only during the puberty period does the second stage of the genital phase begin. In girls this is the transfer of excitability from the clitoris to the vagina, which however is usually incomplete due to developmental disturbances. (All of this is very crudely schematized.) Each of these phases is thus connected with an essential bodily function, the oral phase with food reception, the anal with defecation, and the genital with micturition.

Each of the three main phases is usually subdivided into *two stages*, according to change of the libido's *aim*. The tiny infant wants to suck (first oral stage). (The independence of the need to suck has been demonstrated experimentally by D. M. Levy in a number of animal experiments.) As soon as the first teeth appear, the goal of biting and devouring more and more takes the place of sucking (second oral, also called the cannibalistic, stage). In the anal phase, too, there are two stages. First defecation itself, i.e., elimination, is pretty much the central matter. Only later, when the child has learned to control the sphincter muscles of the anus, is retention of the excrements more pleasurable. At the same time the child changes his behavior toward the things of the outer world, strives less for the destruction of the object than for the control of it. (Because of this pattern the anal phase is also called the anal-sadistic.) In the genital phase the two stages are widely separated. During the first genital step (about the fifth year of life), the development of the libido comes to a standstill. Only after the termination of the latency period, at the beginning of puberty, does it resume its development. The mode of satisfaction in the first genital step, masturbation or, as I prefer to call it, ipsation (the term stems from the Polish physician Kurkiewicz of Krakau, and was later taken over by Magnus Hirschfeld and other writers), is taken up again at the onset of the second genital step. Cultural factors actually to a great extent determine the time when the sexual drive reaches its actual aim, the sexual act.

Finally, the development of the object series is complicated by the fact that at first no object exists which is separated from the ego. There is reason to suppose that the neonate at first cannot differentiate the maternal breast from his own body. Very young infants are thus autoerotic, the self and the external world still flow together into one. Only gradually does a clear self percept arise (probably by way of perception of other persons as part of the external world). But even at the beginning of this period (in about the second year of life) the child is still primarily narcissistically oriented, only knows love of self. However, his oral libido is already using objects of the external world as physical objects. Gradually, too, a psychologic tie is formed with the external world, a constantly growing part splits off from the initially exclusively narcissistic libido and becomes object libido. This takes place to the same degree to which the original tie to the mother is given up,[11] and in the adult there is a rough equality of narcissistic and object libido. However, in case of disappointments, object libido can always be transferred back into narcissistic libido. (Freud compares this process with the amoeba's retraction of the pseudopodia. A comparison with a snail which retracts its tentacles would also be appropriate.) This re-transformed narcissistic libido is called secondary narcissism. It plays a great part in the neuroses. The first, tender object libido, however, still shows clear traces of its origin in narcissism, for it is passive object love: the child wants to be loved. The objects of this state of passive love are naturally those people who take care of the child, and above

[11] See: Edith Buxbaum, Transference and Group Formation in Children and Adolescents, in "The Psychoanalytic Study of the Child" I, London, 1945, p. 355.

all the parents. Gradually the parents are more actively desired, object libido is strengthened into active object love. But already in the first genital stage, the first beginnings of a liberation from these incestuous objects takes place. The sexual aim is still autoerotic, and the emotional yearning for the parents only shows the tender striving; the sensuous component is split off. Here we speak of active object love with genital exclusion. This splitting of the libido into its sensuous and tender components still continues throughout the greater part of puberty, until a unification of these two strivings into full psychophysical love signifies the termination of the puberty period. As a rule, a number of transition objects have taken the place of the parents in the meantime: teachers, superiors, movie actors, and the like. These unconscious parent substitutes are called parent images. Physical objects which hold a strong positive affect for the child during the anal period are primarily his own excrements, for disgust of these is by no means innate. Here, too, the connection with the preceding oral-narcissistic period can be seen. His own excrements are, indeed, the first object in his external world produced by the child himself. They are his own product, and as such they are treated with the same love and admiration as the child receives from the mother, or as intellectual and material achievement receives from its creator. In individuals who have fixated at this level, money, the symbol for excrement, takes its place. Depending on whether the fixation is upon the first or the second anal stage, they will have a tendency either to lose or squander money (they cannot "hold on" to it), or to keep and collect it (and usually other objects also).

Side by side with this development of the love drive runs the development of aggression. It has been less investigated because it is less easily accessible. It becomes evident only in various forms of ambivalence, i.e., in the simultaneous contrasting drive aims, of love and hate. In the first oral step, the child is still pre-ambivalent, and there is no object cathexis. According to Theodor Reik, who describes the growth of ambivalence in four steps,[12] this is the period of undifferentiated drive. Next come the coinciding antagonistic drives (incorporation-destruction). (This takes place during the second oral phase.) In the anal and at the beginning of the second genital phase there is a period during which the various drive components live side by side, each with its separate satisfaction (losing-keeping, destroying-collecting). In the first genital step, love and hate still co-exist in an ambivalent manner in the complete Oedipus complex. This development is concluded in puberty with the post-ambivalent orientation, the subordination of the distinct partial drives to the primacy of

[12]Theodor Reik, Der eigene und der fremde Gott, Internationaler Psychoanalytischer Verlag, Wien, 1923, p. 234, footnote 2.

genital sexuality and the tying together of love and hate in a total emotional unit which is preponderantly one or the other.

Since this entire development coincides approximately with specific years of the chronological age (only very approximately), this libido development may be simplified and crudely schematized as in Table 1.

## THE OEDIPAL SITUATION

We must isolate one detail of this "map of the development of the drives" and present it in greater scale. We here refer to the ambivalent situation during the first genital stage known as the Oedipus complex. At this stage, the bisexuality existing in all higher organisms plays a decisive part. Sexual differentiation has at this age already developed so much in the child's psychologic life that he shows a clear preference for the parent of the opposite sex, while rivalry is developing toward the parent of the same sex. The origin of the Oedipal situation develops by the boy first identifying himself with the father. This is a "narcissistic identification," characterized by Freud as "the earliest exertion of an emotional tie to another person," as "the earliest form of emotional tie to an object."[13] This identification expresses "what one wishes to *be*." (Freud, op. cit. p. 60). Along with this the child develops an "object cathexis to the mother," who becomes the ideal of "that which one wishes to *have*" (Freud). But the opposite is also true, although to a lesser degree. The homosexual component of psychological love is repressed to a far lesser degree in the child than in the normal adult. As a result, two opposed strivings toward each parent coexist during the Oedipal period. This is called the complete Oedipus complex. In this connection it should be noted that the homosexual strivings are somewhat more strongly developed in the girl than in the boy, since her first object love is of the same sex: the nurturing mother, who is already vaguely perceived as an object during the oral phase. (Our above diagram is only a crude simplification of the facts in the situation!) In the girl a reorientation from an inclination to an object of the same sex to an object of the opposite sex (to heterosexuality) must first take place (the "passivity push," Helene Deutsch). This situation may be expressed diagrammatically as Figure 2 without doing much violence to the facts. The square symbol indicates the male; a circle, the female; a solid line stands for positive (love) strivings, and dots for negative (hate) strivings.

This Oedipal situation decreases gradually toward the end of the first genital stage. The psychological processes involved here are extremely complex: they are some of the most difficult aspects of depth psychology. An extensive characterization of these processes would exceed the avail-

[13]Sigmund Freud, Massenpsychologie und Ichanalyse, Wien, 1923, pp. 58 and 62.

## TABLE 1. LIBIDO DEVELOPMENT (Schematic Representation)

| A G E (very approximately) | | Relation to vital bodily function | Source | Aim | |
|---|---|---|---|---|---|
| I. Stage: to six months | oral | Intake of | Mouth | Sucking | |
| II. Stage: six months to one year (cannibalistic) | phase | nourishment | Mouth | Biting Devouring | |
| I. Stage: 1-2 years | anal sadistic | Defe- | Anus | Destructive: Elimination of excrements Destruction of object | |
| II. Stage: 2-3 years | phase | cation | Anus | Conservative: Retention of excrements Domination of object | |
| I. Stage: 3-5 years (phallic) | | Micturition | Penis Clitoris | Ipsation | |
| Genital phase | | LATENCY PERIOD | | | |
| II. Stage: 12 years— | | | Penis Vagina (Clitoris) | Ipsation; later, sexual act | |

| Object | Ambivalence | | |
|---|---|---|---|
| (Mother's breast and self not differentiated)<br>No object<br>(Autoeroticism) | Pre-Ambivalent<br>(no object cathexis) | | |
| Ego (Narcissism)<br>Physical: objects<br>(total incorporation) | Incorporation-destruction<br>(in coincidence) | | |
| *passive object love* { Parents<br>Physical: excrements<br>(Partial love with incorporation)<br><br>Parents<br>Physical: excrements<br>(Partial love) | AMBIVALENT { Retaining-destroying_<br><br>Retaining_<br>destroying | ____<br>____ | side<br>by<br>side |
| Parents<br>(active object love with genital exclusion) | Love and hate<br>side by side<br>in the complete<br>Oedipus complex | | |
| **LATENCY PERIOD** | | | |
| Parents and Parent images,<br>later sexual partner<br>(Object love) | Post-ambivalent<br>(subordination of partial drives) | | |

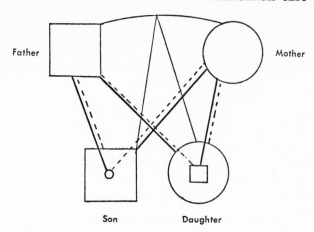

Father                                                          Mother

Son                    Daughter

## FIGURE 2.  THE COMPLETE OEDIPUS COMPLEX

able space. In addition, the development of boys and girls is considerably different. Suffice it to say here that in the boy, as Freud puts it, the Oedipus complex is "destroyed" by the castration complex. That is to say, it disappears by means of a retribution anxiety which is inherent in the phylogenesis and which is repeated in each individual. In the girl, however, the castration phase precedes the Oedipus complex in that the "passivity push" is in part made possible first by the notion that the mother has endowed her child with "too little."

Superego (conscience) formation goes hand in hand with the gradual dissolution of this dramatic conflict situation. For the final giving up of the parents as sexual objects is first achieved by means of an "object-libidinal identification" with them and their demands (i.e., an identification with "that which one wishes to have"). From now on this process takes place each time a love object is unachievable or is lost, and each time traces of the loved object remains in the ego. (The "character of the Ego" is determined by "the remnants of abandoned object cathexes," Freud.) [14] At an earlier period it was "you should" for the child, now he begins to feel the "I want." The regulating moral demands are no longer external but internal; they come from the child's own ego. In this manner character is built out of a double identification with both parents, and bisexual traits are retained into adulthood, not only biologically, but also psychologically.

### THE INSTINCTUAL VICISSITUDES

Whether the development of the drives, which has here been outlined very crudely, takes place in a fairly normal manner or not, depends—as

[14] Sigmund Freud, Das Ich und das Es, Kap. III.

in all human character formation—on two factors: the hereditary endowment and the regulating environmental influences, whose effect, in turn,
largely depends on the instinctual constitution.[15] Thus the latter also de-
termines the kind and strength of superego formation, that which Rudolf
Brun calls the inhibiting "secondary drives," or the "cultural counter
drives." They are the same forces which we have in this book designated
as braking mechanisms. In the following survey, which has been derived
from Brun's textbook, we shall try to show under what conditions and by
means of what mechanisms development either becomes normal, or turns
into perversion or neurosis. (The numbers in parentheses refer to the pages
in its second edition.)

Instinctual Vicissitudes (232, 236-239, 240-243)
(Balance of forces in instinctual constitution)

Definitions (according to Freud):

Perversion        =  Manifest expression of either the inverting of the sexual object
                     or of isolated partial drives, exclusively and compulsively.
                     (Three Contributions to the Theory of Sex.)

Neurosis          =  Repressed perversion (the "negative of perversion").

1. Normality      =  Medium strength in the archaic primary drives + medium to
                     strong development of the inhibiting secondary drives (braking
                     mechanisms) (232, 235/236).
                     a. Unrepressed remnant in original form (236) = forepleasure
                     b. Repressed drive energy =
                        (i)   reaction formation
                              (turning into the opposite with overcompensation)
                        (ii)  substitution
                              (activity with a substitute object)
                        (iii) sublimation
                              (the aim-inhibited libido is put into the service of the
                              repressive force)

2. Perversion     =  Abnormal strength of the archaic primary drives + weakness
   ("born-            of cultural counter-drives (232)
   criminal")
                     a. Inverting of the sexual object, but retaining the normal
                        sexual aim (240/241)
                        = homosexuality, inversion
                        (i)  sexual intermediate steps (hereditary)
                        (ii) acquired homosexuality (misidentification)
                     b. Inversion of the sexual aim (isolation of a partial drive)
                        = paraphilias (Stekel), perversions in the stricter sense.

3. Neurosis       =  Constitutional increase of one or more primary drives +
                     strongly developed secondary drives (232)
                     (Inhibitions) (242/243)
                     (Fear of drives breaking through
                     + defense mechanisms, above all unsuccessful repression.)

[15]Rudolph Brun, Allgemeine Neurosenlehre, 2 edit. p. 193.

## Differences Between the Psyche of Children and Adults

We now return to the neuroses, and must remember that they are to be viewed above all as infantilism or disturbances of psychological development. In order that these terms not be just words, we need to clarify in what respects the child's psyche differs from that of the mature adult. These differences are as follows:

1. *The difference in integration.* Reality perception, i.e., the critical appreciation of impressions from the external world, is an intellectual function which appears only in the course of the individual's development. The brain and the psyche of the child are much too inadequately integrated to be able to exercise this complex function. Only at about the age of eight is the reality sense developed to a reasonable degree (Bühler). Younger children do not draw any sharp boundaries between fancy and reality. They do not yet think logically, but rather magically like the primitives ("pre-logical thinking," Lévy-Brühl). Fantasy percepts may have the same effect for the child as reality. They have psychic reality (Freud). For this reason, little children cannot "tell lies," they simply do not understand the difference between the true and the false. In almost all neurotics traces of this pre-logical thinking are found, as well as of disturbed, but not basically demolished, reality perception. (It is severely disturbed or essentially lacking in the psychoses.) An almost complete fixation on this pre-logical level is found in the pseudological or mythemanic psychopaths.

2. *The difference in libido development.* As we have seen, the libido of younger children has not yet reached the genital phase, or at any rate it has not gone beyond the first step in that phase. In the first case we say that the libido of the child (and of many neurotics) is pre-genital.

3. *The topologic difference.* We have seen also that superego formation, the development of conscience, is a process which takes place in the child's ego only toward the end of the first stage of childhood. The ego develops first (at the beginning of speech acquisition, many children still refer to themselves in the third person), and the superego only much later. The small child has as yet an undeveloped conscience.

4. *Two dynamic differences.* The dynamics of the different drives, i.e., the distribution of force in them and their mutual shifting as a result of external stimulation, are different in the child as compared with the adult.

(a) First of all the young child is still *predominantly narcissistic.* Object libido, the attachment to love objects in the external world, takes place only gradually, a slow development lasting for years. By nature the child is egotistical.

(b) Furthermore, the ratio of mixture between the two main drives, *aggression and libido,* is not the same in the child as in the adult. Children have much larger quantities of free aggression because libido and aggression have not yet become so closely tied in with each other as in adults. Hence the natural "wildness" of the child, his strong compulsion for activity and his immediate aggressive reaction whenever his interests are trespassed upon.

5. *The difference in libidinal economy.* The manner in which the child quantitatively manages his libidinal energies, is not that of the adult either. At first the psychologic apparatus of the young child is directed only toward the immediate satisfaction of his needs, the direct attainment of pleasure. Along with Freud, we are speaking here of the *pleasure principle.* Only after the ego has attained a certain measure of differentiation does it gradually learn to substitute the avoidance of displeasure for immediate satisfaction of the drive in some situations, in other words, to postpone certain pleasures. Freud calls this modification of the pleasure principle the *reality principle.* It is the goal of education gradually to replace the pleasure principle of the young child with the reality principle of the adult. Good education will seek to attain this goal with the least loss of activity on the part of the child.

Two other differences are to be added to the above:

6. In instinctual life, as in the motor pattern, the several functions are not at first able to cooperate too well. In other words, in the child all *partial drives* (oral, anal, urethral, phallic, sadistic, masochistic, exhibitionistic and voyeuristic tendencies) still appear in isolation and, as Freud puts it, the child is "polymorphously perverse."

7. Finally, the separation between libido and aggression has the effect of making the *ambivalence between love and hate* stronger and causing it to display itself more openly in the child than in the post-ambivalent adult with his firmer genital primacy.

### Various Aspects of the Neuroses

Keeping in mind these differences between the psyche of children and adults, we can now go on to the different points of view under which the neuroses may be considered and classified.

#### 1. THE NEUROSES AS PREGENITAL FIXATIONS

The purest form of fixation on the oral narcissistic phase is found not in the neuroses but in the psychoses, mainly in schizophrenics. (In melancholia the fixation is partly at the oral phase and partly at the first anal stage, but here there is a defense against the anal libido. Paranoia is considered as a regression to the anal-sadistic phase with narcissistic object cathexis.) However, oral fixations appear secondarily in the neuroses as well, especially in compulsive neurosis, which hardly ever shows a "purely" anal character; and also in the addictions, primarily of course in alcoholics.

The typical fixation point of compulsives is in the anal-sadistic phase (chiefly the second stage), while phobics quite generally regress to the pregenital phases without a more definite fixation point. Hysterics, finally, are fixated at the infantile-genital (phallic) phase. Treatment of hysters is a relatively promising task because, in order to complete their development, they have a markedly shorter span than other neurotics to catch up with. In terms of development, they are closely related to phallic-narcissistic character neuroses.

## 2. NEUROSIS AS SHIFT OF EGO STRUCTURE

The neuroses may also be differentiated on the basis of the typical structural system (between ego, id, and superego).

In hysteria the conflict is between ego and id. The ego suppresses geni-tality, the id circumvents the superego and finds discharge in the physical innervation of the ego.

In compulsive neurosis the relation between superego and id is disturbed. However, the relations between ego and id, and between superego and ego remain intact. Id impulses are constantly influenced and distorted in the ego, owing to criticism by the superego. The ego regresses to the magical (pre-logical) stage, and the id to the anal-sadistic. The superego turns to sadism against the individual himself, and guilt (aggression originally directed against others) is atoned for by self-torture.

(For purposes of comparison: In schizophrenia and in the psychoses related to it, a conflict goes on between ego and reality. The relations between superego and ego, *and* between superego and id are disturbed. The superego is weakened and there is a short-circuit between ego and id [manifest perversions]. More precisely, the conflict between ego and superego is projected outward, and it then becomes an apparent conflict between ego and reality. Recognition of the paranoid projection mechanism plays an important role in Rorschach test diagnostics [see chapter 13 concerning involutional paranoia]. In manic-depressive psychoses there is conflict between superego and ego; in the melancholic phase the ego succumbs to the point of suicide, in the manic phase the superego succumbs, and its identifications are nullified.)

Roughly speaking, then, hysteria and phobia may be called id neuroses because in them the disturbance originates in the id. Compulsive neurosis, on the other hand, would be a superego neurosis. There are also neurotic states with ego disturbances. These are the depersonalizations, which, however, really represent a transition to the psychoses (e.g., in the psychotic forms of hysteria with ego splitting, and to a lesser degree in psychas-thenia).[16]

As we have seen, the central feature in neurosis is *anxiety*. This topical categorization of the neurosis is closely related to the different kinds of anxiety. It is all the more important for the Rorschach diagnostician to be intimately acquainted with them, in that the different types of anxiety can to a great degree be differentiated in the Rorschach protocol.

"The ego is the actual locus of anxiety," says Freud,[17] but it is dependent on the outer world (with which it is in direct contact through the sensual organs), on the instincts of the id, and the moral demands of the superego. Anxiety may be classified on the basis of these dependencies, and we may then differentiate reality fear (ego anxiety in the narrower sense), libidinal anxiety (id anxiety), and conscience anxiety or castration anxiety (superego anxiety).

Reality anxiety is the normal anxiety of the healthy individual which warns against outside dangers. It is a basic feeling which arises from any threat to the life drive and which aims to make the organism ready for fight or flight or for playing dead.

Libidinal anxiety comes from within; it is transformed love or aggression and, consequently, is better termed drive-anxiety.[18] It is a free floating anxiety which, in the form of so-called anticipation anxiety, attaches itself to any possibility. In anxiety neurosis, it arises through the damming up of drives, and it is found also in hysteria, where, however, it is not experienced as anxiety but is converted and remains bound to the symptom. If the original fear of the internal drives is bound to an object through the mechanism of displacement, it becomes a phobic anxiety (situation anxiety).

Conscience anxiety also comes from within. Originally referred to ex-ternal objects as normal fear of punishment, it is later introjected. In its neurotic form, in compulsive neurosis, it is again a displacement anxiety, in which the fear of punishment is displaced onto a small detail.

Because of their great importance, we shall again present these relation-ships schematically (following Rudolf Brun's "Neurosenlehre," second edi-tion, pp. 113, 114, 115, 126, 264, 364, 365, 391/392).

[16]The situations described above refer to disturbance of ego *structure*. So far as ego *functions* are concerned, the physical expression of the ego (the organs) is disturbed in hysteria, the psychologic ego (thinking and feeling), in the compulsive neurosis, and in schizophrenia (in addition to the other functions) the perceptual ego is disturbed. (See Nunberg, Allgemeine Neurosenlehre, p. 274.)

[17]Sigmund Freud, Das Ich und das Es, Kap. V.

[18]The words of Freud, "regardless . . . . whether aggression or love" in the XXXII. lecture of "Neuen Folge" (Gesammelte Werke, Vol. 15, p. 90) have been over-looked by a number of critics, such as Karen Horney.

## Anxiety

Introductory remarks:

Anxiety is always produced and experienced by the ego, but can be related "to the three kinds of dependence of the ego, viz., on the external world, the id and the superego" (Freud).

Basic biological condition: threat to vital interests (when the normal course of an already activated primary drive excitation seems suddenly to be made questionable or appears threatened by an obstacle) (113, 126, 364).

1. *Reality Fear* (Ego      —   Basic, fundamental feeling
   (from without)               (threat to life urge) (113)
   (normal)                       preparation of the organism for defense or flight (violent random movements) or reflex of playing dead

2. *Libidinal Anxiety* (Id)
   (from within)

   a) (Anxiety neurosis)    =   Free floating anxiety (basic, fundamental feeling) (114)
   (analogous: anxious restlessness after loss of object)
   (restlessness in animals and anxiety neurosis of widows) (264)

   b) (Hysteria)[19]      =   Anxiety bound in the symptom, converted ("stiffened"), not experienced as anxiety

3. *Phobic Anxiety* (Id)    =   Fear of object
   (psychoneurotic anxiety)      with displacement substitute (complex anxiety) (114)
   (from within)           (originally fear of danger from one's drives) (364)
   (phobia, compulsive neurosis)   (situation anxiety) (365)

4. *Conscience Anxiety* (Superego)
   (fear of punishment, "castration anxiety")

   a) (Normal)      =   α) related to object (extraverted), fear of consequences (reality fear, infantile form) (115, 126)
   β) introjected, pure conscience anxiety (objective basic feeling) (115, 126)
   (threat to moral counter-drives) (adult form)

   b) (Compulsive neurosis)    =   Displacement anxiety (with projection onto a displacement substitute)
   (displacement onto a small detail) (391-392)

[19]In hysteria, it is an anxiety which, like any anxiety, originates in the ego, but which here depends on the needs of the id, a fear of loss of love. However, it has been repressed into the unconscious and has been bound to a symptom ("converted"), and thus is no longer affectively manifest.

3. NEUROSIS AS CHANGE IN THE INTERRELATIONSHIP BETWEEN THE
DRIVES

Neurosis, however, is also a dynamic structural shift in the energy relationship between the drives and their components.

First, a heightened *narcissism* is common to all neuroses. In the apparently more constitutionally caused, so-called narcissistic neuroses (states
related to the psychoses, but without their reality disturbances), it is mostly
a matter of a fixated primary narcissism. But also all transference neuroses
involve an increase in narcissism, which, however, here is a secondary narcissism, that is, object libido is retransformed into narcissistic libido. This
is the origin of the well-known egocentricity of the neurotics.

But the relationship between *libido and aggression* also undergoes a shift.
Due to partial re-differentiation, aggressive energy is liberated, but it cannot be abreacted or can be done so only furtively. Since on the other hand,
due to anxiety, the normal positive aggression component of the drive
cannot be satisfied, much accumulation of aggression occurs. This, in turn,
whenever it cannot be discharged in some form such as a hysterical "scene"
or attack, is inhibited and then leads to depressions, dysphorias, shyness,
fatigue and general loss of activity. In some cases this mechanism dominates the entire picture so strongly that it is quite feasible to focus therapy
directly on the liberation of the aggressive energies.[20] Experience shows
that these neuroses play an unusually important part in countries whose
mores present fewer obstacles to libidinal development but where "fine
manners" and fixed form in interpersonal relationships have been made
middle class ideals.

However, disturbances of the aggressive drives are found in *all* neuroses,
and the Rorschach test is a particularly sensitive instrument for measuring
their effects. Instead of the normal connection between aggression and
the self-preservation drive, we find, for example, free aggression in its
negative form in social contacts (so-called neurotic obstinacy), while at
the same time the individual's energy is reduced in his vocational life,
and he is taken advantage of in his struggle for existence. These people
find fault with everything and everyone, but take no steps toward improv-
ing their situation or defending their interests. Instead of normally connecting object libido with aggression, they engage in timid withdrawal
from the opposite sex with simultaneous fantasy excess, which is concerned
with sadistic or masochistic imagery.

But it is not only aggression which lacks anchorage or is split off. All
drives may re-differentiate themselves, and thus the neurotic shows isolated

[20]Tora Sandström, Ist die Aggressivität ein Übel? (Stockholm, Albert Bonniers,
1939).

sadism, masochism, exhibitionism, voyeurism, orality, anality, and of course also the inversion of drive objects (homosexuality, arising out of the normal homosexual component in the Oedipus complex). But all of this takes place in repressed or isolated form or as reaction formations (the "negative of the perversion"). This re-differentiation of the partial drives is the immediate cause of neurotic ambivalence (love and hate co-existing side by side). The two components of genital sexuality, sensuality and tenderness, are also separated out, just as was the case in childhood and puberty.[21] This separation is closely related to the fixation on the old incestuous drive objects of childhood (father and mother) which prevented an integration of these two strivings. Thus in many cases the tender tie to the mother is transferred to an adored "Madonna," who is not desired sexually. Sensuality, on the other hand, is satisfied through a prostitute, who is not loved.

#### 4. NEUROSIS AS ANXIETY DEFENSE

The various anxiety defenses employed by the neurotics are, if anything, even more important for understanding the neuroses than the various forms of anxiety.

Anna Freud[22] enumerates ten of them: repression, regression, reaction formation, isolation, undoing, projection, introjection, turning against the self, turning into the opposite, and sublimation (displacement of the drive aim). She then adds an additional three, which serve more as a defense against external discomfort and danger, namely: denial in fantasy, denial by action or word, and ego-constriction. These forms will be further discussed in relation to the amphithymias. Ego-constriction is already known to us in the shape of neurotic intelligence inhibition.

Turning into the opposite is a transforming of an active process into a passive one, a reversal of the direction of the drive, e.g., sadism becomes masochism. It is therefore not (as in reaction formation) a change of aim with the object remaining constant, but an inversion of the object libido in the narcissistic libido and thus usually a turning against one's own person. (As Nunberg points out, the various kinds of defense often overlap.[23]) In reaction formation, however, the old object remains; the aggressive child becomes tender (still toward the mother) and love of dirt becomes love of cleanliness.

---

[21]The reader will find an excellent survey of the psychic development in puberty, a knowledge of which is indispensable in order to understand the neuroses, in Ernst Kretschmer, Medizinische Psychologie, Georg Thieme, Leipzig 1939, pp. 136-137.
[22]Anna Freud, Das Ich und die Abwehrmechanismen, Wien, 1936, p. 52.
[23]op. cit. p. 210.

The above defense mechanisms are not equally distributed among the various neuroses. Each neurosis has its favorite kinds. Hysteria primarily utilizes repression (of the genital libido). The hysteric is silent in his resistance, he just has no ideas. Reaction formation is also found in the hysteric. Regression takes place only in his imagination and expression, the drive itself remaining on the genital level. Compulsive neurosis prefers isolation. The compulsive is not silent in his resistance, "but he destroys the connection between his ideas."[24] His regression comprises the drive itself, his libido actually regresses to the more primitive pre-genital structure. Compulsives also show a great deal of reaction formation and undoing, i.e., magic. Projection is also found among the compulsive defense mechanisms, but is otherwise the specific mechanism of the paranoid states and psychoses. Sublimation, finally, is the only defense mechanism which mainly occurs in normals.

## THE CHARACTER NEUROSES

The character neuroses represent a special group among the neuroses. The concept and term "character neuroses" is derived from a paper by Franz Alexander: "The Neurotic Character" (Imago, 1921). Wilhelm Reich later developed it further. According to Reich,[25] the character serves the resistance; it is a "chronic hardening of the ego." This hardening (armor) appears in three ways: 1. identification of the ego with the chief frustrating person; 2. through introjection of the aggression against the frustrating person; and 3. by reaction formation against the sexual strivings, their energy being used as a defense (Reich, p. 168). The following general conditions apply in these situations: "The result of character formation depends on: the point in time at which the frustration of the drive occurs; the accumulation and intensity of the frustrations; the drives in which the central frustration is effected; the ratio between the permitted expression and the frustration; the sex of the predominantly frustrating person; the contradictions in the frustrations themselves" (Reich, p. 171).

Reich calls the "normal" character the "genital" one, because he believes that only the "normal" individual has full orgastic potency, although many neurotics actually have excellent orgastic potency. But this is not of crucial importance because orgastic potency is only important as one of several other criteria of normalcy. In addition to the normal character, Reich distinguishes between the instinct ridden and the instinct inhibited characters. The latter fall into four groups: the hysteric character, the

[24]Anna Freud, op. cit. p. 42.
[25]Wilhelm Reich, Charakteranalyse, Copenhagen, 1933.

## TABLE 2. SYMPTOMATOLOGY IN THE NEUROSES*
### The Actual Neuroses

---

**Neurasthenia (85, 86, 91, 107/108)**

(functional affection of the vegetative brain centers) (91)

Basic symptoms: "irritable weakness" (Beard)

1. Hyperaesthesia of the sense organs (lowering of the stimulus threshold for all cerebro-spinal and vegetative excitations) (85)
   Insomnia (disturbances in falling asleep)
   Pseudo-neuralgic pain

+2. Insufficiency of the emergency functions of the sympathetic system (85) (Abnormally rapid exhaustibility of motor efficiency):
   General physical weaknes
   Tremor
   Easy fatiguability

Vegetative Symptoms (86)
   Vasomotor disturbances
   (Increased skin excitability, lability of the pulse)
   Breathing disturbances
   Lability of blood pressure
   Disturbances of the gastro-intestinal functions

"Sexual Neurasthenia" (86)
   Increased pollutions
   Intensive Masturbation
   Ejaculatio praecox
   Impotence
   Hypochondria, anxiety and guilt feelings

Psychasthenia (Janet) (86, 87)
   Increased affective readiness (affective lability)
   Rapid mental fatiguability
   Inability to concentrate
   Tendency to depressive moods

Hypochondria (psychoneurotic superstructure) (107/108)
Tendency to increased self-observation
Faulty interpretation of symptoms ("agglutinated causality" Monakow)
Activation of guilt feelings

---

**Anxiety Neurosis
Symptoms (115-117)**

1. Acute anxiety attack (out of a blue sky)
   (Cardio-vascular symptoms, fear of choking)
   Also protracted anxiety attacks, fear of anxiety

2. During the interval:

   Anxious expectation with increased sympathetic tone
   (insomnia, dizziness, irritability, hyper-aesthesia of the sense organs, easily startled, tremor, perspiration from anxiety, diarrhea, psychic lability, cardiac lability, sighing, threatening fantasy content)

   Anxiety equivalents (without subjective anxiety)
   (Bodily anxiety reflexes, hypnagogic night terrors, frequent urination, increased nocturnal urination, nocturnal ravenous hunger)

   Night terrors in children

   Types of fearfulnes (situation anxiety)
   Agoraphobia
   Fear of being alone (118/119)
   Fear of darknes
   Fear of thunderstorms
   (Pseudophobias, not analysable)

   Hypochondria of the anxiety neurotics (heart) (117/118, 120)

   Secondary psychoneuroses
   Genuine anxiety hysteria or compulsive neurosis (120/121)

   Analogy in accident neurosis (cf. commotion neurasthenia):

   Panic neurosis (126, 127)
   with psychologic overlays:

   Panic hysteria
   (Hysteria or anxiety hysteria) (127)
   (Traumatic neurosis)

---

* The numbers in parentheses in Tables 2 and 3 refer to the pages in Brun's "Allgemeine Neurosenlehre," second edition.

## SYMPTOMATOLOGY IN THE NEUROSES
### The Psychoneuroses

---

**Defense Psychoneuroses (382)**

| Hysteria | Phobia (Anxiety Hysteria) | Compulsive Neurosis |
|---|---|---|
| Abnormal form and course of excitation: (78)<br>Abnormally increased auto- and external-suggestibility<br>Tendency to keep painful impressions away from consciousness, (fending off, blinding oneself, repression)<br>Tendency of startle reflexes and startle attitudes to become rigid, increased capacity for affect displacement and for conversion, unduly long duration of visceral reflexes (pupilar tonus) ("primary incapacity of psychic synthesis") (Janet) . | Anxiety due to instinctual danger from within (364)<br>Repression of the instinctual danger and binding of anxiety in psychoneurotic symptoms (365)<br>Situational anxiety (365)<br>Anxiety is unappealable (368) | 1. Abnormal form and course of excitation: Primary increase of ambivalence of all feelings (78/79, 396) (Doubt, paralysis of readiness to act) (397)<br><br>2. Drive constitution: (397) Strong primary sadism, with excessively strong anal erotic fixation (pedantic exactness, stubbornness, obstinacy) (397, 398)<br><br>3. Mechanism of symptom formation (391-395):<br><br>   a. Strong active sexual impulsiveness in childhood (Oedipus complex) with late repression<br><br>   b. Repression of primary self accusations and displacement to other thought contents (displacement on to a small detail) with "undoing" of action through reactive compulsive acts<br><br>   c. Hostile feelings against individuals who suppress one's impulses<br><br>   d. Defense against and repression of these sadistic impulses and inversions into their opposite (reaction formation) (pathological increase of the moral counter impulses) (Strict superego)<br><br>   e. Insurance against breakthrough of drives through compulsive acts (compromise with the repressed sadistic impulse) Faith in all-powerfulness of thoughts<br>   Overestimation of thinking (Intellectualization of the instinctual life) (pseudo=sublimation)<br><br>   f. Secondary repression of the original drive object (automatization of the compulsive act) |

compulsive character, the phallic-narcissistic character, and the masochistic character. A special sub-type of compulsive character needs to be mentioned here, which we may call "intellectualization neurosis." In these character neuroses, which are very frequent today, especially among young professional persons, the patient attempts to master his anxiety by means of extensive intellectualization of his affects. These persons discuss ad nauseam but experience nothing. Yet, because of their compulsive isolation, they do not understand that their intensely analytic thinking and endless discussion is due to fear of experience. They usually believe that they know themselves extremely well, and because of their iron-hard shell they represent a hard nut to crack even for experienced analysts.

Drawing on the works of Brun and Reich, we now present a short summary of the most important structural characteristics of the character neuroses. A detailed knowledge of this is indispensable to the Rorschach diagnostician.

### The Neurotic Character Types
#### (Based on Reich and Brun [Brun 402-405])

1. *The instinct ridden character*
   Undisguised and uninhibited sexual drive (also perversions)

   Affirmative attitude of the ego to the drives (the drive itself serves as a defense against imagined dangerous situations) — Distinction from compulsive

   Extensive rationalizations — neuroses

   Vivid relations to the external world (No splitting off, reality testing preserved) — Distinction from schizophrenia
   Insoluble conflict between prohibition and impetus
   Isolation and repression of the superego
   Need for punishment (resulting from the effect of the repressed superego on the ego) (Masochism, "crimes resulting from guilt feelings")
   Satisfaction and unburdening of need for punishment through self-injury
   Genesis: sudden traumatic frustration after extensive drive satisfaction

2. *The hysteric character*
   Coquetry plus fear of genitality (fear of orgasm)
   (Play-acting without sexual experience)
   (Men: soft, feminine and excessively polite)
   Lability and strong suggestibility
   Inclination to fantasy and to pseudologia (Reich 214)
   Little inclination to sublimation (because of fully developed genital strivings)
   Bodily conversion symptoms and anxiety
   Genesis: genital fixation on incestuous objects

3. *The compulsive character*
   Anal traits and reaction formations (pedantry, brooding, thriftiness)
   Reactions of pity and guilt feelings (repressed sadism)

Indecisiveness, doubts, mistrust
Control to the point of complete affective inhibition (muscle tensions)
Defense against the genital (phallic-sadistic) instinctual impulses
Regression to the anal level (binding of aggression through anal-erotic energies)
Bodily and psychological tendencies to retention
Behind the affective inhibition, anal (beating, crushing, bruising) and phallic sadism (piercing, boring) (Reich 225)

4. *The phallic-narcissistic character*
Self assured, arrogant conduct
Aggressive courage with insufficient reaction formation against aggression
Strong object relationship with considerable social productive capacity
Contempt of the female with no tender strivings (incapacity to love), with unconscious sadistic revenge impulses (also active homosexuality in both sexes)
Genesis: Inhibition of the genital object libido at the peak of genital aggression through a powerful prohibition

5. *The masochistic character*
Inhibition of all desire to aggression through intense castration anxiety
Constant fear of being left alone
Chronic feeling of sorrow and tendency to complain (Reich 244)
Chronic tendency to self-injury and self-depreciation (Reich 245)
Awkward and clumsy conduct in everyday relations (at times amounting to pseudodementia) (Reich 245)
A need to be loved, which is so heightened that realistic satisfaction is out of the question, accompanied by provocative behavior toward persons by whom one feels disappointed (Reich 250/251)
Normal: The genital character
Libido on genital level with heterosexual object
Oedipus complex definitely resolved
Full orgastic potency

With this, we shall close the section, which has not been meant to be a "Theory of the Neuroses" (that would require many more important details), but only a short summary of certain lines of thought and principles of classification which are of great importance in the daily practice of Rorschach diagnosis.

## PRINCIPLES OF FORMAL RORSCHACH DIAGNOSIS IN THE NEUROSES

As in any Rorschach test evaluation, the Rorschach diagnosis of the neuroses begins with the formal aspects, since the content frequently offers no diagnostic reference points at all. Rorschach calls this formal diagnosis the formal psychogram. He defines it as follows (p. 215): "I designate as the formal psychogram all those conclusions drawn from the formal

## TABLE 3.  ETIOLOGY AND STRUCTURE OF THE NEUROSES
### The Actual Neuroses

**Neurasthenia** (91-94, 94-95, 95-96, 97-101, 102, 105)

Etiology:

1. Exhaustion (91-94)

2. Inadequate libido release in the sexual ⟵⟶ act (97-101)
   (Prevention of orgasm, masturbation with guilt feelings and anxiety) (97-101)

3. Individual's honor is offended, chronic anger, grief and sorrows, haste on the job (102)

   or isolated psychologic shock (especially anxiety shock)

4. Chronic toxic effects (94-95)
   a. External (carbonic oxide, sedatives, intoxicating poisons, nicotine)
   b. Internal (auto-intoxication from stomach and intestinal tract, especially in chronic constipation)
   c. Following infectious diseases

5. Mechanical shock (95/96)
   (traumatic or commotion neurasthenia)
   (Analogy in accident neurosis, cf., panic neurosis under "anxiety neurosis")

   Symptoms:
   Lability of the vegetative nervous systems: pressure in head, dizziness (especially in sudden changes of position), insomnia, low tolerance for alcohol, tremor, sweating, dermographism, cardiovascular symptoms, increased liquor pressure, cerebral sugar secretions;
   Psychologically: inability to concentrate, retardation of thinking process, increased irritability, depression

6. Constitutional neurasthenia (105) (primary insufficience of the hemoencephalic barrier)

**Anxiety Neurosis**
Hormonally released free floating anxiety (objectless anxiety) (117, 365) ⟵——

Pathogenesis:

1. Libido Accumulation (121)
   (forceful inhibition of libido release) (97)
   (Anxiety neurosis only in potent men and non-frigid women) (124)

   Conditions:

   Frustrated sexual excitation (e.g., coitus interuptus)
   Virginal women and children
   Courting
   Sudden discontinuation of regular sexual activities (widows, discontinuation of masturbation)
   Aged people (with temporary reactivation of libido without satisfaction) (124/125)

+2. Constitution (123)

+3. Acquired disposition (123)
   (Resulting from physical weakening, e.g., after infectious diseases, alcoholic excesses, dietary errors, or hard taxing labor) (123, 124)

## ETIOLOGY AND STRUCTURE OF THE NEUROSES
### The Psychoneuroses

| Hysteria | Defense Psychoneuroses (382) | |
| --- | --- | --- |
| | Phobia (Anxiety Hysteria) | Compulsive Neurosis |
| | →Release of anxiety is bound to certain objects or situations (conditioned anxiety) (365) | |
| | Binding of anxiety in psychoneurotic symptoms (365) | |
| | Kind of defense:◄————————►Kind of defense: Anxiety and flight (382) | Reaction formation (382) |
| Repression of affect representation (not of objects) (342, 373) | Repression of object representation, + displacement of affect to a symbolic substitute object or a substitute situation (374) | |
| Affect conversion into◄►Affect conversion into its opposite (314) (pleasure into anxiety, desire into repulsion) | bodily symptoms (342) | Affect conversion into its◄► opposite (Reaction formation) (392) |
| Anxiety affect has disap-◄►Anxiety affect remains (265, 374) peared (365) | | |
| Fixation point: genital level (380) | Fixation point: Pre-genital steps (connection with old childhood anxiety) (380) | Fixation point: Sadistic-anal stage (397) |
| Materialization of the drive conflict in the form of a condensation resulting in an innervation process in one's own body (394) | In the drive conflict the fear of id strivings predominates (394) | Control over the drive conflict in the form of reactive thought compulsions or a reactive act (393, 394) (Projection into the external world and conjuring by means of symbolic substitute objects) |

qualities of the protocol alone, excluding consideration of the content of the interpretations, and obtainable irrespective of whether the subject is known to the examiner or not."

GENERAL CONSIDERATIONS

Rorschach has based the formal diagnosis of the neuroses mainly on color shock and on M repression as well as on appearance of white space percepts, at the same time referring everything to the experience type and to the remaining factors of the experiment. So certain typical neurotic syndromes emerge which will be further discussed below. Since the "pure" forms of the neuroses are relatively rare, and since today in the majority of cases the neurosis is found to be mixed or presents an atypical structure, it is useful to determine first what the formal factors reveal specifically of the neurotic structure in the individual instance.

We will search for the fixation points in the libido development and for the disturbance in object libido, then in general we will try to clarify the number and intensity of the anxiety symptoms; and finally attempt to determine the type of anxiety. Where secondary narcissism dominates the picture, this will appear in the protocol, too. Finally, we must find out whether an increase or shift in the aggressive energies merely plays a part or actually forms the nucleus of the neurosis.

1. The *fixation points* of the neuroses are generally seen most clearly in the complex responses (oral, anal, phallic, genital). However, we shall refer once more to Zulliger's remark (Bero, p. 106), that also the modes of approach are related to the developmental level of the libido, where W represents orality, D genitality, Dd anality, and Ds aggressiveness. These "equations" cannot, of course, be applied mechanically *ad modum* of the Egyptian dreambook, since the manner of approach alone cannot show whether we are dealing with original, manifest or repressed drive energies that have not been deflected from the goal, or with socialized and sublimated energy. This will only appear from the other factors of the experiment.

2. *Disturbances of object libido* exist primarily in the "classical" psychoneuroses (hysteria, phobia, compulsive neurosis). They can be determined from the color responses, especially the color type, and the shock phenomena.

(a) *Color type* directly discloses the developmental level of affectivity. The stronger the C and the CF (right type) are, the more infantile and primitive is the affectivity. If the pure C dominates the picture, the differentiation of the object libido has not at all been effectively achieved. Libido organization is at the primitive level of the neonate who attains his affective balance simply through explosions. In the middle type, with predominantly CF responses, beginnings toward affective object cathexis are usually present (usually represented by a smaller number of FC), or they *have been* present, i.e., the subject may still or again (after a disappointment) be on the unstable stage of "search for stimulation." Genetically this corresponds to the level of the young child with his as yet weak object libido and his predominantly egocentric attitude. Only the left type with the predominance of FC and perhaps occasional CF displays the normal object libidinal cathexis of the adult, i.e., affective stability.

Color type, however, only shows something about the developmental level, or developmental disturbances (fixation or regression); it does not indicate whether these are neurotic, psychopathic, or psychotic. This can only be ascertained from the entire protocol.

(b) *Shock phenomena* indicate whether we have a case of repression of libidinal (or possibly aggressive) energies, or a conversion of libido or aggressiveness into anxiety.

(i) *Color shock* always indicates affect repression, and is therefore the most common index to neurosis. Any color shock proves the presence of neurotic mechanisms (which also may be present as an additional finding in diagnoses of other disturbances, even in the psychoses!). But not every neurosis need display color shock, though it is rarely absent. On the other hand, it is to be noted that milder color shocks appear in almost all individuals who are virtually normal in today's Western civilization. This is apparently a characteristic of our "neurotic age."

Binder[26] only recognizes direct color *shock*, i.e., the manifest form of affective stupor, as typical of the neuroses. He does not consider that we have an index of neurosis in mere flight from color (circumvention of color) and in the "disguised" forms of color shock (description and flight into Ds responses, into the fantastic, abstracts, symbolic percepts, and the like). He may be correct regarding clearly clinical cases of neuroses, cases which are rich in symptoms and in which there is a splitting off of affect-laden ideas (complex formations). But if we include the character neuroses and the numerous cases with mild neurotic trends, his limit is too narrow. Neurotic mechanisms enter the pathological picture in almost any psychological abnormality, from the mildest character neuroses up to the most severe psychoses, and affect repression is to be assumed in practically all forms of color shock.

One may generally follow Rorschach's rule that color shock in extratensive experience type points to hysteria, in introversive experience type

---

[26]Hans Binder, Die klinische Bedeutung des Rorschach'schen Versuchs, in "Psychiatrie und Rorschach'scher Formdeutversuch," Zürich, 1944, pp. 23/24.

to neurasthenia (possibly pseudo-neurasthenia) and psychasthenia (the latter, however, is not always introversive); and in ambiequal experience type to compulsive neurosis.

In evaluating drive-intensity we must keep in mind that "drive-intensity" occurs not only in cases with many color responses (especially with right color type), but appears also in the form of inhibited drive-intensity with comparatively few color responses and severe shocks or other indications of anxiety.[27]

(ii) As we have seen, however, the repression mechanism does not predominate in all the neuroses. It is most pronounced in hysteria (and here, too, color shock tends to be more severe). In compulsive neurosis, repression is less prominent than isolation, and in phobia only the object representation is repressed with the affect being displaced onto a substitute object. At the same time, the affect is converted into its opposite, anxiety, and this anxiety remains. At almost any point at which there is manifest anxiety, *dark shock* is found. (But *red shock,* in the meaning of blood shock, is also frequently combined with anxiety, and this also applies to the color shock of the phobics.) Just as color shock is the most general sign of affect (specifically anxiety) repression, so dark shock is the most general indicator of phobic anxiety, regardless of whether the total picture presents a classical phobia, or whether phobic traits are only incidental as in a number of compulsion-like mixed neuroses or psychopathies. This conversion of affect into anxiety usually concerns the *libidinal* energy. Where we are dealing with *aggression* energy, either the Ds responses are increased (in introversive or ambiequal experience types), or dark shock and/or color shock are displayed preferably as descriptions. But also the complex-determined responses may betray a conversion of aggression, as in phobics who see animals smashed by vehicles in card VI.

3. The *anxiety symptoms* of the Rorschach test were summarized as early as in 1933 by Zulliger.[28] Anxiety is present in all neuroses, but it may be bound up in the symptom and thus be latent, as in hysteria. Zulliger enumerates the following anxiety symptoms (for manifest *and* latent anxiety):

Prolonged response time
Reduction of the number of responses
Reduction of the W
Increase of Dd, Do, Ds

[27]Olav Gärdebring, High P per cent in the Rorschach Test, Zeitschr. f. diagn. Psychologie II, 1954, p. 142.
[28]Hans Zulliger, Die Angst im Formdeutversuch nach Dr. Rorschach, Zeitschrift für psychoanalytische Pädagogik, VII, 1933, pp. 418-420, now enlarged in: Der Tafeln-Z-Test, 1954, pp. 257-258.

Tendency to an approach D-Dd-Ds, frequently also Do
Decrease of M and color responses, coarcting of the experience type
Occasionally increase of CF
Increase of the number of light-dark responses (of all kinds)
Occurrence of MLD (then mostly persecution ideas)
Increase of A per cent and often also of P per cent
Decrease of the H per cent
Hd > H; in intelligent children frequently Ad > A
Increase of the Obj per cent, of plants, with intelligence complex, of Anat per
cent as well
Decrease of the Orig+ per cent, in less endowed persons occasionally increase of
Orig—
Reversion of sequence during the test; it either becomes rigid (in pedantics) or loose
to confused (because of embarrassment)
Production of color shock and/or (with manifest anxiety) of dark shock
Rejection
Avoidance of the interpretation task by fleeing into descriptions, "marking time"
talk
Mention of symmetry, alarm because of lack of symmetry

In addition to these there is also the search for symmetry (Zulliger, Bero, p. 71) as well as specific insecurity symptoms: object criticism, "either or" responses, perspective percepts, negating one's responses, or putting them in question form. Finally, the content is also significant, (blood, mutilation, some flexor movements).

The way in which the Subject reacts to his anxiety may also frequently be seen from the test. In this connection, Zulliger (Tafeln-Z-Test, p. 256, 257) gives the following rules: If, besides several of the above-mentioned anxiety symptoms, *flexor movements* occur, the Subject has the tendency to withdraw from the anxiety situation, to turn away from the outer world. This is a reaction of paralysis (similar to playing dead in response to acute anxiety). If, on the other hand, *extensor movements* occur where no direct signs of aggression are present, a readiness to flee exists, but if direct signs of aggression (CF, increased Ds, content) are displayed, then the anxiety is neutralized by aggression. If a color or dark shock is added, the aggression takes an inward course, and masochistic traits develop.

It must be added that as Zulliger states, on the basis of an observation by Oberholzer (Tafeln-Z-Test, pp. 79 and 187), people who produce a color or red shock in response to card II and immediately after give a CF or C response (mostly with blood), will display *manifest* anxiety. If at the same time the experience balance is introversive, it is a matter of *panic* anxiety, i.e., they lose their heads in difficult situations. (See also "phobia.")

In most cases, it is quite possible to determine the *type of anxiety* from the test:

(a) *Libidinal anxiety* may find expression in all anxiety symptoms, and can usually be recognized by the presence of several pure C in the protocol (libido accumulations; see below under "Anxiety neurosis").

(b) The central symptom of *phobic anxiety* is dark shock. It is indicated as well by reversed sequence, Do responses with good F+ per cent, Dd and light-dark, or light-dark-form responses. In the content one usually finds facial stereotypy in addition to threatening ghosts or animals and mask responses (Group II).

(c) *Castration anxiety* (*conscience anxiety, fear of punishment*) also seems to prefer Do responses in combination with good F+ per cent, and usually several M are present, but ordinarily no dark shock. (In compulsives with dark shock there is ordinarily a phobic admixture in addition to the compulsive symptoms.) Moreover, in conscience anxiety we usually have an increase of Dd and Ds.[29] In reference to content, frequently mutilations appear, at times in the Do response itself, such as a wooden leg and a real leg as a Do response to the lateral extensions of card V, or only "leg without a foot" in response to the thicker of these two.

4. A neurotic individual's *narcissism* (predominantly secondary narcissism) cannot generally be directly determined through the Rorschach test, but this may be done indirectly by ascertaining the psychologic attitudes connected with it. Thus:

(a) Oral fixation (seen by the complex-determined responses and greater prominence of the W factor, see above under: 1. The fixation points);

(b) General infantilism (infantile responses including infantile M, inverse interpretations);

(c) Decreased content factors (FC, P, possibly also D) with the exception of H, which may also occur in narcissism, and frequently flexor movement, with

(d) Simultaneous egocentricity (CF, C), but only occasional egocentric-extratensive experience type; narcissistic persons very often show even a strongly introversive experience type.

(e) Only in very gross cases (mostly perversions) is there also a direct hint of narcissism in mirror percepts as M. The usual mirror responses like the bear with the rock formation which is reflected in the water, seen in card VIII, only express symmetry. They do not belong here. In the narcissistic mirror percepts the reflection lies upon the axis of the symmetrical figure itself, e.g., the black part in the upper detail of the midline of card VI: "A man who views his reflection on the wet pavement."

If narcissism is found in connection with hypochondriacal self-observation, an increased number of anatomical responses also appear.

5. The *increased aggression* of the neurotic is seen primarily in an increase in Ds responses. It may appear in three forms. In an *introversive*

[29] See also: Hans Zulliger, Jugendliche Diebe im Rorschach-Formdeutversuch, Berne, 1938, pp. 164-165.

experience type, Ds are a sign of introjected aggression, i.e., insecurity and self-distrust, hesitancy and circumstantiality, "a mixture of phlegm and asceticism" (as Rorschach calls it, p. 200), but above all, feelings of inadequacy. In an *extratensive* experience type, aggression is directed outward, and is thus manifested as defiance, obstinacy, a tendency to polemics, to contradiction and querulousness. In the *ambiequal* type, aggression is directed in both directions, and the result is constant doubt and skepticism, indecisiveness, affective ambivalence, compulsion toward thoroughness, need to consider all sides of a question, collector's mania and the strong urge to complete things. But even in experience types which are not pure, whether introversive or extratensive, both sides of the formula are always to be inspected. The following crude rule may be set up: in predominantly introversive experience types (e.g., 6:3), inferiority feelings are more conscious and the need for self-assertion more unconscious; in predominantly extratensive types (e.g., 3:6), the need for self-assertion and the urge to dominate are more conscious and the feelings of inadequacy more unconscious.

Neurotic defiance, however, is only indicated if, along with increased Ds and an extratensive experience type, the colors are predominantly labile (right type). With stable color values (left type) and only moderate Ds increase, we usually see a kind of opposition which is more objective, one based on the individual's philosophy of life. In such cases we are not dealing with a neurosis.

But there are also neuroses with Ds increase and stable color values (left type). In most cases, when Ds are exorbitantly increased, a strongly introversive experience type is usually present. These neuroses are particularly frequent in Scandinavia. From the point of view of the older theory of the neuroses, they are difficult to understand, because in them the libidinal development need not be disturbed at all or at least not to a significant degree. However, the development of the aggressive drive is definitely disturbed. Here, then, we find fewer libidinous inhibitions than inhibitions of aggression, with the following consequences: depression, embarrassment, inhibitions in occupational activities, etc. Development of intense anxiety with dark shock, Do, etc., may also be based on inhibition of aggression without necessarily an increase of the Ds. In those cases, however, there are usually either numerous descriptions, or the content betrays the condition (animals which are torn open or which are seen in the act of pinching or piercing; fierce animals, pliers, etc.). Therapy in such neuroses must vary accordingly. Relaxation therapy (e.g., *ad modum* autogenous training, J. H. Schultz) and psychotherapy aiming at freeing the aggressive energy will be accented in such cases.

6. *Reaction formations,* especially against aggression, are sometimes visible in a high P per cent (or corresponding absolute number of P), combined with drive-intensity (see under: 2. color shock).[30] The "flight into banality" is also only a special case of reaction formation.

### THE INDIVIDUAL NEUROSES

1. *Neurasthenia.* The transition between neurasthenia and psychasthenia is a fluid one. Brun defines psychasthenia only as "the primary psychologic symptoms of neurasthenia." Strictly speaking, only psychasthenia can be determined by the Rorschach test. However, if the following factors are present in a protocol, we may conclude with reasonable certainty the existence of neurasthenia: introversive experience type with flexor M, and at the same time the psychasthenia syndrome (cf., section on psychopathies). In most cases an increase in anatomy responses is found (due to the tendency to hypochondriacal reactions).

2. *Anxiety neurosis* with its free floating anxiety is almost always caused by frustrated sexual excitement. However, similar states may also be found after hyperventilation carried on over extended periods of time,[31] something which does not happen spontaneously. In the Rorschach test pattern, just as in the clinical picture, it is at times difficult to draw the line between a genuine anxiety neurosis and the phobic neuroses, since in most cases an anxiety neurosis has secondary phobic accompaniments. Usually only a part of the anxiety is free, while the rest is bound up in phobic and other symptoms.

The rule may be set up that in cases in which the phobic syndrome (see below) occurs together with several pure C (libido accumulation), we must reckon with free floating anxiety, that is with genuine actual neurosis. This is especially true when no facial stereotypy, and few or no phobic complex-determined responses appear in the protocol.

3. *Phobia.* Phobic neuroses, like the compulsion conditions, are mostly based on a psychasthenic constitution, but the latter may be more or less pronounced. The prognosis for recovery will vary according to the firmness of the constitutional foundation. Where the constitutional factor is of medium strength, the prognosis for psychotherapy is usually good, and where this factor is mild (the state being predominantly psychogenic), psychotherapeutic expectations may even be very good, whereas, in cases in which the constitutional component is strong and predominant, the

---

[30]Olav Gärdebring, High P per cent in the Rorschach Test, Zeitschr. f. diagn. Psychologie II, 1954, p. 142.

[31]Gustav Heyer, Das körperlich-seelische Zusammenwirken in den Lebensvorgängen, Munich, 1925, p. 15.

prospects for psychotherapy are not of the best. The Rorschach test in most cases makes possible a reasonably adequate picture of the relationship between constitutional and psychogenic factors, and this fact makes it an especially reliable tool for diagnosis of the phobias.

In the Rorschach test, the phobic syndrome based on a psychasthenic constitution of medium degree looks as follows: color shock is most pronounced in the responses to cards II and/or III, with blood percepts almost always appearing. These may be manifest or latent (for example, "menstruation," "mouse which has been run over"). Sometimes a simple red shock replaces color shock. Dark shock, which is present at the same time, does not result in the interference phenomenon at card VIII in this group of psychasthenics. Among the determinants, several light-dark-form responses are almost regularly found; among the modes of approach, Do responses may appear; and in the content Hd percepts almost always outweigh H. This is due to the facial stereotypy, which as a rule is present. Expressions of embarrassment, such as mention of symmetry and illusions of similarity, may also occur, both occasionally. Complex-determined responses are not infrequent, mostly threatening faces, devils, wild animals, startling ghosts; also masks, the Group II variety, at times also eye-responses. Percepts of a more sadistic type replace these threatening complex-determined responses only where inhibition of aggression is an essential or even a central feature in the etiology, i.e., where the anxiety is to a high degree converted aggressive energy. Typical of such responses would be, "A cat run over by a steamroller" or the like to card VI, or the above "mouse that has been run over" in response to one half of card II (in the side position).

If the psychasthenic basis is pronounced, the interference phenomenon may appear at card VIII. Fortunately, this is quite rare in the relatively "pure" phobias. (It is different in cases in which the phobic symptoms are purely secondary, as in the compulsion type neuroses.) If there is no significant constitutional basis, dark shock may be entirely lacking. In such cases the phobia is entirely psychogenic and generally rather monosymptomatic (e.g., fear of examinations). Such cases have good prognosis and they offer excellent prospects for psychotherapy.

Phobic symptoms (situation anxiety) may occur in various experience types. If the experience type is introversive, it is a case of the above mentioned "panic" anxiety (Oberholzer); these cases may often also show the interference phenomenon at VIII and must then be classed among those with a psychasthenic basis. In the ambiequal experience type, it is rather a matter of a compulsion neurosis with secondary phobias. In these cases, too, we must often reckon with a psychasthenic basis (if interference phenomenon at VIII is present). If the experience type is clearly extratensive, this indicates a phobia in the sense of Freud's anxiety hysteria, i.e., manifest phobic anxiety with displacement substitute, frequently (namely if combined with strong color shock also in the case of cards VIII-X) *concurrent* with converted anxiety bound up in hysterical symptoms (anxiety equivalents, like attacks of perspiration, diarrhea, enuresis, vomiting, etc. *without anxiety affect*). The symptoms in these cases may sometimes change from the phobic form (e.g., agoraphobia) to the hysterical (e.g., dizziness) or the reverse (alternating symptomatology).

The essential feature in the phobic syndrome is therefore the central position of the color shock, or pure red shock in response to card II and/or III without manifest, or latent, blood content. Light-dark form responses also seem to appear rather regularly. Everything else is more incidental.

4. *Hysteria* is known as the most "classical" form of neurosis. It is also the one best known in the Rorschach test. It consists essentially of a combination of extratensive experience type with inclination to coarctation, color shock and right color type, i.e., predominance of CF and C. This opposition of attraction to and rejection of colors in the shock is an expression of the hysteric's affective ambivalence. The affective contact of the hysteric is generally low (little or zero FC), and ordinarily rather high stereotyping is found.

The problem is as yet unsolved whether it is possible to differentiate, in the Rorschach test, between the "pure" neurotic cases and those in which the hysteria includes psychopathic traits (due to stronger constitutional anchorage).

5. *Compulsion neurosis,* as we know, is the neurotic form in which the affective ambivalence already has a strongly constitutional basis and hence dominates the entire picture. This is also expressed in the Rorschach test, where not only color shock and labile color values are found together, but where the experience balance, entirely or approximately ambiequal, already discloses the individual's ambivalence. Here also, however, a tendency toward coarctation is found; the compulsive neurotic neither "comes entirely out of his shell," nor does he "withdraw into himself entirely." As Rorschach observed (p. 112), the more introversive compulsives have a tendency toward compulsive fantasying; the more extratensive ones toward compulsive acts (compulsive movements) ; and the exactly ambiequal ones tend toward pathological doubts and pedantry. In compulsives, color shock is either combined with red shock, or red shock is found without color shock. In the latter case it is often combined with dark shock. The primarily increased aggressiveness, the sadism of the compulsive, displays itself above all in an almost regular increase of Ds, but also frequently in a notable

increase in Dd, the latter representative of specifically anal aggression. The strong and labored suppression of the compulsive's ambivalence and aggression is revealed in his high F+ per cent (often up to 100) and a tendency to Do percepts. His M are usually not numerous as a result of coarctation tendency (stiffening of the affectivity and of kinesthetic resonance). The number of W is usually also somewhat reduced (tendency to accessory depressions due to inhibition of aggression). The sequence is either markedly rigid or loose; it is rarely just orderly. Most compulsives produce predominantly extensor movements, and their complex-determined responses often betray castration anxiety (mutilation responses). According to Kauko K. Kaila,[32] a normal approach type and the occurrence of pure C responses argue against a compulsive neurosis.

6. *Kleptomania* is a special case of the compulsive neurosis, in which the stealing of certain objects is the compulsive act. Correspondingly, the kleptomaniac shows an almost ambiequal experience type, with predominance of color, but usually no FC.[33] In addition to this, since he is a neurotic and his stealing is not due to a general lack of control, the kleptomaniac displays color shock, while his central symptom is represented by confabulatory W and D.[34]

Clinically pure examples of any specific neurosis are quite rare, as also Klopfer and Kelley have noted (op. cit. p. 392). As a rule, various neurotic structures merge into one another. For this reason, it is not easy to find appropriate examples for illustrative purposes.

## EVALUATING THE COMPLEX-DETERMINED RESPONSES

In general, the formal Rorschach diagnosis of the neuroses permits only a rather crude classification of the neuroses. To penetrate more deeply into the structure of the individual case we must resort to the complex-determined responses. Unfortunately, these appear in only a minority of the cases.

It has been repeatedly pointed out that the evaluation of the Rorschach test protocol should always begin with the formal aspects. This does not mean that content aspects can be neglected. Rorschach, himself a psychoanalyst, placed great emphasis on the depth psychology evaluation of the content, especially in the last protocols he left to us. For this purpose

---

[32]Kauko K. Kaila, Über den zwangsneurotischen Symptomenkomplex, Copenhagen, 1949, p. 207.

[33]Hans Zulliger, Jugendliche Diebe im Rorschach-Formdeutversuch, Berne, 1938, p. 71.

[34]Hans Zulliger, Erscheinungsweisen und Bedeutung des Farbschocks beim Rorschach'schen Formdeutversuch, Zeitschrift für Kinderpsychiatrie, Vol. 4, 1938, p. 151.

first of all the "complex" responses are used, this term being used in a broad sense here. One may speak more precisely of the *responses, relevant in respect of* their *content.*

"Complex" responses, of course, occur not only in the neuroses. Besides occurring in virtually healthy individuals, they are also found in psychopaths and psychotics. Since the technique of determining and evaluating the "complex" associations is always the same, the following considerations apply to all cases in which such responses are found.

DETERMINING THE "COMPLEX" RESPONSES

First, the "complex" responses should be noted and written out at the end of the summary of the special phenomena. The method of determining them is based first of all on formal aspects. Only in very exceptional instances, where the content offers especially striking and clear hints in regard to the complex, are responses to be included which are less arresting formally. In the following types of responses, the diagnostician may suspect complex-determined content. First all original and individual responses which are at the same time M or C (all subgroups). Next the DsF(C), which are usually apprehension originals, as well as other apprehension originals. The DsW and certain categories of F also belong here, particularly the MF responses, abstractions and symbolisms, the intersexual responses, percepts of defects and of eyes. In addition, responses should be at times included which are not arresting in regard to form, but are in regard to content.

The procedure recommended would therefore be first to proceed like the poor student in the restaurant who traces the prices on the menu with his finger, stops at the lowest price and orders the herring opposite it. Similarly we will go through the last row and check each Orig as to whether it is M, a color response, DsF(C) or otherwise an apprehension original, and then look more closely at its content. After having thus found the basic stock of "complex" responses, we shall once more go over *all* the responses. To find the rest of the "complex" responses then becomes relatively simple. This procedure in two stages has the advantage of allowing us to ascertain the main theme in the complex-determined content before racking our brains about the doubtful "complex" responses. It simplifies the task.

THE KINDS OF "COMPLEX" RESPONSES

Evaluation of the content of "complex" responses depends on their formal qualities.

1. *M Orig* responses contain an unconscious tendency, a basic *expectancy attitude.* As Rorschach (p. 207) acutely notes, they point to that which

has been lived through but not necessarily that which has been experienced. They express an attitude, a role, which the Subject plays in life, frequently without being aware of it. The girl at the abyss (see above under "censorship") who felt morally threatened by the dangers of the big city, probably had no suspicion of the real motives behind her actions and attitudes.

It is sometimes possible to trace repressed events by this means. One such case may be mentioned here in which the Rorschach test first made it possible to direct suspicion to an undesired pregnancy. This was at a point in time when the patient had still repressed the entire experience and told the examining physician in good faith that she had never had any dealings with a man, and would never do such a "filthy thing," even if she were married (!). The Rorschach protocol yielded the picture of a depression (for which she had been admitted to the clinic), but with no formal reference points beyond this. The protocol, however, contained four original responses, all to card X, of which two were arresting. The dark brown spot inside the middle yellow was a "child's face," and the projections of the outer yellow (> position) was a "kneeling woman." (This detail in fact suggests the famous sculpture "The Kneeling Woman" by Lehmbruck.) This last original was M and yielded the clue to understanding the patient. There she was on her knees, desperate and praying (the patient belonged to a pious sect), and from the child's face one could deduce the rest. The urine specimen was positive, but only after several weeks could the patient recall the events which had led to this pregnancy.

But that which has been lived through is not always unconscious. In some instances the Subject is very much aware of his problems but will not communicate them because of shame or other considerations. Entire family histories of unhappy marriages, of lovers kept apart, etc., may sometimes be deduced from the "complex" responses. The so-called "nervous breakdowns" with incomplete amnesia are frequently gold mines for such "complex" responses. For example, a sensitive insecure female psychasthenic, whose marriage was unhappy because of the insufficient potency of her husband, was admitted to the clinic because of her phobic fear of cutting and piercing instruments and because of compulsive thoughts (to harm her child). The husband had had a nervous breakdown earlier when he discovered that his wife was unfaithful to him. The woman thought that the husband did not know, and initially concealed the matter from the physician. In the test she interpreted card III with the remark, "Well, what is this? This looks like two people who agree." The center of card V looked like "two people who like each other," and the lower section of the upper portion of card VI were "the shoulders of a person who holds a cloak together" (light part). While this last response contained the urge to conceal (enveloping, hiding oneself), the other two "complex" ones revealed a secret love. The discussion showed that the patient fostered a secret love for a married man, whose wife was incurably ill, and who urged her in letters to marry him later on.

At times we find M Orig responses referring to several persons, e.g., mother and child, father and son, king and beggar, etc. These associations usually arise as condensations and are to be understood as double identifications, e.g., identification with mother *and* child by an effeminate infantile man. Even where the identification with one of these figures is compellingly suggested, identification with the other figure often cannot be precluded with certainty. For example, an individual with inhibited aggression interprets the entire lateral contour of card VI in the < position and its two extensions as a man who stands in triumph over his slain opponent (the small projection is the stretched out arm). In this example it is to be kept in mind that sadistic and masochistic traits are usually united in the same individual.

2. *The original color responses* are usually to be "translated" as symbols which betray an *affective relationship* to some latent content. The most frequent responses of this variety (frequently not even Orig) are "explosions" and "fire and smoke"; and recently also the atom-bomb explosion at Bikini. It is quite obvious that these themes express strong affective liabilities and ambivalences. The response "broken heart" to the middle red of card II (CF Orig) is more specific. It was given by a paranoid woman patient, who thought that she was persecuted by her husband's family and that they wanted to estrange him from her. Here again a clear relationship to the central affect is obvious.

3. *DsF(C) responses* (or DsDF[C]) contain mainly *wish fulfillments,* as Rorschach has already pointed out (pp. 199-200). He cites the three-dimensional architectural responses (fortresses, towers, temples, etc.), as expressions of the wish for greater inner stability, projected in these buildings. Such wishes appear in children at a simpler level, as in the case of a small boy who, in response to card VII, sees a "flyer" in the tiny space detail over the "hinge" together with some of the gray. Day and night this boy dreamt of being a pilot. The fairly frequent interpretation of the inner space detail of card II, together with the black pointed detail, as "decanter with stopper," is more ambiguous, however. In people who enjoy a good drink, it may simply reflect "love of the bottle." Where, however, the closing of the bottle with the stopper is especially accented, it may well be the wish of the alcoholic to control his passion (the wish that the bottle may be closed to him). Prognostically this would, of course, be of great significance. One must therefore be a bit careful in evaluating such responses.

4. *DsW responses* occupy a special position. As we have seen, they ordinarily indicate a conflict of environment. If M "complex" responses show that which has been expressed in action, the color "complex" responses that which is felt, the DsF(C) that which is asked for, then the DsW indicate *that which is feared.* The content in these usually points to the area in which the environmental difficulties exist. It is usually a matter of a "pressure situation," Sjöbring's term, by which he understands a chronic conflict situation. This may be demonstrated in a few verified examples: Card II interpreted as "stage prop with a grotto," indicated a daughter's conflict with her mother; Bero card VII in ∨ position (upper space figure), interpreted as "face of a Russian with fur cap and decorations (cockade)," indicated a conflict of a police official with his (uniformed) superior; Bero card VII seen as "introitus vagina with torn parts of the hymen (above) which have remained," indicated difficulties in sexual adjustment in a man who had recently divorced his wife; Bero card VIII seen as "film cartoon figure with head (gray), arms (red), and small legs (brown); stands there like a gorilla," betrayed inadequacy feelings in a man owing to his appearance (the response is at the same time M!) and his clothes, together with resentment because his social position did not permit him finer clothes; Rorschach card II seen as "section through a uterus," showed sexual problems at puberty in a gifted schizoid.

In general, this procedure can be applied only if the DsW responses are SW in Zulliger's sense (the Ws responses usually have a neutral, objective content), and some knowledge of the Subject's life circumstances is necessary in making the interpretation. Even with a thorough knowledge of depth psychology, and especially the symbolism of depth psychology, which is an absolute prerequisite, it is necessary to proceed with the greatest care in this kind of interpretation. It is not always possible to find the correct solution. The procedure in most cases is not applicable to the interpretation of mask responses of Group I.

5. General rules cannot be set up for the interpretation of the complex-determined responses in the *F category.* F associations are usually not complex-related because they are conscious and objective. Only in rare cases do complex-determined themes occur here. Rorschach mentions (p. 210) skeletons, bone structures, and the like, as expressions of inner emptiness, aridity, and coldness. He further mentions wrappings, disguises, and masquerades as indicating tendencies to concealment, to dissimulating affective states. According to Rorschach (p. 214), abstract responses occupy a middle ground between M and color responses, "between the unconscious attitudes and the affect-colored goals of the unconscious." With reference to abstract and symbolic responses, reservations are in order. Not every-

thing that looks like a symbol and which could be a symbol always is a symbol. We must keep in mind Siegfried Bernfeld's famous bon mot: "The Zeppelin is not *only* a phallic symbol; we can even fly to America in one." Form responses which are MF play a special role. These are percepts of anthropomorphic animal movements in non-anthropomorphic animals (without these animals themselves being anthropomorphized as is done in movie cartoons). As mentioned earlier, deeply unconscious attitudes may sometimes be deduced from these associations. In view of the colossal misuse to which these responses have in recent years been subjected, the greatest caution is once again recommended in their interpretation.

Another category of "complex" responses is much more important, these being sometimes M, but very often simple form responses. We have in mind those responses which betray some *sexual mis-identification,* i.e., unconscious mixed sexual attitudes, feminism in men and masculine traits in women. Three degrees of them may be differentiated: 1. "androgynous responses" are the most pronounced ones, such as women with beards, men with breasts and the like. 2. Next are the "hermaphroditic sexual responses," i.e., male genitals seen in details ordinarily perceived as female genitals (e.g., top of IV, middle of VII); or vice versa, female genitals seen in the details usually understood as male (e.g., the pointed detail in II). 3. The weakest forms of such "complex" associations are those striking Orig M in which the sex is opposite to that of the Subject. Caution is again in order here. An M Orig response with female content in a male Subject (and vice versa) may stem from mis-identification, but this is not always the case.

It has already been pointed out when we dealt with compulsive neurosis that the so-called defect interpretations are of the nature of "complex" interpretations and that they usually express a castration complex. It should be added, however, that according to Friedemann,[35] organisms, organs or objects with defects in D or Dd ("woman with mutilated arms," "chest cavity torn open," "nose broken off") are frequently found in organically sick people. He also found that defect responses with M ("limping beggar") appear in climacteric disturbances as well as in brain trauma.

A type of *eye response* to which little attention has been paid hitherto, should be mentioned as still another group of form responses with "complex" content. These are eyes which are frontally directed and look at the observer "reproachfully," in an "evil" or "hostile" manner, often in the mask percepts. They are to be interpreted almost always as paranoid themes, from which a fear of persecution may be deduced. This basic conscience

[35]Adolf Friedemann, Bemerkungen zu Rorschach's Psychodiagnostik, Rorschachiana II, Berne, 1947, p. 63.

anxiety projected onto the external world in a paranoid manner is found mostly in schizoid personalities, with or without a compulsive character, and occasionally in the phobic neuroses. In the case of paranoid schizoids there are usually a number of other schizoid symptoms in the same protocol. Isolated eye interpretations of this nature will by themselves cause suspicion of paranoid self observance and persecution ideas. Possessing the same value, as Merei and later Beck[36] and Zulliger[37] also have observed, are the "usual" eye responses when they occur in numbers in the same protocol, even if they appear only as a mention of a minor detail in human or animal faces, and especially if no other details of the face are mentioned.

Furthermore, attention is called to the group of *denied responses* and, above all, to the *suppressed M*, which may represent specific compromises in conflicts between intellect and affect.

In the form responses, the embellishments and more detailed elaborations deserve attention, especially in the cases of elaboration originals. But even a not so original response may sometimes yield important clues. For instance, a Subject with oral difficulties sees the two dogs in Bero card II with "a chicken bone between them, at which they are nibbling," while another Subject with claustrophobia says, "The two dogs are standing in front of a garden gate and are sorry because they cannot get out."

6. It must finally be admitted that there are "complex" associations which one cannot recognize as such. Occasionally, and only through extensive knowledge of the Subject and his history, can their relation to the complex be understood. For example, a monk once interpreted a detail as a specific part of France, in itself quite a "harmless" geography theme. It became clear, however, that this monk, a convert, had taken his vows at that place. Only in connection with the preceding and the subsequent responses could a meaning be arrived at, which, however, without knowledge of the Subject's life history would have remained quite obscure. Furthermore, without this communication the response could not have been recognized as complex-determined.

## CONTENT OF THE "COMPLEX" RESPONSES

We have so far discussed the content of the "complex" responses only in connection with their formal characteristics and the manner in which they are to be evaluated. Now we should go on to ask what categories of content are in general to be found in these responses? Three broad main categories may be differentiated: fixations, identifications and actual conflicts.

---

[36]Samuel J. Beck, Roschach's Test III. Advances in Interpretation, p. 128.
[37]Hans Zulliger, Der Tafeln-Z-Test, Berne, 1954, pp. 77, 186, and 224.

1. The most frequent kind of "complex" response is the *fixation* on pre-genital phases (oral, anal) or on the phallic phase, as well as on certain isolated partial drives (sadistic, masochistic, exhibitionistic responses).

*Oral* complex responses include teeth, animal fangs, mouths and the like; and also, very frequently, Hd responses as M, that is, faces sticking their tongues out, spitting, blowing, opening their mouths, etc., and possibly also widely opened animal mouths. Bottles, beverages, people and animals drinking, are also frequently oral complex responses, and, of course, all food responses. Female breasts are also usually to be understood as oral complex responses.

Nor do *anal* complex responses usually present great difficulties. Excrements belong here, animals "that drop something," and similar topics; above all, direct anus percepts. Not infrequently they are given, and very significantly, as alternatives for percepts of genitalia (e.g., the response to card VII, middle, "the female organ or the anus," sometimes given, very suggestively, as "the anus of a woman."

While the frequent penis and vagina responses are *genital* percepts, the rather rare specifically *phallic* responses, in the sense of a fixation on the phallic-sadistic phase, appear mainly as symbols of piercing and boring (boring, injection syringes, at times also fever thermometers).

*Sadistic* complex responses are usually very easily recognized. They are war-like scenes, beheaded humans and animals (which may at the same time indicate castration anxiety), the above mentioned triumphant opponent, animals flattened out (by steam roller) or cut open, pliers, scissors, and similar instruments, etc.

*Masochistic* motifs are at times more difficult to recognize as such. They are not always as clear as in "kneeling woman with head cut off" in response to card II in > position. A great many flexor movements belong here (bent, weak, collapsed figures, etc.). The kneeling woman with her head cut off is, of course, also such a response.

Genital responses in a narcissistic syndrome provide suspicion of *exhibitionism*. The same is true of responses such as, "ladies whose skirts are lifted up by the wind" (if seen by a woman), and the above noted "carrot which sticks out of the ground the wrong way," or (typical of psychologic exhibitionism) "an opened-up cranium that one can look into" (red of card IX). *Voyeurism* may be revealed by responses such as, "animals who are looking into a periscope to see what is taking place above the water" (gray middle of card X); or "a rabbit holding a pair of binoculars to its eyes with both paws" (green middle of card X).

*Homosexual* responses have been discussed under "sexual misidentification." They do not usually offer marked difficulties in M responses such as "two girls kissing each other." In overt homosexuality, a conflict with the environment often enters into the picture (as when the men in card III are described as wearing swimming trunks, a DsW response).

2. The *identifications* are almost always M. They were discussed at length previously. They yield information about the family and childhood of the Subject from the point of view of his own experience. They thus explain a number of character traits. Identifications with the opposite sex are, of course, quite important.

3. The *actual conflicts* are directly apparent in some M responses as well as in the wish responses and the DsW responses (friction with environment, pressure situations). Indirect light is often thrown on these by color originals reflecting the affective traumata of the past which gave the actual conflicts their pathological significance. Denied responses and the suppressed M contain re-actualized conflicts, so to speak.

### THE GROUPING OF "COMPLEX" RESPONSES AND THEIR APPEARANCE IN SERIES

After the "complex" responses have been ascertained, and after their content has been determined, it is necessary, if they are numerous, to group and order them according to content, placing the oral, anal, homosexual topics together and so on. This simplifies the task of surveying them and of making an accurate reconstruction of the neurotic structure. Above all, it makes it easy to tell whether or not a theme is repeated a number of times and where. It is just this repetition of the M Orig which simplifies its interpretation and makes for great certainty about it.

It may also be observed that several "complex" responses which occur in a consecutive series often represent a story in a continuous context. Thus a woman physician first sees, in Bero card VI, "a person who carries a male patient on her arms" (black, middle); then, "an idol in the background and in the center a person coming to offer a sacrifice" (W); then "a walrus jumping into the water with extended flippers" (black, middle—birth fantasy!); and then, "a Gothic madonna," as a wish percept (S). The Subject's meaning here is that in the profession one must "sacrifice" oneself for one's patients, and thus give up the possibility of starting a family. The paranoids in particular will often tell an entire story about their prophetic role in this wicked world. In rare instances, almost the entire test is a continuous story. The interpreter must beware of hasty conclusions, however, and of wild "imagining into" the percepts!

## THE CHARACTER NEUROSES

So far, there has been little systematic investigation of the character neuroses. This may in part be due to the fact that what we have said of the neuroses applies even more to the character neuroses, namely, that they are rarely found in "pure" form. In addition, many character neuroses, especially former phobias, are strongly assimilated and thus as hard to diagnose clinically as in the Rorschach test. Such protocols belong in advanced Rorschach seminars, and it is almost impossible to set up general rules for their interpretation.

Although the last word is far from having been spoken about Rorschach diagnosis of the character neuroses, we shall nevertheless offer a few scattered observations about the various types.

THE INSTINCT-RIDDEN CHARACTER of Alexander and Reich is relatively rare. Some cases designated as "hypereroticism" by the clinicians probably belong here. Nymphomania which has grown out of penis envy shows all the essential traits of the instinct-ridden character, especially the utilizing of the drive in the service of defense.

The essential features of the Rorschach picture of the instinct dominated character appear to be an attraction to the red (mostly food responses), a certain attraction to color, and relatively many CF and C with zero or only few Ds (see Schneider's above-cited communication "Eine diagnostische Untersuchung," Zeitschr. f. Neur. 1937, p. 7). The common element in all these factors is a positive attitude to the impulsiveness and to the individual's own affectivity. Average reaction time seems in most cases to be faster, especially for the colored cards. (In one case we found .62 for all cards, .75 for the achromatic, .64 for the black-red, and .44 for the colored cards; these figures are in minutes per response.) In nymphomanic women, moreover, masculine identification and penis envy responses seem to play a part (very numerous penis symbols and responses symbolizing the number 3).

In terms of differential diagnosis instinct-ridden character is distinguished from the anti-social psychopath by the fact that the Ds response does not increase the way it does in the anti-social individual, and by the fact that in contrast to lack of control we here find normal braking factors.

The contrast to the instinct-ridden character would be the neurotic armor, particularly in the compulsive character.

THE HYSTERIC CHARACTER can be distinguished from the hysteric neurosis only with great difficulty. The Rorschach test picture also presents a fluid overlap. The M values may be a little higher and variability somewhat greater (smaller A per cent). If no conspicuous conversion symptoms appear, the labile color values are usually somewhat less, too. But even where such values approach normality, the hysteric character may frequently betray itself in women by a stuporous reaction to male sexual symbols (fear of genitality); and in men by feminine identification in the M Originals.

### THE COMPULSIVE CHARACTER

1. The difference between the compulsive character and the compulsive neurosis is generally only a quantitative one. In one type of compulsive character, the experience type is ambiequal but more coarcted (values of 1:2 as opposed to 3:5 or more in the compulsive neurosis), the color values are a little less labile, and the absolute Ds values and Dd are somewhat lower (however, they are still relatively increased). In other words, in this group the structure is the same as in the compulsive neurosis, except that the ambivalence tension is somewhat lower, i.e., the picture offers fewer symptoms. These are just stiff, dry, precise people.

There is, however, still another type of compulsive character, one more strongly pervaded with oral traits. This group is of a predominantly or purely introversive experience type, while Ds and Dd responses are increased as usual, and Do responses may also appear. These types ordinarily also produce oral-sadistic complex responses (teeth, fangs of animals, etc.). This introversive experience type may be understood in the light of the fact that introversion may arise out of anal tendencies toward retention, as well as out of a displacement of the infantile desire to suck into an intellectual "sucking in" of knowledge.[38] Due to their inhibition of aggression these types also manifest a depressive mood.

In compulsive characters, color shock may at times be delayed (without dark shock having to be present), and sometimes it only appears in the form of red-avoidance (preference for blue and green) (Zulliger, Bero-Test, p. 64).

2. *The anal retention character* is a form of compulsive character in which the retentive tendencies (thrift, miserliness and the corresponding psychological attitudes), which are among the anal traits (pedantry, obstinacy, thriftiness), have developed to a very high degree, and have become second nature to the individual. Certain peculiarities sometimes appear in the Rorschach pictures of such individuals.

Here, too, the experience type is either ambiequal or introversive, but with a certain repression of M (inhibition of productivity). (Extraordinarily high M values in compulsive characters almost always indicate certain oral components.) Color shock may be weak or delayed. There is a general anxious reticence, productivity is low, and the number of responses

[38]Karl Abraham, Psychoanalytische Studien zur Charakterbildung, Vienna, 1925, pp. 19 and 49.

is therefore below average. If quality ambition is also present, the approach type comes close to the W+ type. In most cases, however, only a W± type is achieved, since, due to these people's aversion to anything "well-formed" their indefinite F− are rather numerous ("skeleton of some animal," "an object that is cut open," etc.). Do and light-dark-form responses may also be found, as in any type of anxious reserve. With such excessive carefulness, the level of achievement is naturally lowered, and because of the indefinite F−, the F+ per cent decreases (which is otherwise rare in compulsive characters). Poor anatomy responses also show up. Response time is usually markedly prolonged (the subject hems and haws), which is also consistent with the generally (slightly) depressive basic mood. Mention of symmetry is also typical of this picture. It corresponds to the frequent "need for symmetry" in the anal character (Abraham, op. cit., p. 29). Aggressive fault finding (Dd, Ds) at times seems to be somewhat relegated to the background. However, it is seldom completely lacking. It should also be emphasized that an increase in Ds among compulsive characters is not *only* an indication of heightened aggressive tension, of anal sadism, but is also a direct expression of the anal "tendency to deal with the reverse side of things,"[39] to do everything differently from other people. Rorschach was well aware of this when he characterized the Ds of a compulsive neurotic (p. 146) as an "attitude of energetic oppositionalism, so that the Subject attempts to demonstrate viewpoints which are usually overlooked," or when on p. 199 he speaks of an urge "to look at things from all angles, the need to hear the other side of the story." Finally, it is noteworthy that the anal lack of contact in the retentive character is sometimes expressed in the fact that there are no H and Hd responses in the content, whereas a variety of objects are found (interest in the possession of things).

3. *The hyperintellectualized character* is also a special case of the compulsive character. It occurs whenever the belief in the omnipotence of thought has developed to a specially high degree. In that case, the anxiety defense is effected more or less completely through the mechanism of intellectualization. These types usually display certain special forms of color shock in which descriptions (inhibition of aggression is quite regularly present here as well) and abstract, conceptual and symbolic responses play a dominant role.[40] Red avoidance and preference for yellow also are found (Zulliger, Bero, p. 64). The descriptions and comments about symmetry may pervade the entire protocol. This type of compulsive character is frequently found today among neurotic professional persons.

[39]Ernest Jones, quoted from Karl Abraham, op. cit. p. 30.
[40]See Hans Zulliger, Einführung in den Behn-Rorschach-Test, Berne, 1946, pp. 69, 169, 180 and 71.

THE PHALLIC NARCISSISTIC CHARACTER with its power to act belongs to an extratensive experience type, but does not lack M responses. Color shock is the rule, or at least red shock, and the color values are rather labile. So far, this type resembles hysteria, (which is also genital), but if they are socially adjusted, phallic narcissistic characters have a higher F+ per cent than the hysterics, and they show marked aggressiveness (Ds, Dd). The approach type is usually W-D-Dd (generosity and in addition anal aggressiveness). Sequence is usually loose. M responses are predominantly extensor and display exhibitionistic narcissistic ideas of grandeur in their content (magicians, orators, medicine men, jugglers, sword swallowers, etc.). They produce also quite specific "complex" responses which represent piercing and boring actions ("piercing" sadism). The asocial varieties belonging to this type score a lower F+ per cent and display a tendency toward confabulation. Homosexuality may also appear in them.

THE MASOCHISTIC CHARACTER has scarcely as yet been investigated by the Rorschach test. Judging from a few occasional examples, this type shows rather marked color shock and at times also dark shock, usually with an introversive experience type and definite flexor movements, at times with masochistic content. Do, Dd and Ds increase, indicating castration anxiety and need for aggression, which has been heightened by this castration anxiety but has been introjected.

## APPENDIX: THE PERVERSIONS

Some authors include the perversions among the psychopathies, among them Eugen Bleuler, Eugen Kahn, and Maurice Levine, and so does the Statistical Guide of the State of New York. This has some justification since the development of manifest perversions generally presupposes a constitution (at times found with criminality) marked by an especially strong development of certain partial drives. In addition we find a weakness in the braking factors, in the "cultural counter drives" (in Rudolf Brun's terminology) which also appears to be largely constitutional. At any rate, this ego weakness of the pervert is closely related to the ego weakness of the psychotic, for in the families of perverts we frequently find psychotics. Nevertheless, the genesis of the perversions shows so much similarity to that of the neuroses that we are warranted in considering them a phenomenon somewhere between the neuroses and the psychopathies.

The only Rorschach symptom which applies generally to the perversions is based on the ego weakness typical of these conditions. This symptom is initial censorship; it may be used in diagnosing a perversion if there is no evidence of a psychosis. Wherever we are fortunate enough to find initial censorship in addition to the corresponding "complex" responses in a non-psychotic individual, we may conclude the manifest presence of the particular perversion.

Otherwise we are restricted for our evidence to the "complex" responses, though it is not usually easy to see whether they stem from a manifest perversion, or from the repression of the perversion in a neurosis.

In this regard the inversion of the drive object, *homosexuality*, is no exception, even though it occurs rather frequently in its manifest form. It is even less possible by means of the Rorschach test alone to determine whether the homosexuality in any given case is only a psychologic accompaniment to an intermediate sexual constitution, or whether it is more of a developmental disturbance. Any kind of homosexuality, constitutional, psychogenic, manifest or latent, is expressed in the same kinds of "complex" responses (see above). In some cases, however, it is possible to make a safe guess as to the existence of manifest homosexuality, based on the psychologic conflicts arising reactively and due to the social condemnation of homosexuality. The homosexual usually attempts to conceal the true nature of his sexual life from society ("sexual mimicry," Magnus Hirschfeld). As a result of this wish, homosexuals sometimes produce DsF(C) responses, often with fusion of figure and background, in which there is an effort to conceal own genitality, e.g., the men in card III wear swimming trunks (space figure between waist and legs), or they wear a white apron (figure between arms and legs). Unfortunately, however, we cannot conversely deduce manifest homosexuality simply from such responses, since the same wish shows up in the frequent masturbation conflicts as well as in nymphomania. In both of these groups, the same responses actually do appear.

Among the paraphilias *sadism* and *masochism* (often in the same person) are of the greatest practical significance. The same considerations obtain here as above: the "complex" responses only indicate the quality of the perversion, but do not give us any idea of whether it is latent or manifest. This, however, may be deduced with some probability from the experience type and the strength of the braking factors. A subject with increased Ds, conspicuous sadistic complex responses, and a strongly extratensive experience type (possibly even with pure C), and with inadequate braking factors as well (M+, W+, F+ per cent), raises a strong suspicion of sexual sadism. The certainty of this diagnosis will partly depend on whether the sadistic complex responses express only a generalized aggressiveness, or whether a specific sexual component is revealed. The corresponding observations apply to masochism (but with an introversive experience type).

*Exhibitionism and voyeurism* (also frequently in the same person) betray themselves in very specific "complex" responses. But it is extremely difficult to determine from the total protocol to what degree these tendencies are manifest or latent.

*Fellatio* may generally be looked for in the phallic narcissistic character neurosis. A preference for *cunnilingus* may be present if the corresponding "complex" responses appear (faces with their tongues stuck out as M and so on). Such conjectures cannot, however, usually be checked by the test results themselves. In this area, an especial caution should be made against drawing premature conclusions.

# CHAPTER XI

# *The Psychopathies*

## THE GENUINE (CONSTITUTIONAL) PSYCHOPATHIES

1. PSYCHASTHENIA (SUBVALIDITY). By "psychasthenia" we mean a very specific state, as has been thoroughly described by the Swedish psychiatrist Henrik Sjöbring in his paper, "Psychic Energy and Mental Insufficiency."[1] Its clinical syndrome involves the following manifestations. Because they sleep less deeply, people suffering from this condition are less rested in the morning and exhibit only a lower degree of awakeness during the day. They wake up toward evening and work best at night. In order to save energy, they very easily fall into habit grooves, and are often pedants. In their contacts with other people they are extremely passive and thus tend toward egotism. In spite of their easy fatiguability, they are industrious because of their need to keep busy, but they prefer routine and detail in their work. They easily become nervous and tense if they are not busy, also if large demands are made on them, and especially if they have to make any kind of responsible decision. They avoid synthesizing activity and tend to have feelings of doubt and indecision. Compulsive symptoms and phobias frequently develop in them (but these are secondary, just as in Janet's psychasthenia). Their activity is extensively determined by external influences, and so they are forgetful, absent-minded and tend to make mistakes in their reactions. Since larger goals are difficult for them to reach, they develop insecurity, inadequacy feelings, and insufficient self-confidence with a tendency to depressive moods (usually rather superficial) and irritability, and sometimes hypochondriacal ideas. If the demands become too much for them, they at times develop states of clouded consciousness (as protective and defense mechanisms).

This psychasthenia syndrome is to be looked on as a diagnosis of a status. According to Sjöbring's school, this status is in the majority of cases due to organic lesions (traumatic, infectious).[2] Only where an organic lesion cannot be demonstrated, does Sjöbring presuppose a certain negative constitutional variation as the cause. He calls this subvalidity.[3] Sjöbring

[1] Uppsala Läkareförenings Förhandlingar, 1922, pp. 163-214.

[2] I owe especial thanks to Tore Broman of Gothenburg, who called my attention to my mistaken belief that Sjöbring usually equated psychasthenia with subvalidity. This is not the case. Only in a minority of cases is the psychasthenic syndrome based, according to Sjöbring, on a subvalid constitution.

[3] This term can only be understood with reference to Sjöbring's constitution system. It would lead us too far afield to discuss it here. For those interested, reference is made to my paper "Der Psychastheniebegriff (Subvalidät) nach Sjöbring" in "Schweizerische Zeitschrift für Psychologie und ihre Anwendungen," 1948, vol. 7, pp. 179-190.

understands this as a decrease of potential psychic energy due to the low energy density of the various tissue elements. Psychasthenia is thus a "genuine" psychopathy only in the sense of subvalidity. In all cases of organic etiology it would be better to speak of "organic pseudo-psychopathy" (see below).

As has been elsewhere pointed out in some detail,[4] the core syndrome of the psychasthenic Rorschach test protocol consists of a peculiar distribution of shock. Most psychasthenics show dark shock, with color shock, and with interference phenomenon at VIII. Occasionally a clear red shock appears in addition to the two other kinds (see chapter 5 concerning means of establishing diagnosis in these cases). There is even a suggestion that it has a certain diagnostic significance in this connection. The red shock then appears to be the connecting link between the compulsive (color shock with red shock) and the phobic (dark shock with red shock) symptom pattern. Actually, we will find in general that the cases with only color and dark shock and the interference phenomenon at VIII tend to show simple subvalidity, while those with all three kinds of shock (with, or at times without, the interference phenomenon at VIII) frequently represent psychasthenics with a rich array of compulsive-phobic symptoms.

One, or usually several, accessory symptoms are found in addition to this core syndrome: subject-criticism, isolated emphasis on symmetry, either-or responses, denial, responses in question form, forced emphasis on the middle, and possibly perspective responses. All these are indications of insecurity. In addition, we find object criticism and pedantic formulation as signs of caution and pedantry; and finally, descriptions (aggression inhibition!) and a few illusions of similarity, as stupor symptoms. As Roland Kuhn has demonstrated, some psychasthenics have mask responses in their content. This corresponds to their usually weak affective contact, and also (especially in percepts of disguised figures) to their disinclination to assume responsibility.[5]

The practical significance of this status diagnosis is not limited to the medical field. The psychologist Ulrich Moser of Zürich told me, for instance, that he had an opportunity to use the Rorschach test to examine persons who had had difficulty in learning to drive a car, having failed the examination for the driver's license several times. In about half of them Moser found the above psychasthenic syndrome to a high degree. Severe psychasthenics thus seem to be unsuited for driving automobiles. This was again demonstrated by the test apparatus on which these individuals were unable to do two or three things simultaneously and to distribute their

[4] Ewald Bohm, Die Rorschach-Diagnose der Psychasthenie (bezw. Subvalidät), Rorschachiana III, Berne, 1950.
[5] Roland Kuhn, Über Maskendeutungen im Rorschach'schen Versuch, Basel, 1944, pp. 58 and 87.

attention correspondingly. According to Sjöbring, this difficulty is typical for the psychasthenics.

2. THE SENSITIVE PSYCHOPATHIC TYPE. The sensitive type is akin to the asthenic. Many traits of the psychasthenic syndrome are found in such individuals as well, above all the lack of self-assurance. But something additional is found here, an intense sensitivity and a "conscious retention of strong affective imagination patterns" which the person is unable to discharge (Kretschmer). These usually hypermoralistic individuals cannot forgive themselves anything, and in spite of their lack of self-confidence, their inner struggles betray a sthenic component (at times intrapsychic inhibitions, see below). If to all this the projection mechanism is added, this state may even show up as a transition to the paranoid. (As we shall see later, the Rorschach test actually shows a fluid transition from such sensitivity to involutional paranoia.)

The psychasthenic Rorschach syndrome is usually found in these sensitive individuals. As a consequence of their severe dissatisfaction with them-selves, subject-criticism is almost always present. It has, therefore, progressed from an accessory to a primary symptom. In addition, light-dark percepts are almost always present (dysphoric mood). This exhausts the Rorschach test syndrome in the more asthenic varieties. In the more sthenic kinds (i.e., the sensitive individuals in the narrower sense of Kretschmer's defini-tion), we find also an accent on shading (F[Fb]) responses, and regularly accompanied by intrapsychic inhibition, i.e., an emphasis on objectivity, or on topological or temporal distance.[6] These "objective" percepts often follow immediately after a light-dark percept as visible evidence of the inner struggle against the dysphoric moods. Moreover, sensitive individuals usually display an introversive experience balance and in their approach the emphasis is on W (see below, "The Paranoid Presenile Psychosis").

3. THE SCHIZOID PERSONALITY. It is assumed that the concept and content of this constitutional type are well known. The Rorschach syndrome of the schizoid personality is a very rich one, although the individual patient usually manifests only a fraction of these symptoms.[7] If, however, two or more decidedly specific symptoms are found (e.g., M with double mean-

[6]Hans Binder, Die Helldunkeldeutungen etc. pp. 235/236.

[7]To this as to all other Rorschach test syndromes applies that they are ideal types with which the individual protocol may agree only in part. How much or how little is required for a diagnosis is a matter of judgement, and depends on the correct evaluation of the psychological meanings of the various factors. A purely mechanical and statistical counting of "signs" which may have radically different values (as is the practice in some places) usually leads to faulty results. This has been demon-strated by K. W. Bash, among others. The evaluation of a Rorschach test is not a

ings, confused sequence, contaminations, etc.) we can usually count on a schizoid constitutional feature.

If, on the other hand, many schizoid symptoms emerge, it may be difficult to make a differential diagnosis from schizophrenia. The following is offered as a rule of thumb. We are dealing with only a schizoid personality if no dementia is found (good F+ per cent, predominantly good W). Furthermore, the schizoid personality does not usually produce gross contaminations with neologisms, and in most cases no perseverations (except in cases of combination with the ixothymic constitution, which is not altogether rare).

The Rorschach syndrome for the schizoid personality manifests a large number of symptoms which appear also in schizophrenia, except that in the schizoid they are usually not quite so frequent, and they are less pronounced qualitatively, "watered down," so to speak. Number of responses is usually above average, but no hard and fast rule can be laid down. Subject-criticism emerges at times, found by Frankel and Benjamin in incipient schizophrenia, too. Response time is usually shortened. This may not be so if there is overlapping with other syndromes, especially if depression also is present. (But even in definite schizophrenics with depression, reaction time is at times fast.) DsW very often occur (especially in response to card I), and this ordinarily indicates a paranoid attitude to the environment, even more so if they are SW.[8] Also DW, DdW, DdD and odd Dd are not rare. When hypochondriacal mechanisms play a part, there is a clear increase of anatomy responses. In very pronounced cases which are showing a transition to latent schizophrenia, sex and blood responses are almost regular topics, which in another context may be merely a harmless neurosis. H responses usually exceed Hd. Orig+ and Orig− are often found in the same protocol. These include not only the "weak" Orig− of the neurotics or the helpless Orig− of the organics, but often surprisingly curious and deviant interpretations. The occasional appearance of a few F(C) (Binder) with few or no FC and many CF and C is an especially interesting symptom. It reveals the typical inner sensitivity with lack of external contact. This is where the schizoid overlaps with the sensitive personality. We are inevitably reminded of Kretschmer's lively simile: "Many schizoid individuals are like bare Roman houses, villas which have closed their blinds from the glaring sun; in the dampened interior, however, feasts and celebrations are carried on."[9] Sequence is usually pretty

mechanical task, but a constructive one. The summary in tabular form of all syndromes contained in this book is reserved for a later publication.

[8]Böszörményi and Meri first referred to the frequent finding of DsW, especially in card I, and predominantly in process schizophrenia, Schweizer Archiv f. Neurologie und Psychiatrie Vol. 45, 1940, p. 283.

[9]Ernst Kretschmer, Körperbau und Charakter, Berlin, 1944, p. 159.

loose, at times definitely confused.[10] M responses with double meanings are found now and then, indicating a tendency to splitting of the ego functions. The frequent subjective feelings of inner instability in these people is occasionally expressed in perspective DsF(C) responses, or in a pronounced emphasis on the middle of the test card. Contaminations are not rare in the protocols of schizoid personalities, but usually take a borderline form, appearing either as clouds which resemble humans or animals, or as "mixtures," "crossings," and "in between things." That is, they always retain a certain amount of reality testing. However, we may find, although rarely, confabulations, or confabulatory combinations, i.e., responses which are no longer fully consistent with reality. "Number" or position responses are rare in schizoids, but they may appear, like the response "six heads" to card VII. Self-references and evaluating remarks are not rare. The same is true for abstractions, descriptions, impressions and possibly intellectual light-dark interpretations. All four of these represent anxiety defense by way of intellectualization, so common in the schizoid individual. Occasionally, as Zulliger (Tafeln-Z-Test, p. 82) points out, the schizoid will complain of lack of symmetry. Now and then an instance of color naming finds its way into the protocol of the schizoid individual. Initial censorship, the indicator of ego weakness, has also been observed without this necessarily pointing to psychosis. Except in schizophrenics, the very rare kinetic descriptions are probably found only in schizoids. Finally, paranoid complex responses (reproachful eyes and the like or several "usual" eye responses) are now and then found in schizoid personalities of paranoid type. (Also MLD responses may occasionally occur [Zulliger]).

In spite of a certain tendency of the schizoid personality to show an introversive balance, there is no definite correlation between the schizoid personality and introversion. According to Manfred Bleuler,[11] only intelligent schizoid personalities belong to the introversive experience type.

It is a curious fact that the overcompensated color shock is also seen in remarkably many schizoids, otherwise typical of a tendency to psychogenic psychosis. This suggests that these particular psychogenic patterns may be looked on as schizaffinic psychoses (so-called marginal schizophrenic psychoses), the frequent schizoid symptoms of which might be due to a heterozygous schizophrenia gene.[12]

[10]Klopfer has occasionally found confusion sequence in normals, too (Klopfer and Kelley, p. 274). One may gather from his hint that these were "very brilliant, though erratic, normal people" that most of them were schizoid personalities.

[11]Manfred Bleuler, Der Rorschach-Versuch als Unterscheidungsmittel von Konstitution und Prozess, Zeitschr. f. d. ges. Neurologie und Psychiatrie, Vol. 151, p. 576.

[12]For more literature on the problem of the marginal psychoses, see Erik Strömgren, Episodiske Psykoser, Copenhagen, 1940, p. 113 ff. and Poul Faergeman, De Psykogene Psykoser, Copenhagen, 1945, pp. 90/91, both works in the Danish language.

4. THE CYCLOID PERSONALITY. The Rorschach diagnosis of the cycloid constitution is as easy to explain as it is difficult to use. It simply depends on whether the formal factors in a protocol fit into the middle column of our diagnostic table for the manic-depressive group (Rorschach "Psycho-diagnostik," p. 263). In practice this diagnosis is difficult to make because in the cycloid we usually find a status combining both low grade depressive and slightly hypomanic mood. There are two reasons for the difficulty: in the first place the deviations of the cycloids from normals are not very great and hence not very striking. Secondly, the fusion of the depressive and the hypomanic syndrome usually yields such a complicated total picture that the cycloid elements in the protocol may easily be overlooked.

If, therefore, a cycloid constitution is suspected, the best procedure is to prepare a list of the depressive and the hypomanic traits in the particular protocol. One may then determine whether the values of all the factors (F+ per cent, sequence, W, approach, A and Orig per cents, M, colors, response total, time, H : Hd) appear in either of these lists. (There also are various third possibilities, since the values represented by these lists are not simple alternatives, see chapter 13.) In such mixed states the relation of F+ per cent to M need not be an inverse one as in the pure states; i.e., a normal, direct proportion may be maintained, and this may further complicate the recognition of this syndrome.

Whenever the cycloid personality appears in pure phases, i.e., clearly alternating depressive and hypomanic moods, it is, of course, much easier to recognize it.

For purposes of differential diagnosis we must be especially careful about young individuals among whom organic (traumatic, post-infectious) pseudo-hypomanias are frequently found, the organic etiology of which may easily be overlooked. However, these hyper-irritable encephalopathic young people can in most cases be clearly spotted by a careful analysis of the Rorschach test protocol.

5. THE IXOID PERSONALITY. Ixoid psychopathy is something between an ixothymic constitution and a mild form of epilepsy. The ixothymic symptoms are here more pronounced and at times border on a kind of epilepsy, which only offers equivalents without producing motor convulsions. Strömgren[13] offers the following description of ixoid psychopathy. The perseveration tendency is very pronounced, intellectually as well as emotionally. The ixoids therefore tend to lengthy displacements of mood. Their contact with others is superficial but sticky, often characterized by the typical "faithful dog" look. The contact, however, lasts only as long as the other

[13]Erik Strömgren, Om Psykopati hos Börn in "Börnesagens Tidende," 1941, pp. 6-8 of the offprint.

partner shares the interests and moods of the ixoid individual. Ixoid persons are very much creatures of habit, slow in development. The psychological development of ixoid children may therefore lag behind their physical development. Their motor behavior is clumsy and awkward, their voices monotonous without modulation. In expression of affect they are explosive; the slightest difficulty may release outbreaks of rage. Due to their good-nature, however, they later repent their explosive acts bitterly. Ixoid children often display night restlessness, toss in bed, talk in their sleep, and manifest nocturnal anxiety attacks. Adults are mainly hypersocial, conscientious and helpful to others. In spite of this, they have difficulty in adjusting to the family due to their lack of elasticity. At times psychogenic psychoses are found in them. There is a strong tendency to suicide.[14] Very typical of the ixoids is their persistent enuresis which often continues to puberty, but finally ceases by itself. (Where there is suspicion of ixoid personality, this possibility is always to be explored.) Body-build of the ixoid is usually athletic or dysplastic.

The following conditions are found in the families of ixoid persons: epilepsy, migraine, speech disturbances (especially stuttering), left-handedness, tendency to enuresis, frequently also mental deficiency and strikingly many twins (Strömgren, op. cit. p. 6). Closely akin and frequently found in the families of ixoids or ixothymics are the so-called epileptoid disorders, which are better expressed by Karl Kleist as the "group of the convulsion-like illness,"[15] and which would roughly correspond to Szondi's "paroxysmal group." Included here are: affective epilepsy, pyknolepsy, narcolepsy, Oppenheim's psychasthenic attacks, dipsomania, poriomania, and, as already mentioned, migraine (Kleist, op. cit. p. 57). These illnesses share "specific identical elements" with one another as well as with epilepsy and, besides, their constitutional elements have a certain affinity with one another and with epilepsy (Kleist, op cit. p. 62). All these constitutions are independently hereditary, although with numerous overlappings (Kleist, op. cit. pp. 62/63 and 65).

Family anamnesis is thus an important complement to the Rorschach test. When ixoid psychopathy is suspected, it is always to be utilized to support the Rorschach test results.

The type which Rorschach described as "epileptoid" (characterized by anatomic stereotypy with perseveration, extratensive experience type, low $F+$ per cent, fairly high Orig per cent ($\mp$), approach W – D, loose sequence, confabulations, evaluating remarks, and color naming) is only one of several possibilities of ixoid personality. Anatomic stereotypy with

---

[14]Karl Gustav Dahlgren. On Suicide and Attempted Suicide, Lund, 1945, p. 147.

[15]Karl Kleist, Episodische Dämmerzustände, Leipzig, 1926, p. 62.

perseveration is also found in other types, in genuine epilepsy with hysterical character and in traumatic epilepsy (Bovet). Without perseveration, it is found practically everywhere (Zolliker, see chapter 5). Anatomic perseveration is here only a special case of sticking to the theme, which may also occur with other topics, e.g., plants (Bovet).[16]

The ixothymia syndrome (see above, chapter 9) may also find application to the diagnosis of ixoid personality. In ixoids, however, the symptoms tend to be more pronounced, and instead of the frequently stable color values of the more "normal" ixothymics, they usually produce considerably more labile color values, at times reaching the explosive stage.

6. LABILE MOODS in the Rorschach picture roughly correspond to that which Binder has described as "chronic dysphoria."[17] By this Binder understands (p. 240) "the endogenous as well as reactive dysphoria which last for extended periods of time," and also the "autochthonous mood lability." The light-dark responses themselves, which are the principal basis of this diagnosis, only betray the dysphoric displacements of mood, however (Binder, op. cit. p. 240). In cases in which nothing is found beside this accumulation of light-dark responses, one may therefore speak directly of a *"dysphoric psychopathy."*

The syndrome itself consists of increased light-dark responses, frequently in short consecutive series of several such responses. They may just as easily be D as W, and may appear in the first as well as in the later responses to a card. "Dark attraction" may also appear here. The light-dark responses often disclose an affective emphasis, and their content at times betrays "a uniform mood atmosphere" (Binder, op. cit. p. 243). Depending on whether their content accents the mechanism of paralysis, flight, or aggression, we may characterize the mood as *depressive, anxious,* or *irritated.*

Whereas in most cases the depressive mood only goes with light-dark reactions, but with few or no color responses, the *anxious* or *irritated* dysphorias, on the other hand, in addition to an increase in light-dark responses, also manifest an increase in the labile color responses (CF, C), the chief representatives of affective lability. Subjects with increased CF and C belong to the labile mood category in its proper and stricter sense, especially if the Ds responses do not also increase.

Excitable individuals, finally, only show increase in the labile color values *without* increase in the Hd interpretations.[18] If one insists on retain-

[16]Th. Bovet, Der Rorschach-Versuch bei verschiedenen Formen von Epilepsie. Schweizer Archiv für Neurologie u. Psychiatrie, Vol. 37, 1936, pp. 156-157.

[17]Hans Binder, Die Helldunkeldeutungen etc. pp. 240 ff.

[18]Roland Kuhn, Der Rorschach'sche Formdeutversuch in der Psychiatrie, Basel, 1940, p. 43.

ing the category of hyperthymic and explosive psychopathy, these excitable individuals may at times be so classified. In most cases, however, the hyperthymic will turn out to be hysteric neurotics or psychopaths, respectively, or hypomanic cycloids (or a mixture of both); and the explosive types, ixoids.

7. UNCONTROLLED WEAK-WILLED INDIVIDUALS. The core of the Rorschach test syndrome in uncontrolled individuals was also first discussed by Binder (op. cit. p. 246). He started with what he called "common, reactive mood lability" (op. cit., p. 238-240). It is marked by occasional light-dark interpretations which are usually seen as W, and occur as first responses to the cards, usually indifferent in respect to content. If furthermore "insufficient intrapsychic regulation" (p. 245-251) is found, we have an uncontrolled individual. This inadequate self-regulation is revealed in the dominantly labile light-dark interpretations (light-dark form and pure light-dark); in the appearance of "primitive light-dark responses" (and also map responses); in "illusory fantasies," which are projected into the blots (that is, there is confabulation); and (especially in the hysterics whom Binder puts principally among the psychopaths) in moods which are occasionally elaborated in a dramatic and pseudological fashion. Already this makes it clear that there is a fluid transition between lack of control and pseudologia, and indeed the uncontrollable person often reveals mythomanic traits. Depending on the traits which predominate, the patient will be classed in one group or the other.

Our own observations have demonstrated to us that this core syndrome of Binder's may be rounded out in different ways. In the first place, Binder's "primitive light-dark responses" (see chapter 3) closely approach the amorphous black and gray interpretations described by Oberholzer (chapter 5, No. 47). The difference is a subtle one, and it may at times be difficult to decide whether these responses are to be scored color form or light-dark-form. A response like "dirty snow" (card VII) may just as well be one as the other. The effect of an error would not be very serious inasmuch as the uncontrolled weak-willed person at times actually produces both response categories in the same protocol. The increase of CF without a corresponding increase in DS (see chapter 8), observed already by Rorschach himself, naturally also plays an important part here. If M occur, they are typically mainly flexor movements, and any "complex" responses among them often express passivity, and at times betray a mother attachment and mother identification (even in males). Correspondingly, the uncontrolled person also gives infantile responses.

The total syndrome of the uncontrolled would then be as follows: Experience type extratensive; a preponderance of CF (and at times also C), usually without Ds increase; insufficient affective braking; amorphous black or gray responses (Oberholzer); insufficient intrapsychic regulation (including primitive light-dark responses, Binder); flexor movements; infantile responses; confabulations (especially pronounced in simultaneous mythomania); and possibly "complex" responses which express passivity or a mother attachment.

8. THE MYTHOMANICS (PSEUDOLOGICAL), as mentioned before, are rather closely related to the uncontrolled types, in fact they are actually a sub-group of them. Pseudologic or fantastic psychopathy is characterized by an especially labile conception of oneself (in Jaspers' sense). These psychopaths show a tendency to identify with whatever is closest at hand.[19] They share this characteristic with all the uncontrolled persons, whose great suggestibility essentially boils down to an increased readiness for identification.

However, there is something more than this which characterizes the mythomanics, and which is not necessarily related to lack of control, namely, their poorly developed reality testing. In them as in the child, there are no fixed boundaries between fantasy and reality (see chapter 10). From this point of view one may designate them as psycho-infantile. Actually, they are just that, in several other respects as well.

Beside the general characteristics of the uncontrolled individual, the mythomanics are chiefly identified in the Rorschach test by confabulations. These may belong either to the DW type, or merely to the "wild" Orig— which need not be DW. At the same time the "reality testing factors" are reduced (F+ and P per cent). Most of these cases have a clearly heightened need for self-assertion, which the test reveals in their many, but mostly poor W (W∓ or at least W±). Their approach does not necessarily express a pure W type, but the emphasis is in most cases on W. Their need for recognition is frequently also apparent in the content of their responses, since mythomanics like to expatiate on all kinds of topics of which they have hardly any knowledge. Animals and plants are given a "scientific" coloring, or they are exotic. The objects include special instruments, exotic religious objects and the like. The formulations of these responses (frequently mistaken technical terms and foreign words) quite easily betray the Subject's real ignorance, and the accuracy of their forms usually leaves much to be desired.

9. ANTISOCIAL INDIVIDUALS are by no means a homogenous group, but comprise a number of heterogenous symptomatic pictures. No doubt a great number of them have character neuroses, and marking out the con-

[19]Erik Strömgren, Om Bevidsthedsforstyrrelser, Copenhagen, 1945.

stitutional and the cultural factors is especially problematic in this group. From the legal and sociologic points of view, however, it has proved practical to group them together, and on closer examination the several subgroups are indeed found to contain certain common psychological elements, especially their heightened aggressiveness. Thus "moral insanity" (a much disputed concept, based on a semantic misunderstanding,[20] as demonstrated by Wyrsch) arises out of the concomitance of strong narcissism with strong destructive urges.[21] And in fact the entire group of antisocial personalities is characterized in the Rorschach test by an increase of Ds and a lack of FC responses.

Antisocial personalities have been particularly thoroughly studied in Rorschach test research, and two of the best papers in the entire Rorschach literature, by Boss and by Zulliger, deal with them.[22] Boss distinguishes three degrees of antisocial personalities: strong, medium, and weak. The strong ones are the *active-obstinate* antisocials, the medium ones are the *passive* antisocials (uncontrolled, weaklings), and the weak ones are the *relatively adjusted, predominantly neurotic* antisocials with a good prognosis. This last group, which strictly speaking does not belong to the psychopaths, produces the lowest number of Ds. Their experience balance is coarcted or coarctative, and most of them have color shock. Like the other groups, the neurotic antisocials yield few or zero FC and few or zero M (lack of braking), but their F+ per cent is almost 100, and their sequence is cautiously reversed. Thus they are more reticent than the reckless ones. The number of W is normal, they have few Dd (in this, too, manifesting their lesser aggressiveness), a low Orig per cent, and a high A per cent and P per cent. That their antisocial behavior is based on anxiety, may also be seen in the fact that Hd is greater than H, and Ad than A, and in the fact that they give occasional Do responses. In addition, they react with numerous F(C) (in Rorschach's original sense, i.e., including light-dark responses; Binder's paper had not yet appeared).

It is otherwise with the active and the passive antisocial psychopaths. Here the Ds responses show clear increase, more so in the active than in the passive psychopaths (increased aggressiveness). The experience balance is egocentric-extratensive, and there is a predominance of CF and C (right color type). Instead of color shock there usually is only color flight. FC

[20]André Repond, "Gentlemen Cambrioleurs," in Meng. "Die Prophylaxe des Verbrechens, Basel, 1948, p. 57.

[21]Paul Reiwald, Verbrechensverhütung als Teil der Gesellschaftspsychohygiene, in Meng, "Die Prophylaxe des Verbrechens," Basel, 1948, p. 181.

[22]Medard Boss, Psychologisch-charakterologische Untersuchungen bei antisozialen Psychopathen mit Hilfe der Rorschach'schen Formdeutversuchs, Zeitschr. f. d. ges. Neurologie u. Psychiatre, Vol. 133, 1931, pp. 544-575—Hans Zulliger, Jugendliche Diebe im Rorschach-Formdeutversuch, Berne, 1938.

and M are almost completely lacking (as in the first group). F+ per cent is relatively high, even here, but the sequence in the active psychopaths is loose to confused, and in the passive ones it is more orderly. W responses are increased but they are not always good ones (W±), i.e., there is a strong need for self-assertion. Dd usually are increased, more so in the active than in the passive cases (anal admixture in the aggressiveness). The approach typical for antisocial psychopaths is, therefore, $W - Dd - Ds$. In the active psychopaths Orig per cent is high, with low A per cent. In the passive ones it is average with average A per cent (and with corresponding P per cent). Their greater liberation is revealed in the normal proportion H > Hd and A > Ad. Active antisocials also display many objects in the content of their responses. In these two groups, too, the F(C) (in Rorschach's broader sense) increase. Apparently all antisocials are basically uncomfortable (dysphorias). As result of the lack of braking M, with a concomitant need for self-assertion, both of these groups manifest a typical inversion of the W to M+ relationship, consisting of a reversed proportion.

*Thieves* of unsteady character (the uncontrolled) form a special group. According to Zulliger they are characterized primarily by their confabulatory W and by an extratensive experience balance with predominance of CF and C. (Introversive confabulators do not steal, they only lie.) These are the essential factors of the syndrome. The following supporting findings should be added: a loosened sequence, more than one Ds, decrease of H and Hd, and a marked tendency to stereotypy. All this, however, only points to thieving tendencies. Manifest stealing, the carrying out of the act, is to be expected only if the affective brakes are absent, in other words, if there are no M and LD responses. It should also be mentioned that thieving epileptics confabulate in their F responses. Confabulatory M are insignificant in epilepsy, which in itself tends toward M-. Thieves in jail usually show no such syndrome. They have M, preponderantly with flexor kinesthesias and autistic features.[23]

The *kleptomaniacs* have been discussed adequately in chapter 10.

10. ADDICTS. Under this term we subsume chronic alcoholics and narcotic addicts. Opinions concerning the structure of addiction is still rather divided. Some authors believe that it is the schizoid, others that it is the cycloid constitution, which predisposes the individual to addiction. Both are actually found in addicts. In alcoholics it is doubtless the cycloid (orality) constitution which predominates, and in the narcotic addicts it is perhaps more often the schizoid constitution.

[23]Hans Zulliger, Der Tafeln-Z-Test, p. 78, Berne, 1954.

According to Kronfeld,[24] persons suffering from addiction have three psychologic factors in common: flight from their conflicts, a pleasure urge equal to drives, and the tendency to regard the somatic consequences of addiction as an excuse for indulging in the intoxicating agent. The first two factors, the flight from conflicts and the pleasure urge, put the addictions close to the neuroses, and their structure falls somewhere between the neuroses and the perversions. Psychoanalysts suspect, probably with considerable justification, homosexual repression as the latent source of addiction (Karl Abraham, N. Marx).

In the present state of research, it is probably not yet possible to recognize addiction on the basis of the Rorschach test. However, a few hints may be given.

In narcotic addicts one sometimes finds a combination of schizoid constitution with neurotic superstructure. Also most alcoholics show neurotic-like symptoms in the test. According to Klopfer and Kelley (pp. 388-389), the so-called neurotic signs of Miale and Harrower-Erickson were also found in the chronic alcoholics, "although clinically these individuals were not demonstrably psychoneurotic."

Homosexual complex responses are actually found now and then in the addicts, and similarly complex-determined responses which betray a tendency to self-punishment (e.g., humans "without head" as M). So far it has not been possible to determine whether initial censorship (as a sign of the usual ego-weakness) also appears in the addicts. This symptom presupposes a number of "complex" responses with identical content, a case that is rare.

The problem of addiction in the Rorschach test still awaits systematic exploring.

## THE ORGANIC PSEUDOPSYCHOPATHIES

If a psychopathic disorder is essentially an acquired one, we call it a pseudopsychopathy. The great majority of these are organic in nature. The causes of lesions to be kept in view are: head trauma, infection (especially encephalitis and meningitis), intoxication (during the war, for instance, chronic monoxide gas poisoning), tumor or atrophy of the brain, and a number of more rare organic disturbances. More recently, it has been possible to reestablish the older view of the last century, that irregular work shifts, extended over longer time periods (e.g., among railroad personnel) may show up in organic-neurasthenic syndromes (Bo Bjerner, Stockholm).

[24]Arthur Kronfeld, Psychagogik oder psychotherapeutische Erziehungslehre, in Birnbaum, Die psychischen Heilmethoden, Leipzig, 1927, pp. 449-450.

The organic pseudopsychopathies can almost always be clearly differentiated from the genuine psychopathies by means of the Rorschach test. Their organic character is detectable in the presence of some organic Rorschach test signs which do not fit into the framework of the particular psychopathic syndrome.

1. *Organic pseudoasthenia* (or, at times, *pseudo-hystero-asthenia*) is very frequent. It is usually post-traumatic or post-encephalitic, but also is found following monoxide gas poisoning and work in shifts. The Rorschach test syndrome of psychasthenia is found, but usually not with an introversive experience type. (In initial stages of the organic processes, e.g., in brain atrophy, an introversive experience balance may at times also appear.) The organic character of the disorder is usually betrayed in the lowered F+ per cent, a noticeably increased A per cent, the presence of DW, Orig– or perseverations. These latter can hardly stem from oligophrenia, since asthenia is almost regularly accompanied by criticism. At times the organic feature seeps through in the form of amnestic difficulties in finding words.

2. *Organic ixophrenia.* According to Strömgren, ixophrenia is a syndrome with fixated ixothymic (perseverating) reaction readiness, a no longer reversible narrowing of the emotional and intellectual horizon, with tendencies to dysphoric displacements of mood. It is an epileptiform "personality change" ("Wesensänderung" Stauder) of an organic nature.[25] It may appear in epileptics with or without gross motor attacks (according to Stauder, this personality change is more typical of cases with equivalents, twilight states and the dysphorias). It sometimes develops on a traumatic or other organic basis, e.g., postencephalitic (organic ixophrenia). These patients have a tendency toward short, episodic disturbances of consciousness. Ixophrenia is thus a symptomatic picture. Since, however, not all traumatized individuals, encephalitics, etc., develop this reaction type, a specific constitutional basis is probably a factor also where it is not a case of heterozygous hereditary disposition belonging to epilepsy. We are therefore warranted in considering ixophrenia (even in its organic form) as a constitutional psychopathy. Organic ixophrenia would therefore be closer to genuine psychopathy than to the other organic pseudopsychopathies.

It is therefore advisable to follow Swedish psychiatry and designate as *ixoid* those cases which show personality changes based on epileptoid hereditary trends, and to reserve the term *ixophrenia* for the organic cases (traumatic, post-encephalitic, multiple sclerotic, etc.), in which the exogenous noxious element is only the precipitating factor. As a rule, these patients have shown ixothymic character traits in their premorbid state, and these are merely intensified in the organic illness.

[25]Erik Strömgren, Episodiske Psykoser, Copenhagen, 1940, pp. 71/72.

The differential diagnosis in the Rorschach test between ixoid personality and organic ixophrenia is extremely difficult, since the ixoid is so similar to the organic syndrome (perseveration in both!). Affective lability and incontinence, however, are usually more pronounced in the ixophrenics, and color naming is also much more frequent. Ixophrenia also have more Orig–. Perseveration, which is usually extensive, is in the ixophrenics partly epileptiform (sticking to the theme, ruminating type), partly of an organic character (crude form, perseverations directly follow one another). Low A per cent suggests ixoid personality, high A per cent points to ixophrenia. Usually, however, the decision can be made only on the basis of the clinical data (anamnesis, encephalogram). The Rorschach test is only an auxiliary tool! Here then, if anywhere, we must urgently warn against blind diagnosis!

3. *Organic mood lability* is much more easily recognized in the test. It is usually of an irritated or pseudo-hypomanic nature. The following signs are clues to its presence: DW tendencies, Orig–, and naturally the perseveration and possible confabulations, which do not occur in the picture of the constitutional mood lability, especially if the perseveration is of an organic nature.

4. *Organic pseudo-lack of control* occurs especially in young people (post-traumatic, sometimes following birth trauma, or postencephalitic). Clinically this may be easily overlooked, and in such cases the Rorschach test may offer valuable aid. Here, too, perseveration is the most important characteristic, as also a high A per cent. Confabulations, on the other hand, belong to the "normal" picture of poor control.

5. *Organic pseudo-mythomania* appears under conditions similar to those in organic pseudo-lack of control. The diagnosis is thus analogous.

6. *The organic antisocial personalities* are perhaps not quite as numerous as the two pseudopsychopathies just mentioned. However, one must always be prepared for their possible appearance. Both syndromes show the extratensive experience type, the absence of M, the DW and increased Dd, and partly also a high A per cent. We must, therefore, fall back almost entirely on the lowered F+ per cent (which may, however, be due to other causes), and especially on perseveration, which is not found in the "ordinary" antisocial personality.

# CHAPTER XII

# *The Depressions*

SINCE DEPRESSION is an almost ubiquitous symptom, one which may appear in the most diverse disorders and states, it will be expedient to discuss it in a special chapter.

## DEPRESSION IN THE RORSCHACH LITERATURE

The various kinds of depression have so far been treated very meagerly in Rorschach literature. Apart from occasional and scattered remarks, there are only a few papers which have investigated specific groups of depressions. Nowhere do we find any systematic treatment of the entire problem.

Rorschach himself elaborated only the cyclic endogenous depression, i.e., melancholia and the milder depressions in the manic-depressive psychosis. This is the "purest" form of depression. The syndrome which Rorschach found for it stands out in the sea of other varieties like a "rocher de bronze" (rock of bronze). With a single exception, these other forms can all be deduced from the above syndrome. The syndrome of the endogenous depressive displacement of mood looks as follows (as given on p. 263, in our tabular summaries of Rorschach's "Psychodiagnostik"): Improved perception of form (F+ per cent is 80-100); rather rigid sequence; lowered W (0-3); poorer approach (D-Do); decreased variability in content (A per cent—60-80); lowered Orig (0-10 per cent +); and constricted experience type, i.e., decreased M (almost zero) with complete loss of color response. Response total is below average; response time is lengthened; F+ per cent is inversely proportional to M, and Hd exceed H.

In the more severe form, melancholia in the true sense, A per cent is higher still (70-90 per cent), but the number of responses is somewhat greater, usually within the average range, and response time is also lengthened. Number of H responses falls to near zero or zero, there are many Hd, and also many objects. In this shifting of the content, the anxiety (Hd > H) as well as the anal character (Obj!) of melancholia, finds expression.

In addition to this classical syndrome, Rorschach mentions, in passing only, the psychogenic depression (Rorschach, pp. 30, 81, and table IX, p. 246). He says that he has found this occasionally in Subjects with very few or few M but without color responses. He does not maintain that all psychogenic depressions must show this picture in the test.

This observation has been taken up by other investigators. Max Müller mentions it in his survey[1] and Ernst Schneider[2] also accepts M as a differential diagnostic sign for "psychogenic or neurotic depression," saying essentially that this picture should be recognized in the cluster of color shock with introversion and without color. Skalweit,[3] too, in his summary of the symptomatic values of the experience type classifies the psychogenic depression among the non-extratensive types. Thus (like Schneider) he makes the presence of M the only (or at least the main) differential diagnostic sign of psychogenic, as contrasted with endogenous, depression. This differential diagnosis is correct for some cases, but it is too narrow, for there are numerous forms of psychogenic depression without M (e.g., some compulsive characters, phobics, hysterics, and some purely exogenous depressions).

Oberholzer,[4] on the other hand, emphasizes the absence of any considerable color reactions in the psychogenic depressions. Similarly, according to Zulliger (Bero-Test, p. 53), "the momentary or the long lasting depressive moods" express themselves "in long reaction time with only few, but very sharply perceived responses, in which W is present but the color responses are absent." This, too, is only true under certain conditions; for there are depressed individuals who produce color responses, even though this is relatively rare. Goldkuhl[5] points out that many psychogenic depressions show only a small amount of inhibition, at times even a loosening up of the thinking processes, with mass production of depressive ideas and affective outbreaks of despair, and with more or less paradoxical affective explosions. Such patients may very well be extratensive in experience type with a considerable number of labile color responses. We have not infrequently come across this kind of depression.

Binder[6] believes that "in most cases" he cannot differentiate an endogenous from a reactive displacement of mood on the basis of the light-dark responses, "because the central affective reactivity on which the formation of the light-dark percepts depends is the same in the endogenous and in the reactive displacement of mood."

Guirdham has devoted an especial study to the Rorschach test diagnosis

[1]Max Müller, Der Rorschach'sche Formdeutversuch, seine Schwierigkeiten und Ergebnisse, Zeitschr. f. d. ges. Neurologie und Psychiatrie, Vol. 118, 1929, p. 617.

[2]Ernst Schneider, Psychodiagnostisches Praktikum für Psychologen und Pädagogen, Leipzig, 1936, pp. 102/103, 110 and 126.

[3]W. Skalweit, Konstitution und Prozess in der Schizophrenie, Leipzig, 1934, pp. 10 and 24.

[4]Emil Oberholzer, Zur Differentialdiagnose psychischer Folgezustände nach Schädeltraumen mittels des Rorschach'schen Formdeutversuchs. Zeitschr. f. d. ges. Neurologie und Psychiatrie, Vol. 136, 1931, p. 614.

[5]Erik Goldkuhl, Efterkrigspsykiatri, Festskrift till Henrik Sjöbring, Lund, 1944, p. 85.

[6]Hans Binder, Die Helldunkeldeutungen, p. 243.

of depression.[7] In Guirdham's opinion the test, at the time of the patient's first examination, is in some cases the only available tool for a differential diagnosis. However, it cannot replace observation over a longer period of time. In 161 depressed patients, mostly psychotics (melancholics, schizophrenics and cases of delusional insanity) he found: marked decrease of M and of color responses; a less drastic reduction in light-dark responses, as well as a loss of F+ per cent; an increase of P and Hd per cents; and an approach of W - D - Dd (with an average proportion of 10 W : 18 D : 3 Dd : 1 Ds). Moreover he observed a preference for the central (especially dark) details and emphasis on symmetry and evil faces. While Guirdham considers the coarctation of the experience type as the most dependable symptom of depression, he was not able to verify the decrease of W, rigid sequence and *extreme* coarctation which Rorschach maintained having found.

Guirdham's results can be understood in the light of the heterogeneity of his material. Since the various types of depression show very different elements of the classical Rorschach syndrome, it is inevitable that such deviations appear if these types are lumped together.

Guirdham observed that the light-dark responses are not more frequent in depressives than in normals, and correctly interprets this to mean that these responses are more representative of neurotic anxiety than of psychotic depression. Since, according to Guirdham's experience, motor restlessness due to anxiety displays not only a lack of M responses but also few or no color responses, we may draw the conclusion that motor restlessness without color derives from anxiety.

In his study of epileptics, Guirdham[8] was able to show that a coarcted or coarctative experience type is present in depressive epileptics as well.

Zolliker,[9] finally has investigated the status of Rorschach factors in depressions due to pregnancy. High Anat per cent with many female sex responses was especially striking. Depressed pregnant women (with the exception of the mentally deficient) do not, on the other hand, produce responses referring to male genitalia, due to their animosity to the male. Snakes, too, only occur after remission from the depression, apparently for the same reason. In general, no unequivocally characteristic Rorschach signs for a reactive depression could be found, so that "a relatively normal appearing protocol does not exclude a severe depression" (p. 75), an extremely important finding.

[7]Arthur Guirdham, The Diagnosis of Depression by the Rorschach-Test. The British Journal of Medical Psychology, vol. 16, 1937, pp. 130-145.

[8]Arthur Guirdham, The Rorschach Test in Epileptics, The Journal of Mental Science, Vol. 81, 1935, pp. 871/872.

[9]Adolf Zolliker, Schwangerschaftsdepression und Rorschach'scher Formdeutversuch, in "Psychiatrie und Rorschach'scher Formdeutversuch," Zürich, 1944, pp. 62-78.

## TABLE 4. DEPRESSIONS

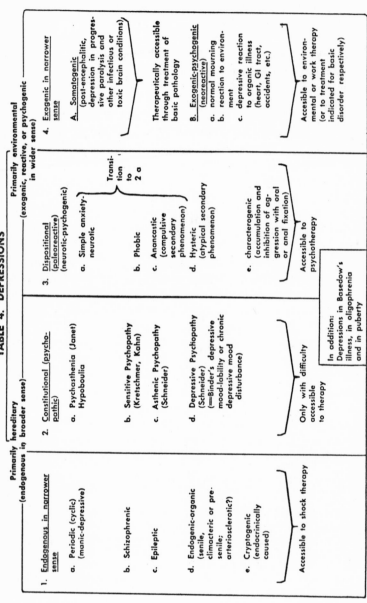

**Primarily hereditary** (endogenous in broader sense)

**1. Endogenous in narrower sense**
a. Periodic (cyclic) (manic-depressive)
b. Schizophrenic
c. Epileptic
d. Endogenic-organic (senile, climacteric or pre-senile; arteriosclerotic?)
e. Cryptogenic (endocrinically caused)

Accessible to shock therapy

**2. Constitutional (psycho-pathic)**
a. Psychasthenia (Janet) Hypoboulia
b. Sensitive Psychopathy (Kretschmer, Kahn)
c. Asthenic Psychopathy (Schneider)
d. Depressive Psychopathy (Schneider) (=Binder's depressive mood-lability or chronic depressive mood disturbance)

Only with difficulty accessible to therapy

In addition: Depressions in Basedow's illness, in oligophrenia and in puberty

**Primarily environmental** (exogenic, reactive, or psychogenic in wider sense)

**3. Dispositional (paleoreactive) (neurotic-psychogenic)**
a. Simple anxiety-neurotic
b. Phobic
c. Anancastic (compulsive secondary phenomenon)
d. Hysteric (atypical secondary phenomenon)

Transition to 2 a

e. characterogenic (accumulation and inhibition of aggression with oral or anal fixation)

Accessible to psychotherapy

**4. Exogenic in narrower sense**
A. Somatogenic (post-encephalitic, depression in progressive paralysis and other infectious or toxic brain conditions)

Therapeutically accessible through treatment of basic pathology

B. Exogenic-psychogenic (neoreactive)
a. normal mourning
b. reaction to environment
c. depressive reaction to organic illness (heart, GI tract, accidents, etc.)

Accessible to environmental or work therapy (or to treatment indicated for basic disorder respectively)

## CLASSIFICATION OF THE DEPRESSIONS

Today the depressions are quite generally divided into two main groups, the *endogenous* depressions and the *psychogenic* or *reactive* depressions. Cyclic depressions are, however, by no means the only group of endogenous depressions. Bleuler[10] believes that aside from the many manic-depressives there "certainly are displacements of mood of different origin which we cannot always differentiate from the manic-depressive ones." Some of these are "no doubt purely psychogenic ('reactive'), others have a physical basis," and finally there is a psychogenic release of genuinely manic depressive attacks (J. Lange has described them). Bleuler also mentions hysteric depressions (op. cit. p. 338).[11] He believes that a symptomatological differential diagnosis of endogenous as against reactive displacements of mood "is not yet possible," (p. 338).

The Finnish psychiatrist Väinö Mäkelä (died 1941) took the opposite view. At the Seventh Scandinavian Psychiatric Congress in 1938 he declared[12] that one must strive to "differentiate the psychogenic and the true depressions," for they are "quite different with regard to form and constitution." But he admits that this differential diagnosis is "quite difficult."

This is one of the important tasks of Rorschach test diagnostics. In many cases the test can give valuable assistance to the psychiatrist in making this difficult differentiation. In order to solve this task, however, it is expedient not to simplify the systematic classification of the depressions more than is consistent with the facts in the situation. Kinds of depression are as numerous as the sands of the sea, for each constitution gives its particular coloring to the depression. In a survey of the problems of postwar psychiatry, Erik Goldkuhl[13] declares that the greatest majority of depressions are hardly related at all to manic-depressive psychosis: for depression is a "common human reaction to the manifold hardships of life," and this reaction may occur in morons, in cases of psychasthenia, cyclothymia, hysteria, and in all individuals who are constitutionally especially sensitive.

If one wishes to take account of this rich variety, it is by no means neces-

[10]Eugen Bleuler, Lehrbuch der Psychiatrie, Berlin, 1937, p. 335.

[11]Maurice Levine arrives at a quite similar division (in Psychotherapy in Medical Practice, quoted here from the Swedish translation, Stockholm, 1946, p. 182). He differentiates among: 1. manic-depressive depressions; 2. depressive reactions in organic diseases; 3. depressive reactions on a psychological basis (reactive depression).

[12]Väinö Mäkelä, Über die Abgrenzung der Neurosen und ihre Einteilung in Untergruppen mit besonderer Berücksichtigung der Formen, die den endogenen Psychosen nahestehen. Report on the Seventh Congress of Scandinavian Psychiatrists, Copenhagen, 1938, pp. 366-367.

[13]Erik Goldkuhl, op. cit. p. 81.

sary to abandon altogether the old basic principle of classification (endo-genous-reactive). One must, however, clearly realize that in the patho-genesis of the depressions there is usually a more or less complex interac-tion of hereditary tendencies and environmental factors, so that in practice we hardly find any purely endogenous or purely reactive depressions. One may perhaps divide the various depressions into four large groups on the basis of the importance of the roles which the hereditary and the en-vironmental factors play in their etiology. In that case the first two groups would be determined predominantly by heredity (*endogenous depressions in the broader sense*), and the second two predominantly by environmental factors (*exogenous depressions in the broader sense*). We have attempted to portray this in Table 4. In it, the predominantly hereditary expressions are placed on the left side, the predominantly environmentally determined ones on the right. The two outer columns comprise those forms in which environment (endogenous in the narrower sense) or heredity (exogenous in the narrower sense) play only very subordinate roles. In between is found the great number of those depressions in which hereditary and cultural factors are more equal, so that in the left middle column heredi-tary tendencies predominate somewhat (constitutional depressions), while in the right middle column the environmental influences lead slightly (dis-positional depressions).

In the first column among the *endogenous depressions in the narrower sense* we find the following: the frequently cyclic and usually periodic depressions of the manic-depressive psychosis (which, as is well known, may often consist of only the depressive phases without any manic phases); moreover, depressions in schizophrenia and epilepsy, a great many of the "organic" depressions (senile, climacteric or pre-senile, and perhaps even the arteriosclerotic ones, because of the predominantly hereditary nature of their basic disorder), and the cryptogenic depressions, which are prob-ably based on endocrine conditions.

In the second column we have placed a number of psychopathies with tendencies to secondary depressions. These depressions are designated as *constitutional.* Here we had in mind Luxenburger's concept of the "ac-quired constitution,"[14] which is composed of hereditary constitution and acquired traits, with a predominance of the hereditary. In *this* sense the psychopathies are constitutional.

The third column comprises the numerous neurotic depressions which we have designated as *dispositional,* because they are based on a disposition in Freud's sense. This means a tendency to neurotic reactions acquired in early childhood through infantile experiences, in which the hereditary

[14]Hans Luxenburger, Eugenische Prophylaxe in Bleuler's Lehrbuch der Psychiatrie, Berlin, 1937, p. 139.

sexual constitution also plays a part.[15] Here the environmental aspect begins to predominate. As has already been suggested in "Rorschachiana I"
(p. 135), the dispositional depression may also be called *paleoreactive*,
since in these cases the depression is based on a reaction thoroughly "ground
in" at an earlier stage of psychologic development.

Contrasted with this are the *neo-reactive* depressions, i.e., the exogenous-
psychogenic depressions in the narrower sense. They are activated by recent stimulation in the external world, or through organic illnesses acquired
later in life, to which the personality reacts by a depression. Somatogenic
depressions, insofar as they are based on infectious diseases of the brain,
also belong in this group of exogenous depressions in the narrower sense.

There is a small group of depressions which cannot be entered into this
classification scheme without doing violence to them. They are such
depressions as are occasionally found in Basedow's disease, in oligophrenia,
or in puberty, and in which it is often impossible to decide whether heredi-
tary-constitutional or exogeneous factors predominate.

Dividing the many forms of depression into these four (or five) main
categories has not only the advantage of easier diagnostic placement, but
allows also for a rough prognostic and therapeutic evaluation. While the
true endogenous depressions (with the exception of the senile forms, of
course) seem to be accessible to shock therapy to some degree, the dispositional (neurotic) depressions are the proper domain of psychotherapy
(especially psychoanalysis). In the neo-reactive depression, simple environmental or work therapy is likely to be sufficient (possibly combined
with the treatment of any organic illness), whereas in the direct somatogenic
depressions, therapy naturally depends on the treatment of the basic disorder. The constitutional depressions are therapeutically hard to approach.
In these shock therapy also very frequently fails.

## RORSCHACH DIAGNOSIS OF THE DEPRESSIONS

The diagnosis of the individual forms of depression by means of the
Rorschach test fortunately is not as complicated as one might at first glance
assume from Table 4. It will be possible to refer to much of the preceding
discussion.

1. *Rorschach's classical syndrome* (see above) should always form the
point of departure. In its pure or almost pure form it is probably found
only in true *manic-depressive psychoses* (and even then only in cases relatively free from the frequent psychogenic admixtures) and, strange to
say, also in the almost pure *exogenous* depressions, especially in *mourning*.

[15]Sigmund Freud, Vorlesungen zur Einführung in die Psychoanalyse, XXIII.
Vorlesung, Gesammelte Werke, Vol. 11, London 1940, p. 376.

"Les extremes se touchent" (the extremes meet), one may say, and this would be correct insofar as the two extremes of our scheme actually represent the "purest" forms of depression, "depression as such," so to speak. The "work" of mourning, which can be caused not only by the loss of persons close to us but also by the loss of objects valuable to us, is very similar to the psychic mechanism of melancholia. As Freud[16] has pointed out, the only difference between the two states is that in mourning there is no disturbance of the self-confidence. While mourning is the work of adapting to a real object loss, melancholia is the reaction to an unconscious loss. As result of a narcissistic identification with an object that has been given up, the accusations which originally stemmed from an ambivalence conflict now turn into reproach and complaints against the self. The general inhibition and lack of interest is in both cases only the secondary consequence of the absorption of the ego into the inner mourning work. The unconscious ambivalence conflict which is part of the manic-depressive psychosis is probably the deeper source of the ambiequal experience type typical for these states. It is common to the endogenous depressions, the sub-manic as well as the manic mood disorders, and to the compulsive neuroses. (The completely arid, coarcted experience type is only a special case of the ambiequal type.)

2. All other forms of depression contain only elements of the classical syndrome (*abortive depressive syndromes*), but enough so that the depression is still clearly recognizable. (Only the characterogenic depression due to pure inhibition of aggression constitutes an exception here. It has its own syndrome, see below.) Either we find a W reduction with the approach shifting more or less to the D - Dd side, often accompanied by occasional Do responses, and ordinarily also an increased A per cent, but with M remaining intact. The color aspect of the experience balance may be lost, but it may also (as in some neurotic depressions) remain intact. Or we find a severe coarction of the experience type and possibly an increased A per cent, with retention of the normal approach and so forth. Almost all possible combinations occur, but the depressive character of the disturbance may usually be detected in the incongruence between various factors, i.e., in the deviation from the normal correlations. In other words, the recognition of the depressive character of the various forms of depression follows the same principles as the recognition of the affective intelligence inhibitions (which are often of a depressive nature). A closer etiological characterization of the state is then achieved by determining the further positive signs present in the protocol (shocks, other special phenomena, specific syndromes).

[16]Sigmund Freud, Trauer und Melancholie, Gesammelte Werke, vol. 10. London, 1946, pp. 428-446.

3. Before we discuss the various forms of depression in more detail, a number of factors *common* to all depressions might be mentioned.

In severe depressions, the act of interpretation is usually experienced as painful. There is as a rule an explicit disinclination to interpret the blots. This is frequently expressly stated. Thus a female melancholic repeatedly complained about the "vague pictures." Many depressed persons will finish their few interpretations of a card with a remark like "That is all," "That is all I can think of," or the like, which Beck terms "the resignation formula,"[17] and which likewise is to be regarded as a symptom of displeasure in making interpretations.

Moreover, we find that in the depressions generally the experience balance is constricted with essentially no change in its qualitative aspect. As has been mentioned above, there are depressive individuals of introversive and even of extratensive experience types. But in such cases one may then assume that these individuals have the same kind of experience balance, more dilated, in their non-depressive states.

Finally, black occasionally occurs as a color value in all kinds of depressions; the same is true of gray, whereas white does not show up as a color value (in contrast to epilepsy and ixothymia, where all three response categories may occur).

### 4. *The specific depressions.*

(a) The depressions of the endogenous group which are not of the melancholic type more or less deviate from the "classical" depressive syndrome. The *depressive schizophrenics,* indeed, have usually a rather coarcted experience balance, but sometimes display more H than Hd and not infrequently a shortened reaction time, in spite of the otherwise clearly present depression. F+ per cent is naturally lower in them. Otherwise, the diagnosis is made on the basis of the schizophrenic signs.

As Guirdham points out (see above), the *depressive epileptics* also are coarcted or coarctative in experience type. In other respects they may, however, deviate considerably from the melancholy-type depressive syndrome. As result of their perseveration, usually not showing much regard for the form, they mostly have a not too high F+ per cent. Because of their confabulations they also tend to have a few Orig–.

Among the senile forms, the *arteriosclerotic* depressions still approach the classical depressive syndrome most closely. But in them, too, F+ per cent is rather low as a result of their dementia. (More details in the next chapter.)

*Senile dementia,* if it shows depression, has on the one hand a less

[17]Samuel J. Beck, Rorschach's Test III, Advances in Interpretation, p. 246.

extratensive experience type, but on the other, tends to retain the DW emphasis in its approach.

The *climacteric* or *presenile* depression, Medow's "depressive involutional psychosis," has been described by Rapaport.[18] Color responses still appear here, but with no pure C. Number of responses is fairly high also. F+ per cent may fluctuate considerably ("may be very high or extremely low"). W responses are still rather numerous. Moreover the high A per cent is also lacking in most of these cases. Elements of the depression syndrome, however, almost always persist since not all the deviations occur at the same time. (Examples in Rapaport.)

(b) *The constitutional* depressions are diagnosed by their psychopathic basis. In most cases they show clear depressive changes in the approach as well as in the experience type. The psychasthenics, however, often maintain an introversive experience balance. Kurt Schneider's "asthenic psychopathy" is a neurasthenic constitution with a tendency toward depersonalization and estrangement, and thus essentially coincides with psychasthenia as conceived by the French school and the Swedish school of Lund.

(c) *The dispositional, paleoreactive* depressions of the neurotics are easily recognized. If the mildly depressive mood, nearly always present in the *anxiety neurotic* and in the *phobic* in addition to their fearfulness, becomes a little more pronounced, this may not appear in the experience balance but is quite evident in the approach. The Dd-Do shift is even more markedly accentuated, the light-dark percepts are even more numerous, and A per cent usually increases. However, one cannot always be sure of a high F+ per cent because of the frequently occurring poor anatomy responses.

The *compulsive* naturally tends toward depression, if for no other reason then by reason of his inhibition of aggression. The depression is displayed regularly in his reduction of M and mostly also of W, the shift of his approach in the direction of Dd and Do (in which connection some Ds usually appear), the high F+ per cent and the dearth of color responses. In more severe degrees of depression, compulsive characters may at times end in complete coarctation. In such cases we often find the maximal discrepancy between an F+ per cent of 100 and zero M.

In *hysteria*, on the other hand, depression is atypical. If clear signs of depression are found in hysterics (mostly not at the expense of color responses, but rather in the approach series), it may either be a case of mixed neurosis, i.e., an admixture of phobic or compulsive neurotic traits, or of a basic psychasthenic constitution with the depression as a secondary psychasthenic trait (in those cases not very deep); finally, the depression

[18]David Rapaport, Diagnostic Psychological Testing, Vol. II, Chicago, 1946, p. 384.

may be based on an inhibition of aggression. Nunberg[19] writes as follows about this third possibility: "Ambivalence makes it understandable that even in hysteria intense hostilities may be concealed under the mask of the symptoms. One of the most common reactions to disappointments in love, especially in childhood, is hatred, rather than indifference. Many love relationships which have long run their course are maintained because of hatred. Thus there are depressive hysterics who cling to their partners with apparent love for the single reason that they have not yet been able to take revenge. Superficial observation gives the impression that they are melancholics."

In addition to the usually already high A per cent and the depressive shift to Dd - Do in their approach, such hysterics also show an increase in Ds, otherwise uncommon among hysterics.

(d) The peculiar form of depression which (in "Rorschachiana I") we called *characterogenic*, does, to be sure, also belong to the paleoreactive forms, because of its pronounced character-neurotic structure. However, because of its widespread incidence and the complete divergence of its syndrome from the "classical" one, it must be discussed in greater detail at this point.

In his paper, "Inhibition, Symptom and Anxiety," Freud[20] had already referred to the fact that the inhibition of aggression plays a great part in causing general inhibition as a component of states of depression. This point of view has come more and more to the fore in later psychoanalytical research (Franz Alexander, Tora Sandström). Gerö[21] later described this mechanism in greater detail in his treatise "Der Aufbau der Depression" (The structure of depression). According to Gerö, psychogenic depression stems from aggressions against an introjected object. These aggressions arise from a libido which, because of fear of genitality, has regressed to a pregenital stage (particularly oral), where the libido makes infantile demands on the external world that are impossible to fulfill. According to Gerö, the so frequently found unconscious guilt feelings and the consequent possible need for punishment, are always based on unconscious aggression.

In the Rorschach test this kind of aggression (which is probably also contained in a number of other kinds of depression from the constitutional and dispositional groups) shows in its purest form increased Ds responses (at times even excessively high quantities) with strong braking and inhibitory phenomena. There are either many M and in most cases also

[19]Hermann Nunberg, Allgemeine Neurosenlehre, Berne, 1932, p. 263.

[20]Sigmund Freud, Gesammelte Werke, Vol. 14, London, 1948, p. 117.

[21]Georg Gerö, Der Aufbau der Depression, Intern. Zeitschr. f. Psychoanalyse, Vol. 22, 1936, pp. 379-408.

W+ with good F+ per cent, or only few M which are then usually accompanied by color shock with numerous descriptions. Oral complex responses (lips, teeth, widely opened mouths, spitting faces, etc.) often occur, and furthermore, the frequently found increase in W is in itself an expression of strong orality (Zulliger). The depression itself in most cases only shows up in a decrease of color responses, an increase of Dd, the appearance of Do and usually in Hd > H. Time is often lengthened, though not always, and occasional light-dark interpretations are present.

In its characteristic form (many Ds, many M, few colors, i.e., Ds increase together with an introversive experience type), this form of depression is the reverse of the antisocial psychopathy as Boss described it (many Ds, few M, much color, i.e., Ds increase together with an extratensive experience type). The experience type is here reversed, but increased aggressiveness is common to both states. Where there is an excess of inhibition in the depressive, there is an insufficiency of it in the antisocial person. The rise in the aggression energy is probably acquired (through education, social environment, early experience, trustee education), while the capacity or incapacity for inhibition (or rather braking) is the constitutional factor. Once the constitutionally normal person has acquired these increased aggressions, he will make use of his capacity for braking and inhibition in order not to become asocial, i.e., he will develop a character neurosis. The psychopath, however, is not capable of inhibiting his aggressions. As has been shown by Ernst Schneider,[22] inhibition in the broadest sense of the word (relating to repression, forgetting, childhood amnesia, physical development) is a specifically human, "cultural" phenomenon.

However, even the psychopath would not have become asocial if environmental factors had not produced excessive quantities of aggression in him. And it is just here that the starting point for psychotherapy is found. It is imposible to plant inhibitions in the uninhibited. But it is possible to enable them to get along fairly well, even without too much inhibition, if their aggressive tensions are dissolved, or if they are enabled to express them in a socially harmless or even useful manner.

Correspondingly, the aggression-inhibited depression is to be attacked therapeutically by way of the aggression rather than of the inhibition. Aggressive tension may be reduced by diverting it onto a socially acceptable goal, while inhibition of the direct ("antisocial") aggression is culturally unavoidable, being the "normal" in these individuals.

The founder of the mental hygiene movement, Clifford Beers, gives

[22]Ernst Schneider, Hemmung und Verdrängung, Schweizer, Zeitschr. f. Psychologie, Vol. 6, 1947, pp. 54-63.

an illustration of this mechanism. In his biography[23] he writes that as a child he was both "excessively shy" (p. 16) and sarcastic (p. 17). The oral admixture is also quite clear; he was a "member of a boy's choir" (p. 17) and was "always very much inclined to verbal contests" (p. 17). Scolding actually played a very great role in the manic phases of his later psychosis. He became orally aggressive at the slightest provocation, and he has portrayed his enjoyment of these moments with fine self-observation.

Finally, let it be pointed out that even in its inhibited form, aggression can in most cases be recognized by the trained observer. Like the complaints of the melancholic which grate on the nerves of the bystander, the expressions of other depressives (neurotics and psychopaths) frequently also show a clearly recognizable "aggressive note." "What is this, a sensitive creature?" asks Oscar Wilde,[24] and then makes the nice reply, "A creature who always steps on other people's feet because he has corns himself." The Ds of the Rorschach test *are* indicators of aggression, *even when* they are associated with an introversive experience type. The inhibition is hardly ever absolute.

## APPENDIX: THE AMPHITHYMIAS

CONCEPT AND TYPES

The term amphithymia, a simultaneous double-mood, was originated by Hellpach, and is also used by Kurt Schneider. Hellpach uses it to mean only a special borderline case of the endogenous manic-depressive mixed state. He writes:[25] "By amphithymia we mean a well-nigh physiological constitutional psychologic state, a natural disposition of strong pathotropic qualities. This internal disposition lies at the physiological limit of the manic-depressive mixed states, similar to the manner in which some physiological phases mark the outer limits which lead from classical manic-depressive insanity via cyclothymia into the normal range. Amphithymia shows, as do the manic-depressive mixed states, elements of increase in the physical and psychic achievement, intimately connected with elements of decrease. Accordingly, two principal borderline forms may be distinguished: the physiological equivalents of manic inhibition and of depressive excitement."

In this discussion we shall use this term not only for the endogenous mixed states or their physiological parallels, but in a broader sense as

[23]Clifford W. Beers, Eine Seele, die sich widerfand (A mind that found itself), Basel, 1941.

[24]Oscar Wilde, Märchen, Die hervorragende Rakete.

[25]Willy Helpach, Über Amphithymie (Zwiemut). Neurologisches Centralblatt, Vol. 38, 1919, pp. 720-721 (own report).

well, defining it as follows: By amphithymia we understand the simultaneous presence of elements of both depressive and elated moods, regardless of whether these mood disturbances are of endogenous or psychogenic nature. In most cases these two moods are located at different levels in the personality. Here we may profitably use Max Scheler's theory of levels. In his phenomenology of feelings, he differentiates four levels of the thymopsyche: 1. sensual feelings, 2. vital feelings, 3. ego feelings, 4. spiritual feelings. The difference of the mood tone at the different levels may be entirely physiological in nature. Amphithymia leads to neurotic ambivalence only if the contrasting moods are located at the same level.[26]

In some cases with rapid mood changes, amphithymia may touch on poikilothymia, a capricious, rapidly changing mood, which likewise may be the product of a psychogenic depression with attempts at compensation.[27]

Three types of amphithymia may be differentiated:

1. More or less physiological forms of endogenous cycloid mixed states, in which, however, psychogenic complications are frequently involved.

2. A chronic endogenous depression with simultaneous reactive flight into banality or exaltation, a state which has some similarity to the purely endogenous depressive excitements.

3. A chronic hypomania with psychogenic depression, corresponding to manic inhibition. This state impresses the outside world as a kind of friendly phlegm.

These are the most frequent forms. There probably are others, for instance those in which both mood disorders are psychogenic. However, in most cases a cycloid temperament is likely to be at the basis of the state.

RORSCHACH DIAGNOSIS OF THE AMPHITHYMIAS

The Rorschach test is an excellent instrument for the uncovering of these interesting mixed affective conditions.

1. The purely cycloid mixed states have already been discussed (see chapter 11).

2. *Flight from depression* may appear in two ways.

a) One of these is the *flight into banality*. Individuals in this category attempt to destroy the peculiarity of their personality, and so they try to join some form of collective life. They want to submerge themselves in the mass so as not to be confronted with the impotence of their loneliness and their fear of being alone. Erich Fromm describes this mechanism very well in his book "The Fear of Freedom."[28] He calls it "automaton conformity." The individual ceases to be himself. He completely adopts

---

[26]Paul J. Reiter, Neuroserne og deres Behandling, Copenhagen, 1945, p. 141.
[27]Ibid, pp. 16 and 41.
[28]Erich Fromm, The Fear of Freedom, London, 1945, p. 160.

the cultural pattern set up for him by the environment. "The discrepancy between 'I' and the world disappears and with it the conscious fear of aloneness and powerlessness." The feelings of being alone and of anxiety are no longer present. In amphithymia, however, the abandonment of one's own personality applies to the surface only. The depressive substructure remains. This forced searching for "conformity" shows itself in the Rorschach in a large number of rapidly produced popular responses. The few remaining responses, however, betray the fact that this is not a matter of "genuine" banality. They may be quite original and so reflect the true level of the personality.

b) The more frequent form of flight from depression is actual *flight into exaltation*, a mechanism reminiscent of Kurt Schneider's "escape mania." Superficially the personality is cheerful and friendly, and at times shows a seemingly hectic urge for company and activity. Beneath the surface, however, the plaintive, depressive mood persists. These people are among the most gracious and helpful, and they usually possess a peculiar charm. We have been able to observe several such cases. The Rorschach test protocol shows markedly faster response time and a dilated experience type (in one case 4 : 9!) with fairly Orig per cent ($\pm$), i.e., giving the external picture of a hypomanic. The other factors, however, offer a contrasting picture: Hd > H; at times (not always) increased A per cent; appearance of Do and light-dark-form responses; partial inversion of the sequence, and at times dark shock. Sometimes this "masking" is so successful that only a very few depressive factors betray the true state. One of our cases shows especially clearly that the flight into banality is but a variant of the flight into exaltation. This Subject's first protocol belonged to the one form (flight into banality), while a second one, a Bero protocol, taken six years later, presents the more "personal" form of flight into exaltation. The "complex" responses are especially telling in this case.

3. *Chronic hypomania* with the superstructure of a *psychogenic depression* yields very similar pictures, except that the hypomanic syndrome may here be even more pronounced. We found almost the entire classical hypomanic syndrome in a case which was re-tested with only a few days intervening. In the first test, this syndrome was complete but at the same time there was an increase of light-dark responses, i.e., a reactive dysphoria. By the time of the second test, the latter had taken root to such an extent that F+ per cent had risen to almost 90, and the relationship of the human responses had been inverted to Hd > H. Other variations are of course possible.

The differential diagnosis of the amphithymias, in particular, distinguishing their purely endogenic forms from the psychotic manic-depressive mixed states, is a problem of quantity and nuances.

# CHAPTER XIII

# *The Psychoses*

## THE SCHIZOPHRENIAS

GENERAL CONSIDERATIONS

THE PRESENT DAY CLINIC uses the diagnosis "schizophrenia" in many different ways, depending on whether the concept of schizophrenia is employed in the broader or the more restricted sense. The more inclusive diagnosis used by Bleuler's school (symptomatic schizophrenia) refers to a group of different psychoses which are defined primarily on a symptomatic basis, and which may vary considerably from a prognostic and probably even from an etiological point of view. The restricted diagnosis of schizophrenia which is being used here, however, refers to a group of illnesses which are much more homogenous prognostically, i.e., it is essentially a diagnosis from the course of the disturbance (process schizophrenia). As is seen from the more recent studies in heredity,[1] this is probably a matter of a group of psychoses which are distinct from the benign forms of psychoses also in hereditary-biological respects.

Autism, i.e., loss of contact, is the most clear-cut characteristic of this restrictively conceived schizophrenia. In Strömgren's opinion,[2] it is "the only really pathognomonic symptom for the schizophrenic process." Another important, although not necessarily pathognomonic, characteristic much emphasized by the Austrian school is the loss of the I-think-feeling, or the I-wish-feeling. This usually goes hand in hand with an Aha-experience (Karl Bühler).[3] These points of reference are useful for clinical diagnosis, but they are extremely problematical in the Rorschach test. In general, loss of the I-think-feeling (or the I-wish-feeling) cannot be directly determined by the Rorschach test. An autistic Rorschach syndrome is known, to be sure, but it is not always found even in unequivocal cases. The autistic syndrome has been described by Max Müller as well as by Monnier.[4] It consists of a low P per cent, few normal D and few or no FC

[1]Erik Strömgren, Om godartede schizofreniforme Psykosers Arvebiologi, Festskrift till Henrik Sjöbring, Lund, 1944, pp. 263-270.

[2]Erik Strömgren, Episodiske Psykoser, Copenhagen, 1940, p. 75.

[3]Fritz Schulhof, Schizo-phrenie, Schizo-bulie, Vienna, 1928, especially pp. 18, 27, 44 and 74.

[4]Max Müller, Der Rorschach'sche Formdeuversuch, seine Schwierigkeiten und Ergebnisse, Zeitschr. f. d. ges. Neurologie und Psychiatrie, Vol. 118, 1929, p. 612—Marcel Monnier, Le test psychologique de Rorschach, L'Encéphale, Vol. 29, 1934, p. 265.

responses. In addition, H and Hd are lacking (though not always), and according to Zulliger, flexor movements may occur.[5]

An additional diagnostic difficulty appears. More recent investigators,[6] have shown that in neither chronic nor acute schizophrenia do the mean values deviate very much from normal. However, especially in the acute form, this is due to a wide scattering of the single values. It is therefore very difficult to determine schizophrenia by applying the Rorschach test in a mechanistic way. In schizophrenia, if anywhere, the principle applies that only "the consideration of the protocol as a whole" can lead to the goal (Tschudin, op. cit., p. 82). Although we will not neglect the formal values, the Rorschach diagnosis of schizophrenia, as Tschudin remarks quite correctly, is based on "further elements in the experiment which we have so far not been able to conceive in statistical form." We may add that it is based in the main on such factors.

## THE SCHIZOPHRENIC RORSCHACH SYMPTOMS

The following peculiarities are found in schizophrenic protocols. Let it be emphasized once more that naturally not all of them appear in each test, and that individual elements of the syndrome may very well be found in other disorders and states as well. The conclusive indication is to be derived from the *accumulation* of these characteristics and the *total* impression they make.

The interpretation awareness is in most cases weak and at times completely lacking. Response total varies. Except in blocked and aboulic individuals it is usually above average. A sometimes markedly shortened response time is a rather frequent finding.

Rejection as a result of blocking or negativism is frequent, even in the "easy" cards, and especially in response to V. It is particularly noteworthy that frequently the P response (the bat) is not seen in this card. Encouragement is ordinarily of no use in schizophrenic rejections. Blocking cannot be overcome.

Precision of form shows wide differences. It often fluctuates from very good to unintelligibly poor forms. As a result, F+ per cent is usually rather low. There are also wide variations in the quantity of production in response to the various cards. Due to the strong difference in form accuracy, a frequent finding is extraordinary Orig+ side by side with completely absurd Orig-. Usually there is increase in Orig per cent.

[5]Hans Zulliger, Der Z-Test, Berne, 1948, p. 35.
[6]Arnold Tschudin, Chronische Schizophrenien im Rorschach'schen Versuch, and Wolfgang Binswanger, Über den Rorschach'schen Formdeutversuch bei akuten Schizophrenien, both in "Psychiatrie und Rorschach'schen Formdeutversuch," Zürich, 1944, pp. 79-100, and pp. 101-121.

Sequence as a rule is very loose, not infrequently even confused. Only in the more integrated patients, especially the paranoids, the sequence may be orderly.

In patients with high W, there are usually numerous W–. But not all forms of the disease show this W increase. DW and even DdW are rather common, usually with very poor forms. Even DsW are not rare, and they are usually seen in response to card I (Böszörményi and Merei). Confabulatory-combinatory W are also present. Contaminated W (and occasionally even D) actually seem to be a specific symptom of schizophrenic thinking, with its condensations. Off and on, however, they also appear in schizoid personalities that are still healthy, in them, however, as borderline contaminations. As a differential-diagnostic sign of process schizophrenia they thus cannot be used.

Schizophrenics have a tendency to bizzare Dd, which may at the same time be found in markedly high numbers (especially in paranoids).

M is usually reduced, but restless or blocked catatonics sometimes produce a normal number of M. This is also true of paranoids, in whom M may even be high. Individual cases may show M–, and if so, usually several.

The color nuances of schizophrenics are predominantly labile (CF and C) just as they are in neurotics. High absolute total values are characteristically found in silly hebephrenics, medium to small values in catatonics, and low in paranoids. Simple schizophrenia (dementia simplex) with its flat affectivity shows the lowest color values (often zero). Color naming is not rare. The more there is of it, the poorer the prognosis.

Light-dark responses are fairly frequent (Tschudin, W. Binswanger, Bochner-Halpern, op. cit. p. 175). They are related to the (frequently hypochondriac) anxieties. In hypochondriasis the anatomy responses are usually also markedly high. (Schizophrenic protocols with 100 per cent anatomy associations are not rare, but neither are they specific for schizophrenia.)

Rorschach found "number" and position responses in schizophrenics only. They have a pretty clear symptomatic value in this clinical area. The fact is, however, that they are not quite as pathognomonic as Rorschach supposed. As mentioned before, we have seen "number" responses in healthy schizoids. Position responses are found occasionally also in deteriorated and in oligophrenic epileptics (Guirdham),[6a] in organics (Klopfer and Kelley),[7] but especially in oligophrenics in the form of the so-

[6a]Arthur Guirdham, The Rorschach Test in Epileptics. The Journal of Mental Science, Vol. 81, 1935, pp. 870-893.

[7]Klopfer and Kelley, The Rorschach Technique, New York, 1942, p. 353.

called anatomic position responses (Pfister).[8] This may make for extra-ordinary complications in the differential diagnosis of the psychogenic psychoses in oligophrenics, as contrasted with pfropfschizophrenia. Pfister, as well as M. Bleuler and Kuhn[9] have called attention to the fact that the diagnosis of pfropfschizophrenia is on the whole very difficult because of the strong effect of the oligophrenia on the pattern.

Responses in the form of abstractions are common to schizophrenics, schizoids, and some neurotics.

Some confused patients show a preference for objects.

Furthermore, alphabetical letters, numerals and geometric figures are found in the responses of schizophrenics, as in those of children and young people.[10]

Moreover, the frequent recurrence of broken, split and isolated things is noteworthy in schizophrenic protocols (Minkowska).[11]

The peculiar self-references occur mainly in schizophrenics and schizoids, but occasionally also in epileptics, ixothymics and egocentric neurotics.

Likewise, the characteristic complaint of lack of symmetry is observed in schizophrenics and schizoids as well as in epileptics and ixothymics.[12]

Stereotypies and perseverations are rather common in unproductive, dull schizophrenics.

Descriptions likewise often occur.

The generally low F+ per cent has been mentioned above. P per cent too, the indicator of intellectual contact with the environment, is generally low, of course. A and Orig per cents, on the other hand, vary considerably. The confused and blocked patients usually are markedly low in A per cent, with at times very high Orig per cent (but poor Originals), whereas hebephrenics are higher in A per cent with average Orig per cent, and simple schizophrenics are very high in A per cent with low to average Orig per cent.

The test sometimes also shows other peculiarities of the schizophrenic psyche. First there is that morbid rationalism which Minkowski has called "perte du contact vital."[13] This severe disturbance of reality testing at

[8]Oskar Pfister, Ergebnisse des Rorschach'schen Versuches bei Oligophrenen. Allgem. Zeitschr. f. Psychiatrie, Vol. 82, 1925, pp. 198-223.
[9]Roland Kuhn, Der Rorschach'sche Formdeutversuch in der Psychiatrie, Basel, 1940, p. 52.
[10]Samuel J. Beck, Rorschach's Test, II. p. 231.
[11]Laignel-Lavastine, Minkowska, Bouvet et Neveu, Le Test de Rorschach et la Psychopathologie de la Schizophrenic, Rorschachiana I, Berne, 1945, p. 82.
[12]Hans Zulliger, Der Tafeln-Z-Test, Berne, 1945, p. 82.
[13]According to Joseph Gabel, Symbolisme et schizophrénie, Schweiz. Zeitschr. f. Psychologie, Vol. 7, 1948, p. 276.

times produces a particular disintegration of the object conception, and in some cases this is formally manifest in the test. Such patients produce completely unintelligible figure-background fusions of miserable form, an interesting Gestalt psychology effect of the structural disintegration in their thinking. The Rorschach test may also uncover the frequent disorientation in the situation, possibly with simultaneous intrapsychic disorientation, the "perte de la fonction du 'moi-ici-maintenant' " (Minkowski).[14] This appears not only in self-references, but not infrequently also in the spontaneous associations which are so often found in schizophrenic protocols. These side remarks may betray a clear misunderstanding of the situation. Finally, delusional images may be introduced into the test, e.g., patients see "ghosts," etc. in the cards.

W. Binswanger has observed a matter of curious psychological interest (op. cit. p. 118), namely, a concretization of speech forms usually intended figuratively. He cites the example, a percept in response to card III, "two men playing with a woman's heart." We have been able to verify this observation on several occasions. A further example (from the protocol of a normal schizoid person) is the response to the lateral part of the upper gray of card VIII, "as if nature were symbolically stretching out her hand in order to help them (the laterally seen animals)." This association from a healthy person shows very clearly the transition from the as yet normal symbolic concept of a schizoid person to the real concretization of a schizophrenic. Such symbolism stands somewhere between concretization and abstraction. As W. Binswanger (op. cit., p. 118) remarks, they are indeed opposites, but both occur in schizophrenics.

Rorschach was mistaken in thinking that color shock does not appear in schizophrenia. We have observed very definite color shock in a number of schizophrenics for whom the diagnosis was quite certain. Beck and Kelley report the same observations (Beck, Rorschach's Test, II, pp. 246, 248; Klopfer and Kelley, p. 364). This is not at all surprising since also clinically neurotic traits frequently enter the schizophrenic picture (Klopfer and Kelley, p. 351).

The experience type of schizophrenics has been the subject of animated discussion. Skalweit[15] maintains that the experience type in schizophrenics tends to shift in direction from introversive to extratensive-egocentric. From this he concludes that "the nature of the schizophrenic psychosis is not a purely quantitative intensifying of a specific constitutional psychologic reaction pattern, but a qualitative change of pattern." In Skalweit's opinion, there is no continuous transition from schizothymia to schizophrenia; rather,

---

[14]According to Joseph Gabel, op. cit. p. 278.

[15]W. Skalweit, Konstitution und Prozess in der Schizophrenie, Leipzig, 1934, pp. 40 and 81-84.

something new enters in schizophrenia, namely, a destructive process. Skalweit shares this opinion with Arthur Kronfeld, Karl Birnbaum, Kurt Schneider and others.

Verification of Skalweit's postulated shift of experience type from the introversive to the extratensive could only be undertaken with any certainty if a sizeable number of cases could be tested before as well as after the outbreak of the disease. This, of course, is only rarely possible, since it would depend entirely on chance. Böszörményi and Merei[16] have described such a case, one in which they were actually able to demonstrate such a displacing of the experience type.

It is certain that an acute schizophrenic episode changes the experience type, but only in patients with catastrophic experience (Carl Schneider's "varieties of psychic upheaval"), in the sense of the dilatation presumed by Rorschach, which is followed by a coarctation in the remission. Conversely, Carl Schneider's "varieties of protective mechanism" display a coarctated or coarctative experience type in the episode, and an egocentric-extratensive-dilated type in remission (Wolfgang Binswanger, op. cit. pp. 104-107).

Skalweit, further, has made the observation (op. cit. pp. 75/76) that in the catastrophic, progressive forms of schizophrenia the approach is displaced toward W, with many W− responses occurring as well as color naming, whereas in the episodic and prognostically more favorable forms, the approach shifts more toward Dd, and only little color naming occurs. Practically important prognostic conclusions derive from this observation.

THE SUBGROUPS OF SCHIZOPHRENIA

1. CHRONIC AND ACUTE FORMS

Skalweit also tried to sketch certain typical differences between the more chronic and the more acute forms of schizophrenia. In chronic schizophrenia (op. cit. pp. 32-33) he found the more extreme approach types, W− and Dd types, predominating. Sequence was very loose or confused. In these patients he frequently found confabulatory and contaminatory DW and DdW, F+ per cent lowered, A per cent either high with low Orig per cent, or low with high Orig per cent. Color values were increased, M reduced, and color naming frequent. In the acute forms of the illness, however (op. cit. p. 56), there was usually a D emphasis in the approach. Here, too, sequence was generally loose or confused, but F+ per cent and W were more normal. Color values were also increased, and he some-

[16]Georg Böszörményi and Franz Merei, Zum Problem von Konstitution und Prozess in der Schizophrenie auf Grund des Rorschach-Versuches. Schweizer Archiv. f. Neurologie und Psychiatrie, Vol. 45, 1940, pp. 276-295.

times found increased M, too, so that experience type in these forms was either extratensive or ambiequal.

The results obtained by Tschudin and W. Binswanger disagree with Skalweit's in the following respects: In chronic schizophrenics, Tschudin found an introversive-coarcted experience type with many self-references, and a dilated type with few self-references (op. cit. p. 88). W. Binswanger, on the other hand, reports a predominantly severely egocentric-extratensive experience type in the acute schizophrenias (op. cit. p. 103).

It is probably impossible to make a blind diagnosis regarding the course which the disorder has run from the test alone, since schizophrenia as a rule cannot be established merely on the basis of the formal factors. For these in turn seem to be dependent primarily on the symptomatological character of the illness (see next section). Finally, too, the typical schizophrenic peculiarities such as differentiation in sharpness of form, absurd formulations with neologisms, symbolizations, abstractions, self-references, etc., appear in both the chronic and the acute forms. However, the above observations concerning favorable or unfavorable prognosis appear clearly to have practical value.

## 2. THE FOUR SUBGROUPS OF SCHIZOPHRENIA

Clinically the illness is usually divided into the following four subgroups: simple, hebephrenic, catatonic and paranoid schizophrenia. Rorschach's syndrome for these sub-groups have on the whole stood the test of time very well. Transitions from the one to the other are naturally found frequently enough in the clinic as well as in the Rorschach test. The boundary between the hebephrenic and catatonic schizophrenia, for example, cannot always be sharply drawn by either method (see also Klopfer and Kelley, p. 323).

In the *simple forms,* the Rorschach picture is that of a simple intellectual and affective deterioration: coarcted experience type with low F+ per cent, high A per cent, and impoverished approach type (D–Dd). The Orig are poor, Orig per cent low to average. Sequence is usually confused, and many Hd are found with zero or only very few H.

In the *hebephrenics,* the experience type is extratensive. Of all schizophrenics, these produce the highest color values, corresponding to their inclination to affective restlessness. Here, too, F+ per cent is low, A per cent rather high, and the approach is impoverished (D – Dd). Orig per cent is medium, of predominantly poor form. The confused sequence they have in common with almost all other schizophrenics. Their more severe psychologic fluidity, even though in a negative sense, is seen in their confabulations. They, too, respond with more Hd than H.

*Catatonia* with its stereotypies, its negativism, and its strong ambivalences, displays certain similarities to the compulsive neurosis. Similarly, the ambiequal experience type recalls the compulsive neurosis. However, in the *aboulic* forms it is coarcted (this being a special case of the ambiequal experience type). Definitely autistic catatonics, however, who are inhibited in their movements, may also be of a strongly introversive experience type, as has been shown by both Monnier[17] and by Kuhn.[18] In contrast to simple schizophrenia, the inner tension of the aboulics is shown by the strong W emphasis in their approach. The pure W– type sometimes occurs here (about 10 W–). Their other characteristics are a very low F+ per cent, a very high A per cent, due to perseverative stereotypy and high Orig per cent (–).

The *blocked* reaction types belong to the ambiequal experience type proper, with affective egocentricity (many CF or even pure C with zero or few FC). Again we find the low F+ per cent, confused sequence, but also A per cent is surprisingly low in this group. Corresponding to this greater ideational richness, their high Orig per cent is qualitatively somewhat better, too ($\mp$). The approach type here is W – D – Ds with a tendency to Ds (negativism). Combinations, confabulations, and perseverations are found.

The *motor-excited, confused* catatonics are also of a dilated ambiequal experience type, with emphasis mainly on the color side (likewise without or almost without FC). Along with poor F+ per cent we here also find the low A per cent, a frequently very high Orig per cent ($\mp$), as well as the richer type of approach W – D – Dd, with frequently rather curious Dd. The sequence here is more confused than in any of the other forms; everything goes unbelievably fast, with numerous combinations, confabulations and contaminations produced in a merry confusion. It is often quite difficult to keep up with them.

MC responses may occur in all forms of catatonia.

*Paranoids,* finally, usually show an introversive experience type, with the exception of the querulous persons, who ordinarily are extratensive. Among the paranoids the FC are at times even more pronounced. F+ per cent and sequence are markedly better, A per cent is average and Orig per cent is good ($\pm$). Approach is in most cases *W* – D or *W* – D – Dd, with a tendency to DW, bizarre Dd and Ds. The relative emphasis on W corresponds to the paranoid's tendency to systematize his delusional ideas. In the genuine schizophrenic forms, however, success in this is only moderate. In highly productive paranoids, small M is also occasionally found. Finally we must mention a tendency to MLD responses.

[17]Marcel Monnier, op. cit. p. 265.

[18]Roland Kuhn, Der Rorschach'sche Formdeutversuch in der Psychiatrie, Basel, 1940, p. 55.

APPENDIX: THE PARANOID PRESENILE PSYCHOSIS
(INVOLUTIONAL PARANOIA IN KLEIST'S SENSE)

The paranoid-schizoid syndromes which at times appear during the involutional period, and may possibly have partial organic etiology, occupy a special position on the fringe of the schizophrenias. They are usually classed with the pre-senile psychoses. In contrast to the depressive forms of the latter, they frequently take root in a sensitive constitution. They may therefore be considered a variation of the sensitive delusion of reference described by Kretschmer. Kleist himself (who later abandoned the term involutional paranoia, which he had himself suggested, and substituted the term "delusional involutional psychosis"), points out that in his pre-psychotic state the patient usually was of "hypoparanoiac" character.[19] By this he understands a character determined by suspiciousness and increased self-assertiveness.

Rorschach mentions this picture only in passing. He notes (p. 81) "A few climacteric melancholias and paranoids with late onset of their illness and who might better be diagnosed as paranoics." For in these cases he found M, without color values, just as in the psychogenic depressions. To be sure, color responses are also found in involutional paranoia, but the experience type seems consistently to be of a clearly introversive nature.

The characterogenic factors of the personality on which these paranoid involutional psychoses are built are indicated not only by the introversive experience type, but also by the usually strong emphasis on W in the approach ($W - D$, or $W+$, or $W\pm$). These two factors already show the tendency toward breeding, generalization and theoretizing. A per cent, corresponding to the individual's age, is usually around 60.

In addition there is the sensitive syndrome with which we are already familiar. It consists of the psychasthenia syndrome (color shock plus dark shock plus interference phenomenon at card VIII, plus accessory symptoms, above all subject criticism), and one or several light-dark form responses; at times $F(C)$ (Binder's) also appears.

The constitutional disposition to (characterogenic) paranoid reactions arises out of this cluster. But it is the presence of similarity illusions, which usually accumulate in very pronounced cases, that makes this disposition of the pre-psychotic personality into an involutional paranoia. The essence of the similarity illusion is the tendency to project inner difficulties and tension onto the external world. The identifying mark of the paranoiac psyche (in contrast to paranoid schizophrenia) may be seen in this projection together with an experience of passivity.

[79] Karl Kleist, über zykloide, paranoide und epileptoide Psychosen und über die Frage der Degenerationspsychosen. Schweizer Archiv. f. Neurologie und Psychiatrie, Vol. 23, 1928, p. 11.

This type is probably only one form of the illnesses diagnosed as pre-senile paranoid psychosis. There are other cases which become chronic, and approach the late schizophrenias more closely. They yield a completely different picture (usually showing an extratensive experience type and clear schizophrenic symptoms, such as self-references, confabulations, etc.). Rorschach test research will probably contribute some significant insights to the more precise characterizing of the various types in this rather heterogenous group of psychoses.

## MANIC-DEPRESSIVE PSYCHOSIS

Although Rorschach's material contained only 14 manic-depressive patients, the syndromes which he worked out for this illness is among the best validated of the foundation stones on which the entire Rorschach diagnostic procedure rests.

### RORSCHACH'S FINDINGS

1. Rorschach's syndrome for manic-depressive *depression,* this most important form of the endogenous depressions, has already been presented as the "classical" depression syndrome in the chapter on the depressions. The same is true for melancholia. Neither need, therefore, be repeated here. In the purely endogenous depressions, this syndrome is rarely accompanied by light-dark interpretations. Color shock probably never appears in the purely manic-depressive depressions, and dark shock also seems to be rare. A possible color shock along with a manic-depressive Rorschach syndrome is always to be considered as a certain sign of a neurotic feature. Dark shock is surely a sign of anxiety, which in this case may be either a phenomenon accompanying an agitated melancholia or a neurotic admixture.

2. Rorschach's syndrome for the *manic mood disorder* is the polar contrast of the depressive syndrome. Form perception becomes poorer ($F+$ per cent $= 60$ - $70$), sequence is loose, number of W increases ($8$ - $10$), approach is richer ($W\pm$ - $D\pm$), variation in content increases (A per cent $= 40$ - $50$), Originals increase but are poorer ($20$ - $30$ per cent $\mp$, and experience type is dilated, i.e., increased M ($3$ - $5\pm$), and many color responses are found (on an average $1$ - $2$ FC, $2$ - $3$ CF, and $1$ - $2$ C). Number of responses is above average, response time is shorter, $F+$ per cent is here, too, inversely proportional to M (but in the opposite direction), and H exceeds Hd.

If the attack increases to the point of *mania,* then form perception becomes even poorer ($F+$ per cent $= 50$ - $70$), and W decreases ($4$ - $7$). The approach therefore becomes poorer again ($DW\mp$ - $D\pm$ - $Dd\pm$). The variability of content is somewhat less than in the hypomanics (A per cent $=$ 50 - 70), and Orig per cent is correspondingly also lower (10 - 30 , $\mp$). M and color responses, however, increase (5 M and more $\mp$, and an average of 1 - 3 FC, 2 - 3 CF, and 1 - 3 C). Response total and time are about the same, and this also holds for the relation of F+ per cent to M. Also, one frequently finds DW and successive-combinatory W, at times confabulatory-combinatory ones. In mania (as in melancholia), object content increases (at times also in sub-manics), possibly indicating a kind of reawakening of the infantile play drives (cf. Conrad's concept of Kretschmer's theory of constitution).

3. As has been mentioned in chapter 11 (cycloid personality), there may be many combinations of elements in the two syndromes of the depressive and the manic mood disorders. This is what we find in the *manic-depressive mixed states* (or in the simple cycloid constitution). It should be pointed out once more that not all the possible combinations of Rorschach factors may arbitrarily be placed in these two syndromes, for these factors present polar contrasts and not alternatives. For example, very low F+ per cent or a medium number but sharply perceived W values cannot fit into either syndrome, any more than a very high number of M or Orig of sharp form, as may be found in artists. The absence of color shock and of other neurotic phenomena serve as a boundary line against such forms of amphithymia in which psychogenic mechanisms are part of the picture.

DIFFERENTIAL DIAGNOSIS

According to Eugen Bleuler,[20] the diagnosis "manic-depressive insanity" may be used only as a "negative diagnosis," i.e., by elimination, especially if no anamnesis is displayed, or if it is a first attack. To a certain extent this is also true for the Rorschach diagnosis of manic-depressive psychosis. The mere presence of the classical Rorschach syndrome of depressive or manic mood disorders is in itself not sufficient, since, as we have seen, exogenous forms of depression and states similar to hypomania with organic or psychogenic etiology, may yield very similar syndromes. Very often the differential diagnosis is made possible by another symptom, one which does not belong to the depressive or hypomanic syndrome and which yields the critical hint, like the organic forms of perversion and object criticism in cases of organic etiology. Other organic signs in hypomanic-like states may raise suspicion of traumatic encephalopathy (see chapter 11, the pseudo-psychopathies). If the hypomanic syndrome is present with a strong color shock, it is often impossible to determine from the test alone whether we have a pure neurosis or a mixture of a "genuine" hypomania with a neurosis (mostly taking a hysteria-like form).

[20] Eugen Bleuler, Lehrbuch der Psychiatrie, Berlin, 1937, pp. 109 and 337.

DETERIORATION IN THE MANIC-DEPRESSIVE PSYCHOSIS

If this illness has lasted for many years (8 - 10 or more admissions to a hospital are by no means rare in this disease) one may sometimes observe a certain deterioration of an organic type in these patients; F+ per cent becomes poor even in the depressive phases, perseveration, confabulation and similar deterioration symptoms appear which may raise suspicion of organic complications. Such complications are actually present in some cases since, as is generally known, the pyknics as such, and especially the manic-depressive ones, have the tendency "rather early to develop arteriosclerosis and other kinds of brain atrophy."[21] In other patients, in whom such a complication cannot be demonstrated clinically, we are probably dealing with a "genuine" manic-depressive deterioration of the kind described by Goldkuhl.[22] This consists of an irreversible lowering of the level of the personality leading "to a loss of the ability to strive for a goal and the general lack of control connected therewith . . . the level of ethical and social feelings in the patient is not necessarily lowered; it is only that there is a lack of power to respond to these instincts" (Goldkuhl, p. 161). Goldkuhl assumes that the seat of these "organic defective states of the deterioration type" are in the deeper brain area, in contrast to toxic damage which is localized primarily in the cortex.

## THE EPILEPSIES

RORSCHACH'S FINDINGS

On the basis of his 20 cases, Rorschach reports the following peculiarities as characteristics of epileptic deterioration. In spite of the extensive Rorschach literature which has in the course of the years accumulated on this problem in particular, his findings still constitute the core of Rorschach test diagnosis of epilepsy.

Response total is usually above average. Response time is prolonged. Experience balance is usually pretty much dilated, though predominantly extratensive. F+ per cent is low, A per cent paradoxically is low, too. However, there are tendencies toward stereotypy in the M and color responses. Orig per cent is relatively high, but the Originals are predominantly poor. The approach is mostly DW - D - Dd. In epileptics who have deteriorated early, it is DW - D - Dd. DW at any rate are frequent. Sequence is usually loose, at times rigid, when epileptic pedantry is very pronounced. Most epileptics yield more H than Hd responses. Secondary M and M— are nowhere as frequent as in epileptics. With the strong tendency to M

[21]Eugen Bleuler, op. cit. p. 334.
[22]Erik Goldkuhl, Über Demenzzustände bei Psychosis manico-depressiva. Uppsala Läkareförenings Förhandlingar, vol. 48, 1943, pp. 145-164.

and also to poor form level, F+ per cent is inversely proportional to M.
Confabulations, evaluating remarks, and self-references are rather frequent
in epileptics. They incline to precise emphasis on symmetry and to color
naming; indeed, they frequently enumerate the colors directly. Pure color
responses are on the whole frequent in deteriorated epileptics; they need
not necessarily take the form of color naming. Oligophrenic epileptics perceive many objects. The most important feature of the epileptic's protocol,
however, is the strong tendency to perseveration, without there necessarily
being any stereotypy of animal parts or body parts at the same time.
(Anatomical stereotypy, found in some ixoids, is particularly rare in
genuine epilepsy.) Now and then Rorschach found black and white as
color values in epileptics (Psychodiagnostik, p. 30).

Rorschach believed that the absolute number of M and color responses
would become larger in cases of increasing deterioration, while F+ would
decrease. The latter no doubt is correct, but it has not been possible to
verify the former with certainty.

LATER INVESTIGATORS

Bovet's[23] paper is one of the most important contributions to Rorschach
test research in the field of epilepsy. Apart from several valuable differential diagnostic observations, Bovet's major contribution is in having called
attention to the fact that the genuine epileptics show preference for a very
definite kind of perseveration. They prefer sticking to a basic theme, which
they keep varying rather than repeating a certain interpretation (as do
organics). In chapter 5, under perseveration, we have discussed this sticking to a theme.

Guirdham was able in his study[24] to verify most of Rorschach's findings.
To be sure, all experience types are found in epileptic patients, but the
epileptic *character* prefers the extratensive and the ambiequal experience
type, and tends toward light-dark interpretations and confabulations. The
approach inclines toward the poorer types (D - Dd with Ds and Do), in
a loose or reversed sequence, with frequent occurrence of DW and DdD.
The actual ideational perseveration occurs mostly in W and DW; and
these DW are often H, confabulated from an anatomical detail. Guirdham also found a "perceptional perseveration" (a preference for similar
forms) in the D and Dd, and this primarily in epileptics of well preserved
intelligence. On the whole, the relation of perseveration to M was an
inversely proportional one. Guirdham further observes the so-called "stac-

[23]Th. Bovet, Der Rorschach-Versuch bei verschiedenen Formen der Epilepsie,
Schweizer Archiv f. Neurologie und Psychiatrie, Vol. 37, pp. 156-157.
[24]Arthur Guirdham, The Rorschach Test in Epileptics, The Journal of Mental
Science, Vol. 81, 1935, pp. 870-893.

cato" phenomenon in epileptics, i.e., "a waxing and waning of the flow of interpretations," independent of fatigue and difficulty of the cards (p. 891). In oligophrenic and deteriorated epileptics, descriptions and position responses also appeared.

According to Guirdham, the main characteristics of epilepsy in the Rorschach test are: (1) lack of abstract synthesis (poor approach type), (2) extratensive factors together with strong signs of confabulation, and (3) the process of perseveration.

Stauder[24a] in his extensive work in Bumke's clinic in Munich attempted primarily to work out the differentiation between character change ("Wesensänderung") and deterioration (attempted by Bumke) also in the Rorschach test. Personality change includes perseveration (sticking to some thought), circumstantiality, pedantry and self-righteousness. It is a symptom of the epileptic disposition (p. 117). It is facilitated by three factors: athletic body build, a special form of the process (accumulation of extended disturbances in the consciousness) and luminal therapy (p. 162). The explosive syndrome, which according to Stauder does not belong to the typical epileptic character change (p. 181), appears mainly in symptomatic epileptics, that is, mentally deficient residual epileptics and severe traumatic epileptics (pp. 117-118). The most important deterioration symptoms in the epileptics, about equally frequent in genuine and symptomatic cases, are disturbances of perception and judgment, as well as a disturbance of recent memory frequently connected with difficulties in finding the correct word (amnesic-aphasic disturbances, p. 118).

Character changes always occur in *genuine epileptics* according to Stauder; the differences are in degree only (p. 82). The converse of this rule does not, however, hold, for a patient without any character change may still develop it. Thus we cannot conclude from the lack of personality change the absence of genuine epilepsy (p. 187). (This is of extreme importance for the Rorschach practitioner, see below.) Among the various signs of character changes, perseveration is the core symptom (p. 85). The change is most pronounced in cases which are rich in symptoms (cases with aura, equivalents, twilight states, dysphorias). Most of these individuals are of athletic body type. Those who are poor in symptoms (patients with only gross motor attacks, with possibly very little aura, but without equivalents) are rarely of athletic build, and the majority of them deteriorate. While deterioration progresses with the duration of the disease and the number of attacks, personality change is independent of the number of attacks.

[24a]Karl Heinz Stauder, Konstitution und Wesensänderung der Epileptiker, Leipzig, 1938.

Stauder now thinks he has found a syndrome typical for character change, which occurs in most instances of chronic epileptic character change, and furthermore takes place regularly when there are disturbances of consciousness, i.e., shortly after attacks and in states of numbness and twilight. While this syndrome can be seen early, in the initial stages of genuine epilepsy (even after 2 - 10 attacks), it is said that it practically never shows up in symptomatic attacks (p. 14).

Stauder distinguishes between several forms of this syndrome, the full syndrome and the abortive ones. In the full syndrome (p. 48), we have about 10 responses with prolonged response time and with perseveration through all 10 cards (10 F, almost all poor), and consequently high Orig per cent (−). (This full syndrome has so far not been observed in such frequency by anybody but Stauder.) The abortive syndromes (pp. 54 - 76) are composed of the following factors: number of responses below medium (average 14.5); lengthened response time; zero or few M (according to Stauder, M is found in only new cases); a modest sum of color responses (frequently even zero); experience type coarcted or coarctative, at times extratensive; low F+ per cent; low to medium Orig per cent (predominantly minus); high A per cent (average 50 - 100); increased W (frequently DW); type of approach W - D; sequence rigid or orderly; value judgments and self-references. Finally as indicators and measures of degree of epileptic character change: strong perseveration (especially also in the formulations); pedantry, remarks about symmetry. (We return later to the various discrepancies between this syndrome and that of Rorschach.)

In contrast to the modest color values of the genuine epileptics, Stauder found an explosive affectivity primarily in the symptomatic epilepsies, especially where mental deficiency was also a factor (p. 59).

*Residual epileptics* (after encephalitis) and other *symptomatic* epileptics did not react with the epilepsy syndrome, but in most cases showed organic traits, such as lengthened response time and extratensive experience type. Only the "provoked" among the traumatic epilepsies, i.e., patients in whom an only slight trauma causes an existing epileptic disposition combined with character change to develop, showed the typical epilepsy syndrome. Only in three temporal lobe tumors did the syndrome of genuine epilepsy appear in the Rorschach test, and such cases are very difficult to differentiate, also clinically, from genuine epilepsy (p. 94).

The papers of Weissenfeld, and of Härtel and Ederle should also be mentioned. Weissenfeld[25] attempts a differential diagnosis between genuine

[25]Felix Weissenfeld, Der Rorschach'sche Formdeutversuch als Hilfsmittel zur Differentialdiagnose zwischen genuiner Epilepsie und Übererregbarkeitsepilepsie. Zeitschr. f. d. ges. Neurologie und Psychiatrie, Vol. 171, 1941, pp. 321-336.

epilepsy with character change and tetanoid epilepsy typified by an accurate and thorough, but petty, character. According to Weissenfeld, the main differences are as follows: genuine epilepsy has low F+ and A per cents, frequently confabulatory DW, sometimes M and frequently many colors, mostly perseveration, at times color naming, self-references and evaluating remarks, frequent pedantry, emphasis on symmetry, circumstantial and profuse diction. F+ per cent is at times inversely proportioned to M. Tetanoid epilepsy, on the other hand, shows relatively high F+ and rather high A per cents, only rarely confabulations, few or zero M, rare color responses (no pure C), rare perseverations (few at any one time), never any color naming, self-references or evaluating remarks. In these cases F+ per cent is always directly proportioned to M.

Härtel and Ederle[26] compare genuine and symptomatic epilepsy (including the traumatic and residual varieties). They hold that it is not possible to make a differential diagnosis between these two groups with the Rorschach test. They base this opinion on a number of averages. They also report a high A per cent (50 - 100) in both groups.

As may be seen from the above, the Rorschach test literature shows that there is disagreement on some points regarding the diagnosis of epilepsy. These center mostly on M, color responses, A and Orig per cents. We have had the opportunity to reexamine these disputed issues in our own material as well as in some special data for 28 epileptics (genuine and symptomatic) whose Rorschach protocols (obtained by another person) were given to us for evaluation by Goldkuhl. This material had been analysed by Goldkuhl from a clinical and psychological-constitutional point of view, and the results were published in 1946.[27] Our inspection yielded the following: Rorschach's findings could be verified relative to all four points at issue. The genuine epileptics showed a tendency to copious M production; in the 19 genuine cases, a total of 70 M occurred, including rather many M− and secondary M. In the symptomatic epileptics, M was less frequent, secondary M was rare in them, and M− entirely lacking. Concerning the color responses, Rorschach's claim that these are rather frequent and increase with deterioration has been verified, and so has his view that with progressive deterioration the color responses shift towards pure color. This all applies to both the genuine and the symptomatic epilepsies. In addition, the especially low A per cent mentioned by

[26]Ruth Härtel and W. Ederle, Genuine und symptomatologische Epilepsie im Roschach'schen Formdeutversuch. Zeitschr. f. d. ges. Neurologie und Psychiatrie, Vol. 176, 1943, pp. 640-670.

[27]Erik Goldkuhl, Rorschach-Tests bei Epilepsie, nebst einer grundsätzlichen Untersuchung. Uppsala Läkareförenings Förhandlinger, Vol. 51, Uppsala, 1946, pp. 283-311.

Rorschach as being particularly arresting, was verified. Guirdham and Weissenfeld also found this, though Stauder as well as Härtel and Ederle have denied it. The total average in both groups (genuine and symptomatic) was around 43 per cent. The average for those who were only deteriorated (37.9 per cent) was a full 10 per cent lower than the average for those who were only (or at the same time) oligophrenic (47.8 per cent). Thus there is no significant difference regarding A per cent between genuine and secondary epileptics, but an A per cent of 50 or more justifies the supposition that a possible intellectual defect in this epileptic person is based entirely or partly on oligophrenia. Finally, this material also shows that the Orig per cent roughly behaves as Rorschach had supposed it to do; displaying relatively high values with poor form with the oligophrenic epileptics showing the highest values. (Guirdham, on the other hand, maintains that it is just the oligophrenic epileptics whose Orig per cent is low, in contrast to the deteriorated.) A differential diagnosis between genuine and symptomatic (secondary) epilepsy could not always be made since perseveration was at times also lacking in the genuine epileptics. Ruth and Walter von Brunn arrived at the same conclusion on the basis of their investigation of 280 epileptics.[28] Moreover these authors ascertained that the Rorshach experiment is less valuable for the diagnosis of epilepsy and especially its sub-classes, than it is for an individualized study of the specific cases for treatment and prognosis. They also observed a decrease of F+ per cent and of A per cent with increasing deterioration.[29] In an investigation of 50 patients (which incidentally contains the most complete and clear summary of the Rorschach literature on epilepsy so far), Delay, Pichot, Lempérière and Perse were able to ascertain that the genuine epileptics (as also many symptomatic) on the whole have a coarctated, the traumatic epileptics an extratensive, experience balance.[30]

RORSCHACH DIAGNOSIS OF EPILEPSY IN PRACTICE

1. GENERAL CONSIDERATIONS

What, then, can the practitioner rely on? Essentially one ought to proceed from Rorschach's syndrome, but not to expect that all or even most of the factors should be in agreement in every case. If only enough characteristic elements of the syndrome are present (as for instance, lengthened time, low F+ per cent *and* low A per cent, perseveration and sticking to a theme), one may safely assume epilepsy. Lengthened response time is

[28]Ruth and Walter L. von Brunn, Die Epilepsie im Rorschach'schen Formdeutversuch. Archiv. f. Psychiatrie und Zeitschr. f. Neurologie, Vol. 184, 1950, pp. 545-578.
[29]op. cit. pp. 560, 578.
[30]J. Delay, P. Pichot, T. Lempérière, J. Perse, Le test de Rorschach et la Personnalité Epileptique, Paris, 1955, pp. 77 and 202.

found in most, though not all, cases. Experience balance varies, but is really often dilated and almost always extratensive. We need not be too particular about M (depressive epileptics have no M, and in most cases no color responses). If we are experienced in the scoring of M (and that is no easy matter), we may be surprised at the richness of the M (and M−) in some epileptics. Low F+ per cent is always found where deterioration has already set in, or where oligophrenia is also present. Only in the latter case will A per cent also be high. On the whole, we can confidently depend on just this observation of Rorschach, the low A per cent. Rorschach finds this "striking" (p. 44) ; we expressed the surmise above (chapter 5, under figure-background-fusion) that this is a result of epileptic dysthymia which produces a quasi-structural lability. Among the other factors, the M−, the secondary M, and the perseveration, are of particular diagnostic value, besides confabulations, evaluating remarks, self-references, emphasis on symmetry and color naming. It should be noted that aside from, or instead of, perseveration "proper," it is Bovet's sticking to a theme which is especially characteristic of epilepsy. The occurrence of black and white as color values (especially when there is perseveration at the same time) is also suspicious. Among epileptics even black and white naming occurs!

In addition to these factors listed by Rorschach, figure-background fusion is not rare in epileptics. Our own experience in this regard was verified by K. W. Bash in some material from the Swiss Institution for Epileptics. In most instances only one such interpretation appears in the protocol of an epileptic. The high quantities noted in the protocols of artists are rarely found in epileptics.

As already mentioned, Salomon and Zulliger often also found inverse interpretations in epileptics and epileptoid types with neurosis.

The Subject's diction is always to be observed. Strikingly circumstantial, pedantic and at the same time verbose diction is found in genuine and in organic epilepsy as well as in ixophrenia.

Franciska Minkowska, who did not so much rely upon the formal evaluation method, as on the content and diction of the record in determining the clinical diagnosis in detail, has made the following observation: epileptics attempt to bind the separated details of the blots into a combined interpretation, in other words, they show a tendency toward simultaneous combinations.[31] She regarded this peculiarity as typical, especially where an adhesion was expressed (e.g., a connection, a "being attached to" or "suspended from," a soldering, a welding, a sealing, etc.; op. cit. p. 352). This trait puts the epileptics in contrast to the schizophrenics: "Whereas

[31]F. Minkowska, L'épilepsie essentielle, sa psycho-pathologie et le test de Rorschach. Annales médico-psychologiques, Novembre 1946, p. 331/332.

in the schizophrenics all decomposes, dissolves and diffuses, in the epileptics all is condensed, concentrated, and agglutinated" (op. cit. p. 345).

In conclusion we may offer a warning: only positive diagnoses are fairly reliable. If nothing is found in the protocol to cause us to suspect epilepsy, we cannot, nevertheless, preclude the possibility of genuine epilepsy with certainty. In the same way that (according to Stauder, see above) the absence of character change does not justify the conclusion that there is no genuine epilepsy, so also a "normal" protocol is no proof against the finding of epilepsy. This is the weak point in the Rorschach test diagnosis of epilepsy. *Only deterioration or character change become apparent in the test.* Where both are absent, an almost normal protocol with only faint hints of pathological traits may mask the true state of affairs. We have seen a case of severe genuine epilepsy with dangerous destructiveness, which did not present the slightest reference points from which to detect such severe epilepsy except for a hint of sticking to the theme, two instances of difficulties in finding words and somewhat pedantic diction in a framework of excellent intelligence (among others 7 M+); and the illness was already of 37 years' duration!

## 2. PROBLEMS OF DIFFERENTIAL DIAGNOSIS

The genuine epileptic (as is the case with most organics) belongs characterologically to the type with "firmness of content." Pfahler.[32] This type combines narrow and fixated attention with strong perseveration. This is the origin of the two most important Rorschach symptoms, the DW and perseveration. This, however, is not sufficient for a diagnosis of epilepsy, since both these symptoms are also prominent in the general organic Rorschach syndrome.

This brings us to the problem of the differential diagnosis between *genuine and symptomatic (secondary) epilepsy.* Here the problem is mainly one of traumatic and encephalitic or post-encephalitic etiology, and also of brain tumors, brain lues, circulatory disturbances, meningitis, eclampsia, and other less frequent organic causes of epileptic seizures. If, in addition to (or instead of), perseveration proper, there also is clear sticking to the theme, it generally speaks in favor of genuine etiology. Moreover, as Bovet has shown, in genuine epileptics the perceptual difficulties, especially those with reference to W, are usually not clearly conscious. On the other hand, they are overtly expressed by the traumatics (criticism!). Anatomical stereotypy is found mainly in traumatics, less frequently in the genuine cases, and then for the most part in hysteric characters. Epileptoid diction

[32]G. Pfahler, Vererbung als Schicksal, Leipzig, 1932, here quoted from Hubert Rohracher, Kleine Einführing in die Charakterkunde, Leipzig, 1934, pp. 70-71.

is *not* a sure differential diagnostic sign. To be sure, it does not generally appear in the traumatics (Bovet), but it is found in other patients with organic etiology (especially post-encephalitics) if they show an ixophrenic character change. In general, if deterioration has not progressed very far, genuine epilepsy is still marked by fairly good forms, and it may show M responses, something which hardly ever happens in organic etiology. (Kelley calls attention to these two important factors.[33]) But not all genuine cases respond with relatively good forms, and not all of them have M. Thus the Rorschach differential diagnosis between these two large groups of genuine and non-genuine epileptics is a very difficult matter, and in some cases it cannot be made with certainty, which is true in the clinic also.

It is different when the differential diagnosis is to be made between *epilepsy and hysteria*. A sharp discrimination between these two illnesses is demanded by purely etiologically oriented psychiatry, a demand which cannot always be completely met either clinically or from the point of view of hereditary or constitutional biology. Karl Kleist says: "It is possible to consider a number of constitutional illnesses as belonging to the epileptic, just as well as to the hysteric, groups of disease. From a constitutional point of view the long tabooed concept of a hystero-epilepsy loses its doubtfulness. And the same way the essence of the older teaching with its concept of mixed psychoses, recently revived by Gaupp, Kretschmer, and Hoffman, here appears again."[34] And Rudolf Brun[35] refers to the researches in heredity conducted by Kraulis, Luxenburger and Mauz, who were able to show a certain hereditary affinity between severe hysterics and epileptics. Stauder too, (op. cit. p. 177) mentions the occurence of hysteric psychopathies with pseudologia phantastica among the relatives of epileptics. Szondi's concept of the "paraxysmal" hereditary group (analogous to Mauz' "iktaffinic constitution") also belongs here.

In spite of this hereditary affinity it is often possible, particularly with the help of the Rorschach test, to arrive at a fairly certain differential diagnosis between hysteria and epilepsy, even where a clinical diagnosis is not on sure ground. These two syndromes are so different that they may exclude each other, although not necessarily; for there are transitional cases in which epileptic and hysteric traits exist side by side, even in the Rorschach test. In such cases, a double constitutional taint is to be considered. Whether we designate such cases as hystero-epilepsy, genuine epilepsy with neurotic superstructure, or hysteria with epileptoid symptoms (hysteria in an ixoid), is a matter of finesse, almost of taste.

[33]Klopfer and Kelley, cit. p. 384.
[34]Karl Kleist, Episodische Dämmerzustände, Leipzig, 1926, pp. 65/66.
[35]Rudolf Brun, Allgemeine Neurosenlehre, Basel, 2 ed. 1946, p. 163.

# ORGANIC PSYCHOSES

## CONCEPT AND DELIMITATION

In former years the traditional designation "organic" mental diseases always meant that anatomical changes had taken place. Today's attitude is somewhat less absolute and it is an accepted viewpoint that organic and functional factors are etiologically not mutually exclusive, but are mutually conditioning. Goldstein's and Kleist's studies show that organic damage offers an especially favorable soil for the development of psychogenic mechanisms, and the organ neuroses have taught us that, conversely, the transition from the neurosis to an organic illness is a fluid one. The physical symptoms of organic and functional disorders are to a high degree the same (v. Weizsäcker).[36]

In order to avoid confusion with older, more apodictic concepts, it is advisable, as is more and more the practice at present, to designate the "organic" states as *lesional*. (In addition, Sjöbring groups together the less severe asthenic lesional conditions with muscular hypotonia and lowered degree of awakeness as the two central symptoms, and he designates them as "hypophrenias.")

In the following sections, whenever we discuss one (or several) organic Rorschach test syndromes, we shall refer *only* to the *cortically* or *subcortically* localized disturbances. Organic changes localized in other parts of the central nervous system show the organic Rorschach test syndrome only if clinically they also produce psychologic symptoms; as, for instance, multiple sclerosis. Pure spinal lesions produce also in the Rorschach test only such indirect effects on the personality as are often found clinically, i.e., the reaction of the personality to the disease. In other words, the "organic" Rorschach symptoms refer to the narrower range of psychiatric organic illnesses, not to the broader neurological ones.

## THE ORGANIC RORSCHACH SYNDROMES IN GENERAL

In the area of the organic psychoses, Rorschach diagnostic principles are as yet relatively poorly developed. In Binder's opinion, "the tasks yet to be solved are far more numerous than those which have already been solved."[37] Even though, as we shall see later, this applies to most of the organic brain disturbances insofar as they are special disease pictures, the situation is somewhat better in regard to the general organic psychologic

---

[36]According to Erik Goldkuhl, Funktionellt eller organiskt, Svenska Läkartidning, Stockholm, 1943, Nr. 20.

[37]Hans Binder, Die Klinische Bedeutung des Rorschach'schen Versuches in "Psychiatrie und Rorschach'scher Formdeutversuch," Zürich, 1944, p. 26.

syndrome. Thus one particular organic Rorschach test syndrome, which in its essential traits is very well known today, corresponds to the well recognized organic psychologic syndrome with its triad of characteristic disturbances in memory, thinking and affectivity (disturbances in recent memory and in recall, especially for single concrete concepts, confabulations, poverty of association, disturbances in judgment, and affective incontinence).

One might even say that the Rorschach test is particularly sensitive in regard to organic disturbances. As has been shown by a special American investigation,[38] it is superior to all testing methods in this area, indeed not only to the testing methods, but also to most clinical and physical methods of examination (the neurological examination, the EEG, skull x-ray, and the pneumoencephalogram, but not to the spinal puncture).[39] It is even true that in many cases the incipient personality change due to an organic disturbance shows up in the Rorschach test before it can be demonstrated clinically (Klopfer and Kelley, The Rorschach Technique, p. 327).

1. OBERHOLZER'S SYNDROME[40] In a study published in 1931, Emil Oberholzer had already isolated most of the traits of the general organic Rorschach syndrome on the basis of a single case. Only a few details needed to be added by later investigators. This Oberholzer syndrome is briefly as follows: prolonged response time, more extratensive experience type with only low affective ability for adjustment (predominantly CF and C), and lowered F+ per cent, reduction in primary W+ due to damage of the abstracting capacity, and instead there is frequently W− and DW due to helplessness, increased Dd owing to narrowing of the mental field and loss of the ability to synthesize, decreased D, increased A and Orig per cents (Orig−), decreased M, inclination to perseveration (to fill in for associational poverty), chiefly in connection with confabulations and often with stereotyped repeated phrases, frequently rejections, and poor interpretation awareness.

The affective incontinence of the majority of organics in this syndrome

[38]Stewart G. Armitage, An Analysis of Certain Psychological Tests Used for the Evaluation of Brain Injury, Psychological Monographs, Vol. 60, 1, Washington, 1946; see Summary: "It is suggested that the Rorschach is the most useful for this purpose." (p. 47).

[39]Jerome Fisher and Thomas A. Gonda, Neurologic Techniques and Rorschach Test in Detecting Brain Pathology. A.M.A. Archives of Neurology and Psychiatry, Vol. 74, 1955, pp. 117-124.

[40]Emil Oberholzer, "Zur Differentialdiagnose psychischer Folgezustände nach Schädeltraumen mittels des Rorschach'schen Formdeutversuchs" in "Zeitschrift für die gesamte Neurologie und Psychiatrie" (vol. 136, 1931, pp. 596-629).

is shown in the following factors: extratensive experience type, mostly with labile color values, and with zero or very few M, few W+ and reduced F+ per cent. Thus we have affective lability with generally inadequate braking forces.

From the point of view of differential diagnosis, this syndrome is to be distinguished from schizophrenia and oligophrenia. As Binder observes correctly (op cit. p. 26), this delimitation is not always possible. Nevertheless, differential diagnostic signs are available. To be sure, they are not always present, but they appear so frequently that for practical purposes a decision is in most cases possible. As compared to the schizophrenics, the organics are distinguished by their eagerness to comply. In general, the organics want to do their best. Hence their inclination to be critical and their tendency to perseverations and repetitions. As Hanfmann and Kasanin[41] express it, "they cooperate too well at times," while the schizophrenics very often lack the desire to cooperate. As Oberholzer himself emphasized, organically deteriorated individuals differ from oligophrenics primarily by their criticism, their insecurity (subject and object criticism, negations, responses in question form), while oligophrenics generally are sure that they have hit the "correct" interpretation. Moreover, organically deteriorated individuals usually do more confabulating and stronger perseverating than do the oligophrenics. In most cases the latter do not perseverate at all.

2. PIOTROWSKI'S SYNDROME. In 1937, Piotrowski set up another syndrome representing the "organic disturbances of the central nervous system." In greatly modified form it was later taken over by Isabella Tarcsay[42] who wanted to extend its application in this field to *all* psychoses (including the endogenous ones). The attempt to make such an extension is based on a misunderstanding, for neither in the clinic nor in Rorschach test diagnostics is there any psychologic syndrome common to all psychoses. Bash[43] has shown that the modification of this syndrome and its extension to include also the endogenous psychoses as well cannot be used in differential diagnosis. The Piotrowski syndrome in its *original* form, however, is definitely useful as a check in regard to the narrower group of real "organics" whom Piotrowski had in mind. In itself it is not as reliable as Oberholzer's syndrome, on which, incidentally, Piotrowski built his. Above all, the absence of the typical W∓ factor and of the extratensive experience type is an obvious shortcoming.

[41]Klopfer and Kelley, op. cit. p. 345.
[42]Isabella Tarcsay, Grundriss der Psychodiagnostik, Zürich, 1944, pp. 185-200.
[43]K. W. Bash, Über den differentialdiagnostischen Wert der Piotrowski-Zeichen und anderer Zeichengruppen im Rorschach-Versuch, Experientia, Vol. 2, 1946.

We now present Piotrowski's ten "signs" in their original form:[44] 1. Number of responses is less than 15. Rorschach points out that the response total of most organics is "usually within the average range, usually toward the lower border, except in the case of the confabulators" (p. 21). According to this most organics should produce 15 responses or more, which actually happens very frequently. But Piotrowski's observation is also verified in many cases. Presumably the typical response totals of organic patients are distributed over a somewhat wider range. 2. Prolonged response time (more than one minute per response). 3. Zero or only one M+. 4. Color naming. This factor is of considerable significance. To be sure, in most organic groups color naming does not occur too frequently. But because of its rarity and its complete absence in "normal" protocols, it always has a high diagnostic value. However, it must not be forgotten that it may also show up in epileptics, oligophrenics and deteriorated schizophrenics. Thus it depends on the pattern that is found! It has been shown that color naming is particularly frequent in cases of acute alcohol intoxication and immediately after electric shock (Klopfer and Kelley, p. 332). 5. F+ per cent is less than 70. 6. P per cent is less than 25. This "sign" is of value, however, only if the response total is really low. With high response totals, in confabulatory or manically disordered organics, it loses its significance. At any rate the absolute values of P are in the main lowered. 7. Perseveration. 8. Impotence. By this Piotrowski understands the patient's inability to improve responses which he recognizes as inadequate (Klopfer and Kelley, p. 333). This observation is a very valuable one. For example, we saw a female patient in whom there was suspicion of incipient Huntington's chorea but who clinically only showed a depression at that time. She called card V a "horse." Afterwards, she herself admitted that this was not a good response. However, she actually did not know how she had produced it (of course, it was a DW), and she was not afterwards able to give a better response! 9. "Perplexity," i.e., lack of confidence in ones' own ability, with request for verifying assurances ("was this right?"). Such uncertainty, however, will also occur in non-organic cases, e.g., in psychasthenics. 10. "Automatic phrases" (taken over from Oberholzer).

According to Piotrowski at least 5 signs must appear (op. cit., p. 533), but the validity of the diagnosis is strengthened by the presence of still more symptoms, especially a displacement of the color type towards the CF and C, whereby these are at the same time increased (p. 534). The most important point is the evaluating of the total record, which should show

[44]Zygmunt Piotrowski, The Rorschach Inkblot Method in Organic Disturbance of the Central Nervous System. The Journal of Nervous and Mental Disease, Vol. 86, 1937, pp. 525-537.—See also Klopfer and Kelley, pp. 330-335 and Bochner and Halpern, p. 196.

intellectual passivity, a frequent lack of subjective clearness in the manner of approach, and a striking qualitative inequality (pp. 535-536). It is, perhaps, once more in order to warn against a mechanical application of these "signs." In Piotrowski's own words (p. 529): "The psychological significance of each Rorschach sign depends on the number and quality of the other signs with which it occurs in a record; in other words, it depends on the general setting. This is the chief interpretative principle of Rorschach records, and cannot be overemphasized."

3. THE "SYNTHESIZED SYNDROME" (general organic Rorschach test syndrome). For ordinary investigation of organic brain disturbances a kind of synthesized syndrome may be utilized which consists of an appropriate combination of Oberholzer's and Piotrowski's syndromes, to which the following two important characteristics should be added: repetitions, in definite disturbances of recent memory (not to be confused with perseveration!); and indefinite F— as a result of inability to recall single concrete concepts. Such a pattern is in fact presented in Bochner's and Halpern's[45] book, although not quite in the same form. This synthesized syndrome looks about as follows:

Ready compliance in the experiment
Poor interpretation awareness
(Criticism in interpretations, if present, differential diagnostic sign against oligophrenia)
Number of responses low, from less than 15 to barely above 15
Response time prolonged
Many W, but preferably W— and DW—
Decreased D
Increased Dd
Decreased M+, often zero and rarely more than one
Low to medium number of color responses, mostly CF and C
Color naming
Occasional position responses (Klopfer-Kelley, p. 353)
Extratensive experience type
F+ per cent lowered, mostly under 70
Inclination to indefinite F—
Increased A per cent
Lowered P (with low number of responses P per cent < 25) (in new cases higher, Bochner and Halpern)
Increased Orig per cent (—)
Perseveration, frequently from one card to the next
Repetition of the same response to the same blot
Confabulations
Automatic phrases
Frequently rejections

[45]Ruth Bochner and Florence Halpern, The Clinical Application of the Rorschach-Test, New York ,1942, pp. 193-196.

RORSCHACH DIAGNOSIS OF SPECIFIC BRAIN DISTURBANCES

Relatively usable Rorschach test syndromes are known only for certain specific organic diseases. Nevertheless, we are not completely helpless when confronted by the others. In most cases the clinic has some definite suspicion in a certain direction, and the Rorschach test may then strengthen or dilute this suspicion on the basis of the presence or absence of sufficient signs of the general organic syndrome. In other cases it may be the Rorschach test itself which, because of its sensitivity to organic ailments, raises the first suspicion of such disorder. It must then be left to the clinic to determine the more precise character of these disturbances. In the area of the organic mental disorders, a close cooperation between the physician and the psychologist is especially necessary. Special warning is in order here against blind diagnoses and exhibitionistic feats by Examiners.

1. *Senile dementia.* In spite of this scanty material, only ten senile demented persons and five deteriorated arteriosclerotics, Rorschach succeeded surprisingly well in elaborating the identifying differences between these two dementias. The Rorschach test syndrome in senile dementia does not differ at any point from the general organic Rorschach syndrome. The inclination toward poor W and perseveration are especially pronounced here. Response time is usually prolonged; however, there are exceptions. Nor is the experience type decisive. In seniles there are frequently slightly depressed or torpid types which are not of the extratensive type. However, most of them do belong to it. F+ per cent is rather low, although not always quite as low (0 - 30 per cent) as stated by Rorschach. Orig– are almost always found, but Orig per cent varies considerably. DW are frequently found, and there are many W–. Sequence, if at all determinable, is usually orderly, at times loose. In most cases there are more H than Hd. Tendency to confabulation is usually as obvious as that toward perseveration.

Approach type and H : Hd relationship differentiate the senile demented from arteriosclerotic individuals. Their infantilisms apparently distinguish them from all other organics. (A reservation is in order here concerning neurotic infantilism, which may of course be found in all individuals as well as in all organic disturbances.) Rorschach himself observed (p. 176) that six to eight year old children, as well as individuals with senile dementia, show a predilection for perceiving plants. The old saying that old age makes a person childish appears to be based on very good observations. For we have been able to establish that the typically infantile inverted interpretations are not rare in the senile demented. Apart from educators, we never found them among other adults. And from a formal point of view, the extratensive experience type and especially the approach, the many but poor W, correspond to the reaction pattern seen in the small child. It is possible that with time we will find still other infantilisms in the protocols of the senile demented.[46]

2. *Arteriosclerotic dementia.* Here, too, we find most of the organic traits: lengthened reaction time, low F+ and high A per cents, poor Originals (Orig per cent is usually lower than in senile dementia). In contrast to the general organic syndrome, and above all in contrast to senile dementia, the (frequently depressive) arteriosclerotics manifest a coarcted experience type and above all a poor approach (D - Dd- Do). Their fearfulness is also revealed in their tendency to reversed sequence and (again in contrast to senile dementia) in their inclination to Hd over H. Perseverations are also found, and confabulations play a part, especially in those patients who hallucinate.

3. *Progressive paralysis (dementia paralytica).* Paralysis cannot be determined on the basis of the Rorschach test as such. Only if, and in so far as, it has produced deterioration, may this be found in the test as organic deterioration. The syndrome indicated by Rorschach deviates from the general organic syndrome at only one point, the good M. He observed this in the sample cited in his book (p. 175). However, it seems to stem from the pre-psychotic personality of the patient. Rorschach himself says of the patient that he is a "formerly very intelligent man." At any rate here is an observation that has not generally been confirmed.

Another factor needs to be kept in mind with reference to Rorschach's paralytics. In his day, malarial treatment had not yet been developed. Thus, none of Rorschach's patients had been treated, something hardly known today. And if a patient should come so early that the illness has not yet even been diagnosed, and hence has not been treated, then deterioration, if at all present, will be so minimal that it will manifest itself only slightly in the test. At any rate, in such cases one cannot expect to find the severe degrees of deterioration that Rorschach found in his patients. We must conclude, therefore, that the Rorschach test picture of the untreated and little progressed paralysis is not yet known, and that the older patients who have been treated cannot be set up against those under Rorschach's observation. At the present time, the same is true for paralysis as for most other organic disturbances, namely, that only a non-specific organic picture can be diagnosed with the test.

4. *Encephalitis.* We know a little more about encephalitis. In most cases it yields rather massive organic symptoms. Perseveration and confabulation are rather pronounced, perseveration usually more so than in

---

[46]In the meantime our surmise has been confirmed. It may today be considered a proven fact that the senility process is a reversing of the development process. Consequently in nearly all Rorschach factors there is a certain similarity between the average values of children and seniles. (See Ames, Learned, Metraux, Walker, *Rorschach Responses in Old Age*, New York, 1954.)

traumatics. According to Klopfer and Kelley, M are supposed to appear in this illness (p. 343), as also a preference for indefinite F– (F+ per cent is between 50 and 70); experience type is extratensive, and sequence disturbances as well as Do may be found. Considerable fluctuations may appear in two successive tests, while marked differences in sharpness of form in the same test are claimed to have been found in progressive paralysis, in certain types of epilepsy, and in brain tumors (Klopfer and Kelley, p. 343).

5. *Post-encephalitic Parkinsonism.* Veit made a special study of the Parkinsonian states following encephalitis epidemica.[47] He determined that the test showed a clear difference between the common and the sticking kind. The sticking score lower F+ per cent, and never M, while the common form showed a high F+ per cent and now and then M. The sticking produced no color responses, the common form a few. The common form produced 4 - 10 W and rarely DW, as also a slightly increased A per cent (50 - 70), while the sticking showed decreased or increased W and a severely increased A per cent (70 - 100). But instead of this high A per cent, the sticking at times show anatomy perseveration. Response time was lengthened in both forms, and color shocks never appeared.

6. *Traumatic encephalopathy, Ritter's encephalosis.* Traumatic encephalopathic states, especially in their most frequent form, the post-commotional states, may often be so slight that clinically they may hardly be recognized as such. In the Rorschach test, too, the organic symptoms appear in these cases in a milder form. Time is often not essentially prolonged, perseveration is usually weak, and at any rate less pronounced than in encephalitis and its sequelae, or in severe organic processes. Diffuse contusions and severe traumas naturally produce severe symptoms, at times with pronounced deterioration.

According to Klopfer and Kelley (pp. 339-340) traumatic encephalopathy shows unusual Dd, confabulatory DW, lowered F+ per cent, disturbance in the sequence, pure C now and then, and a tendency to light-dark interpretations, at times of a depressive, irritated or anxious coloring. Cloud, smoke, and x-ray imagery is frequent. In addition, Oberholzer's amorphous primitive percepts (mostly W, but at times also D) at times also appear here. They are not always interpretations of the gray, but are also found as simple indefinite F–.

Traumatics (like organics generally) often get stuck in the preconfigurations (Sander), a protopathic (Conrad) disturbance in efficiency, which makes it impossible for them to interpret more differentiated W, (especially

[47]Hans Veit, Der Parkinsonismus nach Encephalitis epidemica im Rorschach'schen Formdeutversuch. Zeitschr. f. d. ges. Neurologie und Psychiatrie, Vol. 110, 1927, pp. 301-324.

the combinatory W). After seeing the most common W, an interpretation difficulty develops.[48]

In the test, the organic affective lability and incontinence, especially pronounced in brain-damaged cases, reveals itself in the predominance of CF and C over FC (right color type) with reduced braking forces. We should avoid the error of confusing this affective irritability with heightened aggressiveness. An increase of Ds consequently does not enter the Rorschach test picture of encephalopathy.

Neuroses (traumatic neuroses) are a frequent superstructure of post-traumatic brain damage. If the etiology really is mixed the Rorschach test also shows both (elements of the organic syndrome, with color shock, and often also dark shock).

Purpose neuroses (compensation and insurance neuroses) following accidents, according to Oberholzer (op. cit. p. 620), usually show many anatomy responses, and frequently also expressions of aggravation, while purely organic sequelae show no or only few anatomy responses, and no aggravation. The aggravation is rather simple to recognize. Patients will interrupt their interpreting with subjective complaints that they cannot go on, their eyes hurt, etc. Furthermore, in purpose neurotics we may meet with simulation, something not found in organics. This may be determined by repeating the experiment (possibly with the parallel series). If the formal structure of the first experiment is consistent with that of the control experiment, there is no simulation.

7. *Alcoholics.* The many pictures in the alcoholic psychoses differ so widely that they cannot be treated as a homogenous group.

a. *Chronic alcoholism.* No specific Rorschach syndrome for chronic alcoholism is known to us. The basic personality is often one of constitutional addiction, which in case of alcoholism contains both somatic and psychological factors. The psychologic factors that go with addiction may to a degree be manifested in the test (see chapter 11). Alcoholism becomes an organic psychosis only when traces of organic damage appear. In the Rorschach test the first warning sign may be a seemingly harmless repetition which points to an incipient disturbance of recent memory. As time goes on, other signs of the organic syndrome will also appear, but even in clear cases the test only shows the general syndrome. The specific diagnosis can be made only from the clinical data.

b. and c. *Delirium tremens and alcoholic hallucinosis.* There is an excellent study by Arnold Weber[49] concerning these two forms of alcoholic psychosis, in which he reports the following results.

[48]Horst Meyerhoff, Der Gestaltwandel bei den Deutungsleistungen von Hirnverletzten im Rorschach-Test. Archiv für Psychiatrie und Neurologie, vol. 189, pp. 140, 141, 143.

[49]Arnold Weber, Delirium tremens und Alkoholhalluzinose im Rorschach'schen Formdeutversuch, Zeitschr. f. d. ges. Neurologie und Psychiatrie, Vol. 159, 1937, pp. 446-500.

In their delirium, delirium patients mostly show an F+ per cent of less than 60. After the delirium it rises owing to improvement in D and Dd. M are increased in delirium (average of 2), but not afterwards (.8). M with light-dark, and small M occasionally appear. Color responses are more numerous during delirium than afterwards, so that the experience type dilates during delirium, and shifts somewhat to the introversive side. With anxiety and depression Weber finds black interpretations: in euphoria, white interpretations. Delirium patients see relatively many W; DW are relatively rare; W– are more numerous after than during delirium. Dd increase (more so during delirium); Do are rather rare in the delirium and somewhat more frequent afterwards; but Ds are more numerous during than after the delirium. Sequence is usually loose during delirium and orderly afterwards. In the delirium a peculiar series of W appear, due to a perseverative tendency in the formal perception. A per cent is increased only little. The relationship in the human responses during delirium is that H > Hd, later Hd > H. So far as content is concerned, the so-called "water interpretations" are striking after delirium; such as "lake," "ice," "glacier," "water animals," "water plants," and the like. In delirium, however, occasionally alcoholic and frequently also sex responses emerge. They are lost afterwards. Originals are more numerous and better during than after the delirium (as is the case with the M). Color shock is found in about half the cases in delirium, after the acute episode in almost all cases ("recuperation neurosis"). Dark shock is more rare. Illusions and hallucinations are frequent in delirium, as are perseverations of all degrees and kinds. After delirium there is at times a complete amnesia for the first experiment.

*Oligophrenic delirium patients* have their own peculiarities; low F+ per cent, almost no M, no small M, extratensive experience type, more frequent DW, no Ds and only few Orig. No color shock appears here, and dark shock is rare (found only in delirium). The peculiar series of W also make their appearance here.

The *hallucinosis patients* score the same F+ per cent, 70 - 80, during and after the psychosis. Their M are relatively numerous during the psychosis (average 5.3) and small M are even more frequent. Their experience type is pronounced introversive during and after the psychosis. They see only few W but better forms, and their Dd are much increased. After the psychosis there will regularly be some Do. Hallucinosis patients produce no series of W. They regularly show color and dark shock, but no real perseveration, only stereotypies. Amnesia for the first experiment was not found.

d. The *alcoholic Korsakoff psychosis* has been rather thoroughly described by Rorschach. Because of the strong liking for story-telling in these patients (the interpretation of the blots is experienced as pleasurable), their response totals are increased to levels far above average, and they also produce M, small M, and occasional M–. Experience type is introversive; approach rich (W - D—(Dd)); sequence is loose (but, according to Weber's observation, orderly). Successive-combinatory and confabulatory-combinatory W are frequent. A per cent is at average, and Orig per cent may be very high (±). In these patients, in whom memory disturbances are so prominent, repetitions occur in addition to the perseverations. Of all organic disturbances, the alcoholic Korsakoff syndrome seems to be the one whose Rorschach pattern deviates most from the general organic syndrome.

e. In their *delusions of jealousy*, the alcoholics more or less follow the general organic syndrome, depending on the degree of any existing alcoholic deterioration. In the more paranoid forms of jealousy we repeatedly noted that patients interpreted very tiny details, mostly in response to card V, as "horns" or "heads with horns," apparently a projection of the popular notion of "a man with horns." It is conceivable that these complex determined responses may appear also in the jealousy delusions of alcoholics, inasmuch as this disturbance is at times a transition to more paranoid forms.

f. *Dipsomania.* The dipsomanias belong in the main to the psychopathies, and preferably to the ixoid and circular forms. The diagnosis is to be based on the individual's constitution with consideration of the patient's way of life. A "blind diagnosis" does not appear possible for such conditions.

g. and h. *Alcoholic epilepsy* and *alcoholic melancholia* depend presumably to a high degree on a constitutional taint with epilepsy, or manic-depressive psychosis, respectively. A more thorough Rorschach test study of these less frequent alcoholic psychoses would be interesting, and might yield valuable clues about their constitutional sources.

8. *Lesions of the frontal lobes.* In some patients the psychologic symptoms might yield clues to the localization of the organic impairments from which the symptoms result. This is true also for their manifestations in the Rorschach test. Fränkel and Benjamin[50] had already made the observation that frontal lobe patients emphasized the impossibility of producing a W perception (e.g., "out of context"). This is based on the inability for analytic-abstract thinking characteristic of such impairment. According to Klopfer and Kelley (pp. 336-338) another consequence of this damage is the inability to see the interpretations of other individuals,

[50]Fritz Fränkel and Dora Benjamin, Die Kritik der Veruschsperson beim Rorschach'schen Formdeutversuch. Schweizer Archiv f. Neurologie und Psychiatrie, Vol. 33, 1934, pp. 13/14.

as noted by Piotrowski. If we tell such individuals "Some people see two persons here" (card III), they are not able to locate these percepts in the blot unless they have themselves given this interpretation. This peculiar behavior, which naturally can be determined only after obtaining the protocol, was observed in tumor, hemorrhages and atrophies of the frontal lobes. This phenomenon, incidentally, may be checked by means of Rubin's well-known figure (white bowl on black ground which can also be seen as two profiles). If the subject has first seen the bowl, he is not then able to see the two profiles, even if they are pointed out to him. This reaction is probably no more more than a special and very severe form of organic perseveration.

Freeman and Watts[51] report the following in pre-frontal lobectomy as well as in gross structural damage of the frontal lobes: pure color responses, color naming and color enumeration, low F+ and low P per cents, prolonged reaction time, and low response totals. If these patients continue to get worse, stereotyped phrases, repetitions and perseverations appear. These results of surgery thus constitute a kind of verification of the general organic syndrome.

[51]See: Klopfer and Kelley, the Rorschach Technique, p. 344.

# CHAPTER XIV

# The Rorschach Test in Children

DURING THE LAST FEW YEARS child psychologists have taken to the Rorschach technique so eagerly as to breed the impression among the general public that it is a special technique of child psychology. The question is actually asked now and then whether the Rorschach test is applicable to adults. Since Rorschach built up and validated his technique on the basis of work with adults, the question should be reversed: can this method also apply to children? Rorschach's experience and that of numerous later investigators has shown that it has universal applicability to all nations, all intelligence levels, and all ages. This is exactly its great advantage. The test is applicable from the age of three years on (Ford, see below, p. 93). As might be expected, however, a number of modifications must be made for children, with regard to both administration and evaluation. Besides, Rorschach tests of children usually give less results than in adults or youths.

## THE LITERATURE

First, a very short survey of the more important Rorschach test literature on children is in order. So extensive is the literature that it is not possible even to make reference to all the important papers, to say nothing of the many less independent and less significant investigations found in this area, as in any other.

Rorschach's communications concerning findings in children are rather sparse. He only indicated that the intelligence components develop differently at the various age levels (p. 62), that the experience type of the young child of about two and a half to four years is ambiequal and dilated, that in the latency period during the school years there is a tendency to coarctation, and that during puberty the experience type becomes ambiequal again (pp. 90, 113-114).

The first to undertake a systematic investigation of children with the Rorschach test was Behn-Eschenburg,[1] Rorschach's collaborator, in his studies of school children. His paper was an interesting contribution to the psychology of pre-puberty and puberty (the "physiological compulsion neurosis" of the 14 year old is here described i.a.). One of his findings was that the Rorschach technique was eminently suitable for psychological examinations of children and adolescents.

[1] Hans Behn-Eschenburg, Psychische Schüleruntersuchungen mit dem Formdeutversuch, Berne, 1921.

Then appeared the fundamental investigation by Loepfe[2] of 10 to 13 year old schoolboys in Zürich. Loepfe verified Behn-Eschenburg's result: that the Rorschach test is applicable to children (p. 207). He pointed out some special characteristics in children's protocols, which were found again later; less form sharpness (p. 219), the less positive significance of W (p. 240-241), and the greater tendency toward Dd interpretations. Loepfe holds that in children the Rorschach test is suitable only as a supplement to other examinations (psychiatric, educational).

The next important investigation of school children was done in Geneva, by Marguerite Loosli-Usteri.[3] We shall refer to a later paper in which she has stated her results.

A short time later, Ernst Schneider[4] conducted his Rorschach test study of intellectually inhibited school children. It demonstrated that Rorschach's intelligence factors are also of value in regard to children (pp. 110-111), and that, as an intelligence examination for children, the Rorschach test is the equal of other techniques (such as Bobertag-Hylla, Döring, Binet-Simon, and teacher's judgment). In addition, the test is capable of "taking into account inhibition phenomena," as well as of yielding some qualitative indications (p. 160). The highest correlation coefficient was found between intelligence estimates of the school and the Rorschach test (pp. 161, 163).

A mass application of Rorschach investigations of children began in the thirties and has continued. Only a few papers are mentioned here.

Zulliger's (a teacher's) textbook of the "Behn-Rorschach Test" (pp. 21, 59/60, 64) naturally contained a number of important observations on children (perseveration, color naming, animal percepts as M). At another place Zulliger[5] points to the low P per cent and the tendency to DW and DdW in children.

Marguerite Loosli-Usteri has worked extensively on the application of the Rorschach test to children. In her treatise published in 1942[6] she presents a summary of her experiences in this area. She states that children of 9-12 years yield fewer M and color responses than do adults (pp. 86/90). Consequently, the experience type is coarctatively extratensive

[2]Adolf Loepfe, Über Rorschach'sche Formdeutversuche mit 10-13 jährigen Knaben. Zeitschr. f. angewandte Psychologie, Vol. 26, 1925, pp. 202-253.

[3]Marguerite Loosli-Usteri, Le test de Rorschach appliqué à differents groupes d'enfants de 10-13 ans. Archives de Psychologie, Vol. 22, 1929. pp. 51-106.

[4]Ernst Schneider, Die Bedeutung des Rorschach'schen Formdeutversuches zur Ermittlung intellektuell gehemmter Schüler. Zeitschr. f. angew. Psychologie, Vol. 12, 1929, pp. 102-163.

[5]Hans Zulliger, Jugendliche Diebe im Rorschach-Formdeutversuch, Berne, 1938, pp. 15, 74, 78.

[6]Marguerite Loosli-Usteri, Der Roschach Test als Hilfsmittel des Kinderpsychologen. Schweizerische Zeitschrift für Psychologie, Vol. 1, 1942, pp. 86-91.

and not infrequently simply coarcted. M responses in children are rather a sign of precocity.

The development of the child's approach to the Rorschach cards was studied from the viewpoint of Gestalt psychology and developmental psychology by Gertrude Dworetzki.[7]

In the compendium "Psychiatrie und Rorschach'scher Formdeutversuch," A. Weber[8] gives a survey of his rich Rorschach experience with children. Among his results we again find the tendency of young children to perseverate and make inverse interpretations to which we have already referred several times. There are also a number of interesting observations about the content of their interpretations.

We shall return to the other findings of Loosli-Usteri and of Weber in a more systematic synopsis.

Among the newer works, Mary Ford's[9] should be noted. It is based on material from 123 children aged 3-8 years. In the survey of test results in children which follows, we shall refer to this paper repeatedly.

Moreover, we should mention the thorough study by Verena Gebhart,[10] dealing with intellectual development in the Rorschach test. This author compared the intelligence factors in the test on the basis of very extensive material (1443 protocols in all) from intellectually normal and oligophrenic children aged 6-15 years, and from adults.

Finally, the book "Child Rorschach Responses" by Ames, Learned, Metraux and Walker should be mentioned.[11] This diligent work, however, we could not always make use of here, since the authors have standardized certain categories of symbols ($F+$, D, P) differently for three different age groups. For this reason, great parts of the work are unfortunately lost to us, seen from a developmental point of view, as it is impossible to follow the changes of these test factors through the various ages of development. Moreover, the response total, partly through additions and partly through omission of responses, has been arbitrarily changed (op. cit. pp. 27, 32), for which reason all percentages have of course been rendered useless, as a basis for comparison.

[7]Gertrude Dworetzki, Le test de Rorschach et l'évolution de la perception. Etude expérimentale.—Arch. de Psychol. Geneva, Vol. 27, 1939.

[8]A. Weber, Der Rorschach'sche Formdeutversuch bei Kindern, in "Psychiatrie und Rorschach'scher Formdeutversuch," Zürich, 1944, pp. 47-61.

[9]Mary Ford, The Application of the Rorschach Test to Young Children, Minneapolis, 1946.

[10]Verena Gebhart, Zum Problem der intellektuellen Entwicklung im Rorschach'schen Formdeutversuch, Monatsschrift für Psychiatrie und Neurologie, vol. 124, 1952, pp. 91-125.

[11]Louise Bates Ames, Janet Learned, Ruth W. Métraux, Richard N. Walker, Child Rorschach Responses, New York, 1952.

## SURVEY OF RESULTS OF RORSCHACH TEST RESEARCH IN CHILDREN

The response total in young children seems to be below the average for adults and then up to the age of 10 years rises to the lower limit of the average (Ames et al., p. 102).

✕1. APPROACH FACTORS. There are important differences between approach factors in children and in adults. Except for the youngest children, those under five, children generally see fewer W than adults, and on the other hand they tend to more Dd responses. Children cannot yet differentiate essentials from non-essentials, and therefore often cling to small details. The number of Do is also a little higher in children. It has already been pointed out in chapter 3, that children and adolescents in particular have a greater tendency to Ds perceptions. Do and Ds increase with chronological age among children (Ford, p. 53). As had already been recognized by Behn-Eschenburg and specially emphasized by Loepfe, W are to be evaluated less positively in children, and are to be considered more as a "failure at elaborating details." Weber supports this view and distinguishes between primitive and infantile whole responses (pp. 58, 59). The primitive ("easy-going") W responses (Weber uses the symbol Fp) are percepts which are of no concern to the child, such as "pole," "stone," "piece of wood." These responses show indifference, lack of personal interest, and are arid. The infantile (primitive-infantile) W are awkward but not impersonal. They are taken from the world of technology or toys or they are faces of animals and humans, and the child's attitude is not indifferent, but shows uneasiness or attraction. Sometimes they are somewhat confabulatory, in a manner we know from adult artists.

The development of the approach type follows a wave-line with three phases. Very young children (3-5 years) give many W, but mostly poor forms. At the transition to school age (5-7 years), the W decrease, the approach is displaced towards the Dd, and the forms grow better (Ford, pp. 84-85). At the age of 7-10 years the W again increase, but this time with better forms (van Krevelen).[12] Eriksson arrives at similar results in a comparison between two school-classes (consisting of 7½ and 14 year old children).[13] As Dworetzki has demonstrated,[14] this wave-line comprises

[12]D. A. van Krevelen, Der Rorschach-Test im Fröbelalter, Rorschachiana II, Berne, 1947, p. 88.

[13]Albert Eriksson, Rorschach's Formtydningsförsök. En översikt och ett bidrag till Rorschach-testning av barn. Tidskrift för Psykologi och Pedagogik V. 1, 1943.

[14]Gertrude Dworetzki, Le test de Rorschach et l'évolution de la perception. Étude expérimentale. Arch. de Psychologie, Geneva, 27, 1939.

*four stages of development in the approach:* 1) A *primitive global approach,* in which the child does not yet elaborate the form, but either gives an indifferent designation (which is then most often repeated for the other cards) or interpretations which are vague (e.g., "clouds") or schematic (e.g., "circle," letters) or pars-pro-toto interpretations (e.g., "tree" because of the midline of the blot or "cat" because of its whiskers). 2) A *primitive analysis,* in which the striking details (e.g., the projections) of the figures are given preference. Into this category come either similar details (e.g., "points") conceived and stereotypically interpreted, as Guirdham has observed with some epileptics, or schematic interpretations (perhaps everything lengthy is seen as "stick" or "leg") or descriptions ("lines," "it is hollow") or, finally, completely subjective, fantastic interpretations. 3) An *advanced analysis* with better detail response. The schematic and primitive interpretations now turn into well motivated faces, persons, etc. 4) *Advanced globalizations* with a differentiated synthesis: bilateral, combined, or abstract W with differentiated structuring of the whole or impressionistic interpretations (mostly as FC or CF). The ability to disintegrate and integrate (plasticity of the interpretative structures), and hence the possibility of giving several different interpretations of the same detail, will constantly increase with age. In the Rorschach test, a general psychological law of development is thus confirmed, viz., that the primitive-global manner of approach of the young child is first replaced by an analysing one, which does not always succeed in becoming integrated. Not until a rather late time is the global approach restored, but this time with a differentiated-synthetic structure.

Sequence in the young child is rather loose. With increasing age it becomes more orderly. This is due to the fact that young children proceed by the trial and error method (Ford, p. 86; Bochner and Halpern, op cit. p. 106).

2. DETERMINANTS. Among the determinants, too, there are deviations from adults. M as well as color responses are relatively rare in children, at any rate rarer than in adults (Loosli-Usteri, 1942. pp. 89/90; Ford, pp. 46, 86/87). It should be noted, however, that occasionally children do produce genuine M in animal percepts (Zulliger, Bero, p. 21). Children engage in "more aggressive than compliant" M (Piotrowski).[15] Moreover, children produce small M more frequently than adults (Behn-Eschenburg, Schneider),[16] and, indeed, often in the form of small moving scenes, which

[15]Zygmunt A. Piotrowski, A Rorschach Compendium—Revised and Enlarged, The Psychiatric Quarterly, Vol. 24, p. 570.

[16]Ernst Schneider, Psychodiagnostisches Praktikum, Leipzig, 1936, p. 38.

indicate an interested fairytale-like elaboration, a "make-believe thinking in micro-form" (Zulliger, Tafeln-Z-Test, p. 83).

According to Weber, children before the sixth year produce only few color responses and almost no M (pp. 53, 55). In this connection, Ford observed a peculiar difference between the sexes. Boys begin to use M earlier, girls start to see color responses earlier (identical findings by Ford, Paulsen, and Stavrianos, according to Ford, pp. 59-60). It appears, too, that the reaction to color goes through a peculiar crosswise development in the two sexes: In very young children (M.A. 4-6 years) more color responses (of all three categories) are found in girls; in older children (M.A. 8 - 10) the pattern is reversed with the boys responding with more color. Toward the beginning of school age (M.A. 6-8) these differences tend to disappear (Ford, p. 71). The "crossing point" is thus the age of school entrance, i.e., transition to the latency period. This is by no means surprising if one remembers what is known to any teacher, that during their school years girls are far more quiet and produce fewer disciplinary problems than do boys. This is presumably related to the "passivity push" (Helene Deutsch) in the girls' libido development.

The youngest children give mostly color namings and only rarely real color responses (Dworetzki). When the color responses (perhaps at the age of 5-6 years) do commence to appear in considerable numbers, they are (in the 6-8 year olds) preponderantly CF and C, more rarely FC (Dworetzki; Weber, pp. 53-54). The unstable color values (CF and C) will then decrease and the stable FC increase with increasing age (Weber, pp. 53-54; Ford, pp. 46-48, 90-91). But children in general produce more CF than FC.

Thus, as had already been established by Dworetzki and likewise by Zulliger (Bero-Test, p. 64), color naming appears in healthy young children, too. This is normal only in pre-school children, however, and generally it is not found in those of a mental age of eight years and more, i.e., at full development of the reality sense (Ford, p. 72). (At this age perseveration also ceases, see below.) According to Ames et al. (p. 283), color namings in children of more than 5 years should no longer be considered "normal."

The experience balance, according to Loosli-Usteri (1942, p. 92), is usually purely extratensive but coarctative. The introversive experience type is much rarer, and the completely coarcted much more frequent than in adults. The ambiequal experience balance almost always goes with color shock. It is more frequent in girls than in boys, and more frequent in boys who are educational problem children than in those who are normal. In Loosli-Usteri's opinion, ambiequality in children is almost always a product of precocity and neurosis. Ford verifies (p. 73, Table 17) the coarctative experience type in children. She reports that introversiveness increases in the 3-7 years age period in direct proportion to growth in chronological age (p. 79). This increase of M continues during the age span of 7-12 years in normal children; only among the mentally deficient is no such increase observed (Kerr).[17]

3. CONTENT. Breadth of content increases with chronological age (Ford, p. 91, Ames et al., p. 91) and the proportion of human responses constantly increases (Ames et al., p. 93). Children in most cases have many animal responses (Bochner and Halpern, p. 105). On the other hand, the anatomy interpretations are rarer in children. There was agreement on this point among Anglo-American and Swiss workers (Kerr; Ford, p. 50; Zangger).[18] Actually, anatomy only begins to appear toward the end of school age (ca. 13), but they are somewhat more frequent in neurotic children (Kerr, p. 181/182). Mask responses are also rare in children and most likely point to the precocious.[19] Within the animal group, wild animals predominate in the responses of 3-5 year old children, though in 5-10 year olds they are still playing a considerable part (Ames et al., p. 92). In the content of children's responses, Weber has frequently seen "broken off, cut off legs" (apparently castration complex) and "teeth," related in his experience to the onanism complex. Also Ames et al. (p. 193) frequently found broken and "crooked" things in the interpretations of the 5½ year olds, and in 7 year olds, "decay, damage and mutilation" formed a common subject (p. 221). "Angel," "devil," and "ghost" are also numerous, and similarly responses which show an affective fusion of animal and human (e.g., "two parrots are shaking hands"; Weber, p. 60). Naturally, many fairy tale motifs such as "fairies," "elves," "dragons," appear (Ford, p. 49). Food responses are frequent in young children.[20] Youths with masturbation conflicts will often see pools, dirt, water puddles, running water, something decaying (Zulliger, Tafeln-Z-Test, p. 189).

4. THE PERCENTAGES. F+ among children is generally lower than that of adults (Loepfe, Weber, Ford). (See the last section of this chapter for the consequences of this finding in evaluating children's protocols.) F+

[17]Madeline Kerr, The Rorschach Test Applied to Children. British Journal of Psychology, vol. 25, 1935, p. 183.

[18]Gina Zangger, Die "Versager," Zwischenformen und Anatomieantworten im Rorschach'schen Formdeutversuch, Rorschachiana I, Berne, pp. 103, 105, 107.

[19]Roland Kuhn, Über Maskendeutungen im Rorschach'schen Versuch, Basel, 1944, pp. 46 and 127.

[20]Beck, Rorschach's Test, II, p. 221.

per cent increases with age (Ford, pp. 53, 90), more accurately speaking with mental age (Loderer; Weber, p. 60). M, too, increases with mental age, while the increase of W+ depends on chronological age (Loderer, Weber, p. 60).

In children, A per cent is generally higher, P per cent lower and Orig per cent higher than in adults (Bochner and Halpern, p. 105). P per cent in children is on the average 10 - 15 per cent (Zulliger, Jugendliche Diebe, p. 15).

P of children (rated as in adults) increases with chronological age, and the same is true for Orig+, whereas the very numerous Orig– (hence their high Orig per cent) of children under five years again declines after this age (Ford, p. 51).

Thus there are increases with chronological age in response totals, F+ and Orig+ per cents, and (to a less pronounced degree), M+ (Ford, p. 90). The three latter factors mainly depend, however, on mental age.

On the whole, the mental development of the child (and that, of course, also applies to the corresponding Rorschach factors) is not a linear one, but is subject to *fluctuations*. Ames et al. at the close of their book (p. 289) formulate this in the following summary: "Ages of equilibrium to some extent alternate with ages of disequilibrium, ages of expansiveness with ages of inwardizing. Ages when behavior appears to be well organized may be followed by ages which show marked inner disturbance. Ages at which subjects respond favorably to persons and things in the environment may be followed by ages of marked rejection of and rebellion against the environment."

## 5. OTHER PHENOMENA

(a) *Rejection,* as shock phenomenon, is more rare in children than in adults. Now and then it is found in response to card I (Weber, p. 56). In younger children (of preschool age) rejections seem to be more frequent (Ames et al., p. 105).

(b) *Lowered* or entirely *annulled interpretation awareness* (determination of the blots) is nothing unusual in younger children (up to 4½ years), because reality and imagination flow together (Ames et al., pp. 141, 152, 194).

(c) *Color shock* is found in neurotic children of any age just as regularly as in adults, and dark shock is even a little more frequent than color shock (Weber, p. 56). The latter is not surprising since dark shock is related to phobic states, particularly fear of the dark; and these are far more frequent in children than in adults.

(d) We have already noted that *confabulations* are produced even by normal children (Loepfe; Weber, p. 58; Ames et al., pp. 140, 152/153, 168, 221). Since fantasy and reality are not yet differentiated in the young child, or at least not very sharply, these confabulations are by no means to be evaluated as pathologic. However, confabulations should not occur after the age of 7 in normal children (Weber, p. 59; Ames et al., p. 283). Related to these child-like confabulations are the pars-pro-toto interpretations of the children. A special variation of childlike confabulation are objects (people, animals, things) which "cannot be seen." According to Ames et al., (pp. 222 and 266), they could especially be observed in 7 and 10 year old children.

(e) As already mentioned (chapters 3 and 5) both *contaminations* and *"number"* and *position* responses will occasionally occur in young children (Ames et al., pp. 100, 155, 179, 193). Position responses, however, are only normal up to 4 years (Ames et al., p. 284). Contaminations occur especially in 5 year old girls (Ames et al., pp. 179, 193). Thus, in children of less than 7 years such responses should not be considered alarming symptoms.

(f) Similarly, *perseveration* is a frequent phenomenon in children of preschool age, especially with W (Dworetzki), also if accompanied by confabulations. It is normal up to the first year of school. Later it is still frequently found in the form of "sticking to the theme" (Weber, p. 59). Zulliger calls attention to the fact (Bero, p. 59) that not infrequently this tendency to perseveration is also found with Ds.

This inclination to perseveration in pre-school children stems from the "magic repetition" of the very young child still under three years of age (Klopfer and Margulies).[21] This is understood to mean the complete or partial repetition of the same response to the whole card. In its complete form this generally appears only in children between two and three years of age, and rarely between three and four years. Strictly speaking, this is an equivalent of rejection due to lack of interest or inability to adjust to the task (Dworetzki). Abortive forms (four or more cards with "magic repetition," the others either rejected or, somewhat later, responded to with other interpretations of a crude similarity) occur in children up to about five years of age; in rare instances, six or seven years. But only a certain number of the children (about a third) display this type of response between three and four years (Ford, p. 36/37).

[21]Bruno Klopfer and Helen Margulies, Rorschach Reactions in early Childhood. Rorschach Research Exchange, Vol. 5, 1941, here according to Mary Ford, The Application of the Rorschach Test to Young Children, Minneapolis, 1946, p. 36. Also Ames et al., have observed the magic repetition and confirm the normal appearance of perseveration during entire childhood (pp. 118, 128, 138, 156, 170, 178, 193, 222, 281).

A somewhat more mature behavior is reported by Ford, namely, "magic repetition" in response to at least four cards, but as D and Dd percepts. The similarity in these percepts is for the most part rather problematic (Ford, p. 38). This is a matter of one-sided adjustment to the task, the child going from like to like, picking out either the similar contents (e.g., butterflies) or details of similar form, in the manner of Guirdham's perceptional perseveration (Dworetzki).

Only when several reasonably adequate interpretations are given to most of the cards (according to Klopfer and Margulies, at least seven), has the child achieved the developmental level of logical thinking. The other behaviors just noted correspond to pre-logical thinking (Ford, p. 37).

Regarding perseveration, Mary Ford (p. 38) distinguishes among four levels of development:

1. The pre-logical stage: pure "magic repetition" in response to all ten cards;

2. The confused-logic stage: "magic repetition" to the whole figure in at least four cards; the others are rejected or elicit percepts crudely similar to the interpreted blot.

3. The perseverated-logic stage: "magic repetition" in response to at least four cards, but in the form of D and Dd interpretations; and

4. The true-logic stage: several adequate percepts in response to at least seven cards.

(g) *Infantile abstractions,* i.e., outline interpretations of the whole card, according to Zulliger (Tafeln-Z-Test, p. 82) is a normal occurrence in children up to about 8 years.

(h) Finally, let us mention once more the interesting *inverse interpretations* which Weber found (p. 59) in a good ten per cent of his 500 children's protocols. Ames et al., too, mention these interpretations in 3½ to 4½ year olds (pp. 140, 155, 170). Regarding the psychological problems incident to these interpretations, refer to the remarks of Wolfgang Köhler, discussed under inverse interpretations in chapter 5.

## SPECIAL RULES FOR THE APPLICATION OF THE RORSCHACH TEST IN CHILDREN

1. ADMINISTRATION. Rapport is especially important in administering the test to children. If the child does not know the Examiner, the latter must first talk or play with the child so as to establish a natural affective contact. Should the child sense an examination situation, a stern "pedagogue" or a "school marm," the procedure either will not work, or an unnatural, overanxious, and objectively misleading protocol results. In no test situation do the "scientific" findings depend as much on the

Examiner and his contact, or lack of it, as in investigations of children. In some instances, one may have to postpone the test to another time. Or, if rapport cannot be established at all, one may have to refer the child to some other Examiner in whom the child may have more confidence. Any kind of external features (spectacles, beard, white coat) may release a conditioned response in a child, and prevent any worthwhile cooperation. On the other hand, with children who already know the Examiner, rapport is usually easily established.

Since it is difficult to hold the attention of pre-school children for any length of time, it is advisable to run through the test as rapidly as possible, without much irrelevant conversation (Ford, pp. 16/17). Young children are best tested in the morning when they are fresh and well rested (Ford, p. 17).

With children of any age even more than with adults, the presence of a third person is to be avoided as far as possible. In particular parents, teachers, or any educator, may influence the test situation decisively, in the main unfavorably. Any exception to this rule must be very rare.

The suggestion that children be forbidden to turn the cards (Ford, pp. 18, 33) must absolutely be rejected. This prohibition (based on the opinion that the child's activity-urge would distract him from the task) is so severe a modification of the test situation that the findings so obtained are no longer comparable with the Rorschach test proper. A number of M responses in particular are thereby suppressed, which would most likely be given in the $\vee$, $>$, and $<$ positions (e.g., the female dancers in card VIII; or the various M percepts in the big lateral projections of cards IV and VI).

2. EVALUATION. The same basic principles apply to the evaluation of the test in children as in adults (of same opinion: Klopfer and Margulies; and Ford, p. 21). But the peculiarities of the children's reactions to the Rorschach test, described above, result in a number of deviations in the symptomatic values of the several test factors. These are to be taken into consideration in evaluation of the children's protocols. It is essentially a matter of the following modifications:

(a) *Form responses* must be evaluated liberally since they frequently stem from accidental personal experience (Loepfe, Weber, pp. 56/57). It is to be kept in mind that many children have not yet mastered language to the point of being able to express what they see. For this reason they often say something other than what they mean. Whenever a child gives a very peculiar response, one reminiscent of the confabulatory Orig– of the pseudologic psychopaths, it is well to look into the matter more closely later on. It then usually appears that the child has said something other than what he had in mind. Thus a normal four year old girl produced the doubtlessly surprising W response "piano" to card VI. The parents did not have a piano, and it is doubtful whether this child had ever seen one. It soon became evident that the child had meant a guitar, and for a four year old child this is no poorer than the "fan" or "tennis racket" of adults, both of which have been evaluated as Orig+ by Rorschach.

(b) As suggested by Loepfe, the low $F+$ *per cent* of children is to be checked against the Orig+. The primitive W (Weber's Fp) is to be looked upon as a counter-indication (Weber, p. 57).

(c) The $W$, especially the poor and primitive ones, are to be evaluated in a less positive manner, and rather more as "lack of detail elaboration" (Loepfe, pp. 240/241; Weber, pp. 57/58). As Ford correctly points out, this is why the positive correlation between W and intelligence does not apply in children (pp. 69, 94/95). (Strictly speaking, is does not apply in adults either, because in them only W+ shows a positive correlation with intelligence.)

(d) Loepfe's assertion that some $Dd$ are more frequent in children than in adults is correct. However, his suggestion to score them as D in children is impractical. In the first place it would be very difficult in doubtful cases to determine the boundary between child and adult. Secondly, different scoring for children and adults would prohibit us from conducting investigations in psychological development as it is reflected in these factors. It has further been shown that Loepfe overestimated this problem to some degree. More recent investigations show that "there is no significant difference between the D and Dd of children and adults" (Loosli-Usteri, 1942, p. 89). The exceptions are insignificant. Therefore, no difference in scoring Dd and D in children is warranted. It would be equally inexpedient to change the scoring of some Do to D for children just because Do responses are a little more numerous.

(e) If children perseverate with $Ds$, this is not to be interpreted in the same way as in adults, namely, meaning increased aggressive tension. Only several isolated and widely separated Ds have this symptomatic value (Zulliger, Bero-Test, pp. 59/60).

(f) Instead of the usually loose sequence, it is the presence of *object responses* as D+ which supplies the most reliable criterion of disciplined logic in children (Loepfe).

(g) Caution is in order against giving $M$ a too positive significance in the case of young children, particularly if there are several M. In these Subjects, they are merely a "sign of a certain precocity" (Loosli-Usteri, p. 91). It is different with older children. As has been shown by Ernst Schneider, during the school years M may very well be evaluated as an intelligence factor.

(h) Since *color responses* also depend on accidental individual experiences (Weber, p. 52), their symptomatic value in children under 10 years is very uncertain. Colors are usually experienced by children as free colors, in Katz' sense, rarely as surface colors (Weber, p. 52).

Children under eight whose color responses are predominantly FC are precocious or "overeducated." Due to severe instinctual restrictions, they have become compliant, dependent and without spark.

(i) *Experience balance,* too, has less symptomatic value in children (Loepfe, pp. 242/243). Above all, it is more labile than in adults (Weber, p. 51). The feeling of the moment is expressed more strongly. And coarctation, which is so frequent in children (Loosli-Usteri), cannot simply be interpreted as comparable to coarctation in the adult (Ford, p. 95).

(j) Ford is of the opinion (p. 95) that the *P responses* as scored for adults do not have the same relation to social adjustment in children as they do in adults; but this appears somewhat doubtful to us. In any case, the lower P per cent is to be evaluated as normal (Bochner and Halpern, p. 105).

(k) For *Orig per cent,* too, we cannot simply assume that the same symptomatic values apply to children as to adults (Bochner and Halpern, p. 105). Nor are Orig– to be considered abnormal when found in young children.

(1) The ratio Ad > A must, in small children, be evaluated as a symptom of anxiety in the same way as Hd > H (Zulliger).

Finally, it is always to be remembered that *confabulations* and *perseverations* are normal in children under eight years of age. The same applies to the *color-namings* (Zulliger) which, however (according to Ames et al., p. 283), should not occur in children over 5 years, and to *inverse interpretations* which, according to Zulliger, must no longer be considered normal after the age of six.[22]

The most important of all the considerations that apply to evaluating the Rorschach test in children, however, is that one must always think in terms of psychological development. The same finding has quite a different meaning in a five year old than in a 12 year old. That which in a child of 14 years would mean a developmental retardation (e.g., a certain kind of confabulation), may in a four year old be completely normal, or even a sign of special endowment. It is only when this "thinking on a sliding scale" has become second nature to the interpreter, that the evaluation of children's tests may be confidently undertaken.

[22]Hans Zulliger, Imbezillität in der Spiegelung des Tafeln-Z-Tests, Ztschr. f. Diagn. Psychol. u. Persönlichkeitsforschung, vol. II, p. 327.

# Subject Index

# Author Index